Activity Manual Answer Key

Greenville, South Carolina

HERITAGE STUDIES 6 Activity Manual Answer Key
Third Edition

Authors
Peggy S. Alier
Marnie Batterman
Eileen M. Berry
Ann L. Carruthers
James R. Davis
Annittia Jackson
Laurie Tebbenkamp
Debra White
Dennae White

Consultants
Dennis Bollinger
Sherri H. Vick

Bible Integration
Brian C. Collins

Cover Design
Peter Crane
Drew Fields
Cathryn Pratt

Concept & Page Design
Dan Van Leeuwen

Page Layout
Bonnijean Marley

Permissions
Sylvia Gass
Brenda Hansen
Ashley Hobbs
Joyce Landis

Project Editor
Paul Michael Garrison

Project Managers
Amy Johnson
Faith Larson
Donald Simmons

Illustrators
Paula Cheadle
Preston Gravely
Kathy Pflug
Dave Schuppert
Del Thompson

Previously published as *HERITAGE STUDIES 6 Worktext* and *Student Notebook for use with HERITAGE STUDIES 6.*

Produced in cooperation with the Bob Jones University School of Education, Bob Jones Academy, and BJU Press Distance Learning.

Greenville, South Carolina 29609

Printed in the United States of America

ISBN 978-1-62856-276-7

15 14 13 12 11 10 9 8 7 6 5

Contents

Chapters

Chapter 1 Organizer

Use with Student Text pages 2–18.

Name ______________________________

Fill in the blanks in the outlines as you study the chapter.

The Study of History

I. Where does history come from? (pp. 2–4)

A. The only reliable source that reveals how history began is the ___Bible___.

B. All Scripture was given by ___inspiration___ of God.

C. The first five books of the Bible, written by ___Moses___, are called the ___books of the Law___.

D. The period when humans supposedly evolved is called ___prehistory___.

E. The Bible tells the history of the world from the very ___beginning___.

II. Why study ancient history? (p. 5)

A. The stories of history are based on ___fact___.

B. Accounts from history show us how ___to live___ in the present and in the future.

C. History teaches us ___about ourselves___.

D. History provides an opportunity to ___praise God___.

E. History shows us the mighty ___acts of God___.

III. How do we study history? (pp. 6–7)

A. A historian studies physical man-made objects from the past called ___artifacts___.

B. A historian studies information passed from generation to generation, known as ___tradition___.

C. A historian studies ___written records___ that are firsthand accounts by people in the past.

D. A historian needs to ___evaluate___ the accuracy of the sources.

E. A Christian historian's ___worldview___ (how he sees and interprets the universe and everything in it) begins with the Bible.

F. A Christian historian remembers that ___God___ knows and controls all things.

The Beginning of History

I. Creation (pp. 10–11)

A. God created the world by ___speaking___ it into existence.

B. God created man in His own ___image___.

C. God created people with a job to do—be fruitful and multiply, ___replenish___ the earth, ___subdue___ (rule) the earth, and have ___dominion___ over the earth (Gen. 1:28).

II. The Fall (pp. 12–13)

A. Adam and Eve broke God's law and tried to become ___like God___.

B. Civilizations fall apart because of man's ___selfishness___, ___pride___, and rebellion toward God.

C. People turned away from God and ___worshiped___ gods in their own image.

D. People have within them the sense that ___there is a God___ and that He deserves to be worshiped and obeyed.

III. God's Promise of Redemption (pp. 15–18)

A. Genesis 3:15 promises that God will provide ___salvation through a Man (Jesus Christ)___.

B. History is the struggle between ___God's people___ (the seed of the woman) and ___Satan's people___ (the seed of the serpent).

C. Because man was so sinful, God sent a ___universal flood___.

D. God showed grace to Noah; his wife; their sons, ___Ham___, ___Shem___, and ___Japheth___; and the sons' wives.

E. The people gathered in the plain of ___Shinar___ to build a tower in Babel.

F. God caused the people to speak multiple ___languages___ so they could not communicate.

G. These groups of people scattered throughout the earth and developed ___nations___.

H. History is the story of nations rising and falling according to ___God's sovereign will___.

I. God's promise to Eve to crush the ___head of the serpent___ was fulfilled by Jesus' death on the cross.

J. Studying civilizations shows how man's history fits together with ___redemptive history___ and how the kingdom of God will ___subdue___ all the kingdoms of man.

Studying History

Use with Student Text pages 5–7.

Name ______________________

A. Mark the *two best* answers.

Babylonian artifact

1. Studying history is important because
   - ● it provides an opportunity to praise God.
   - ● it shows us the mighty acts of God.
   - ○ written records are more important than artifacts.
2. Sources that a historian uses to find out about the past are
   - ● artifacts.
   - ○ books written by experts.
   - ● original written records.
3. A Christian historian believes that
   - ○ early human-like creatures lived in East Africa.
   - ● man has always been intelligent.
   - ● God knows and controls all things.

B. Number the steps in order to show how a historian produces a historical account.

__2__ 4. He compares the sources and chooses the most reliable ones.

__1__ 5. He gathers primary written sources about his subject.

__4__ 6. He combines information from several sources.

__3__ 7. He evaluates the sources for strengths and weaknesses.

__6__ 8. He interprets and explains why an event happened and how it remains important today.

__7__ 9. He presents the completed historical account for others to study and evaluate.

__5__ 10. He produces a narrative that represents the majority of his research.

C. Answer the questions.

11. What is a Christian worldview? *seeing and interpreting the universe and everything in it through the Bible*

12. What is tradition? *the passing of information from generation to generation*

13. Why are written records more important than artifacts or traditions? *Written records do not need explanation as artifacts often do and are not usually changed from generation to generation as traditions often are.*

14. How is King Nebuchadnezzar an example of the struggle between man and God? *Nebuchadnezzar declared he was to be worshiped as a god. God taught Nebuchadnezzar that He is Ruler over everything and that no one can question Him or stop Him from doing His will.*

Essay Questions

Name ____________________

Complete teaching instructions are located in the Teacher's Edition.

A. Match the definition with the correct term.

D 1. evaluate
B 2. trace
A 3. analyze
G 4. justify
F 5. classify
E 6. compare and contrast
H 7. predict
C 8. interpret

A. examine critically to identify causes, key factors, possible results, and relationships
B. follow the development or steps of something in chronological order
C. give the meaning or importance of
D. judge something's significance or importance using evidence to support
E. show how things are similar and different
F. sort into groups based on shared characteristics
G. support a position with specific facts and reasons
H. tell what will happen in the future based on an understanding of the past

B. First, plan the essay on your own paper. Then, write it below.

9. Describe the three major sources that a historian uses to gather facts about the past.

The student's essay should include these major sources with a definition of each: artifacts, which are physical man-made objects from the past; tradition, which is the passing of information from generation to generation; and written records, which are firsthand written accounts of the past. The answer should also include at least one or two examples.

STUDY SKILL

Essay Writing Steps

1. Read the question.
2. Underline key words.
3. Plan the response.
4. Order the main points.
5. Write an opening statement.
6. Write the main points with supporting facts and details.
7. Write a closing statement.
8. Evaluate the essay.

Study Guide

Use with Student Text pages 2–7.

Name ______________________

A. Define the terms using the glossary and Student Text pages.

1. prehistory *the period when humans supposedly evolved and when there were no written records*

2. worldview *how a person sees and interprets the universe and everything in it*

B. Complete the section.

3. What does it mean when we say the Bible was given by inspiration of God? *The Holy Spirit guided the men who wrote the Bible, breathing out God's words through them so that what they wrote is the Word of God.*
4. What is the only completely reliable source that reveals how history began? *the Bible*
5. Who was chosen by God to lead His people out of Egyptian slavery? *Moses*
6. List two beliefs that a Christian historian holds that a non-Christian historian may not hold.
   - *possible answers: Man was created in the image of God. Man has always been intelligent. God*
   - *knows and controls all things.*

C. Write *T* if the statement is true. If the statement is false, write the correction for the underlined words.

T 7. Written records are more important than artifacts or <u>traditions</u>.

reliable 8. A historian compares sources and chooses the most <u>interesting</u> ones.

Written records 9. <u>Traditions</u> do not need explanation as artifacts often do.

T 10. A historian evaluates <u>primary sources</u> for strengths and weaknesses.

change 11. One problem with traditions is that they often <u>stay the same</u> as they are passed on from generation to generation.

worldviews 12. Sometimes historians disagree about how to interpret information because their <u>accounts</u> differ.

T 13. When a historian writes, he explains why <u>an event</u> happened and how it remains important.

T 14. A Christian sees and interprets the universe and everything in it through <u>the Bible</u>.

D. Complete each chart.

15. Contrast the biblical beginning of history with evolutionary prehistory.

	Biblical beginning of history	Evolutionary prehistory
Beginning of people	*created by God*	*evolved over time*
Speech and written language	*could speak and probably write from the beginning*	*developed these abilities over time*
Agriculture and cities	*appeared in the first generation of people*	*took thousands of years to develop*

16. Name the three kinds of sources that a historian uses and give an example of each.

Source	Example
artifacts	*possible answers: pottery, artwork, buildings, tools*
traditions	*possible answers: story, song, proverb*
written records	*possible answers: Bible, private letter, diary, official governmental record*

E. First, plan the essay on your own paper. Then, write it below.

17. Analyze the importance of studying ancient history. Include at least three facts.

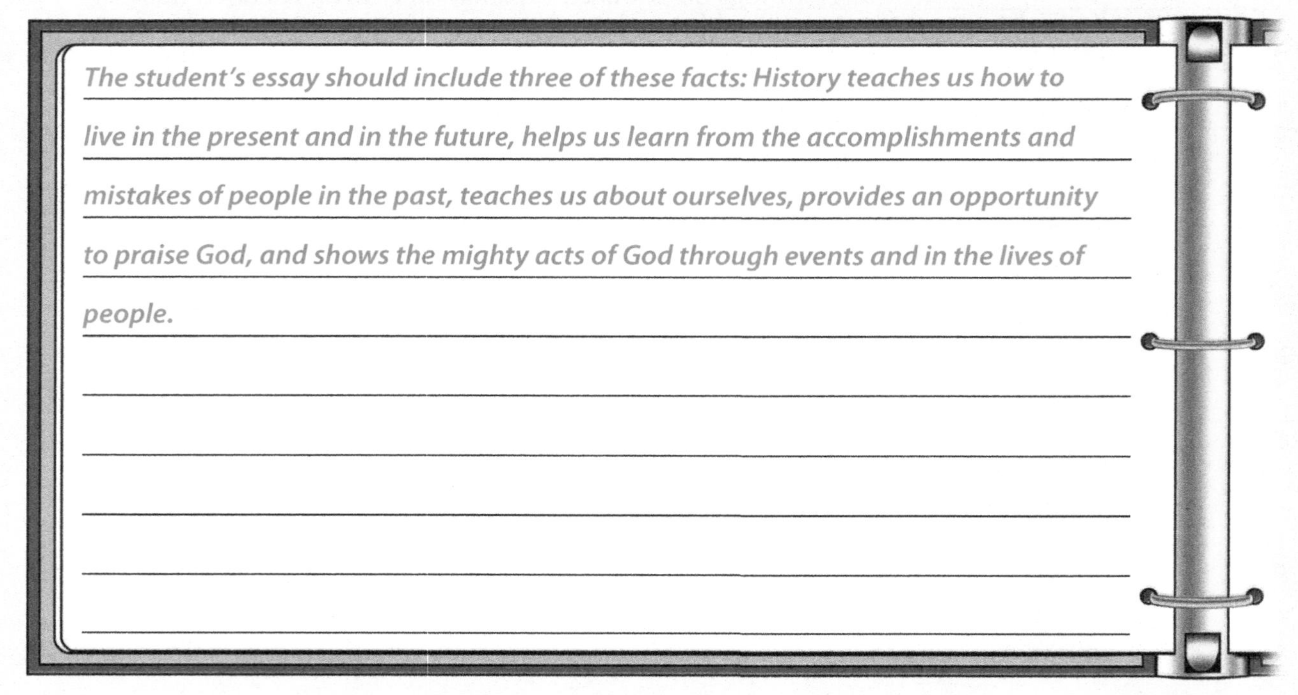

The student's essay should include three of these facts: History teaches us how to live in the present and in the future, helps us learn from the accomplishments and mistakes of people in the past, teaches us about ourselves, provides an opportunity to praise God, and shows the mighty acts of God through events and in the lives of people.

Evaluating Historical Resources Name ______________________

Use with Student Text page 9.

A. Examine each source. Complete the chart to determine whether it is primary or secondary.

Source title	*"Discovered: Stonehenge Village"*	*"Stonehenge, Salisbury, England, United Kingdom"*
Author	*James Owen*	*Ron Tagliapietra*
Written at the time of the event or later	*later*	*later*
Form of information (letter, speech, textbook, encyclopedia)	*magazine article*	*article from a book*
Primary or secondary source	*secondary source*	*secondary source*

B. Determine the author's viewpoint. Record your answers in the chart with examples from the source.

Source title	*"Discovered: Stonehenge Village"*	*"Stonehenge, Salisbury, England, United Kingdom"*
What is the main idea?	*what was found at an archaeological site near Stonehenge*	*reasons that Stonehenge may have been built*
Does the author use Scripture or biblical truths?	*no*	*Yes, examples are Joshua 4:6 and Genesis 1:14.*
Does the author use language that shows emotion or opinion? Look for words such as *think*, *feel*, *best*, *worst*, *might*, or *should*.	*Yes; examples are "wild parties," "they think," "the experts think," and "the theory is."*	*He uses language to show opinions of different people; examples are "they thought," "popularized the view," and "intriguing and provoke many more speculations."*
Does the author provide only one viewpoint or both sides of the event?	*only the viewpoint of the archaeologists*	*provides several different viewpoints of what the purpose of Stonehenge was*
Does the author use factual statements? These statements usually answer *who*, *what*, *when*, and *where* questions.	*Yes; examples are "archaeologists digging near Stonehenge on Salisbury Plain last year discovered the remains"; "the village is less than 2 miles . . . from Stonehenge"; and "remains at the site included jewelry, stone arrowheads, . . . and broken pottery."*	*Yes; examples are "the large standing stone slabs, over thirteen feet high and weighing twenty-six tons each, formed a circle"; "a circle of fifty-six equally spaced holes, now known as 'Aubrey Holes'"; and "modern archaeologists have shown that the ruins date from between 1800 and 1400 B.C."*
What is the author's viewpoint on the topic?	*The author gives only the archaeologists' view, the belief in prehistory and Stone Age people.*	*The author gives many different viewpoints of the purpose of Stonehenge but states that only God knows the true purpose.*

C. Record the strengths and weaknesses of the sources on your own paper.

Civilization Organizer

Name ______________________________

Use with Student Text page 11.

Complete the web as you study about the features of a civilization.

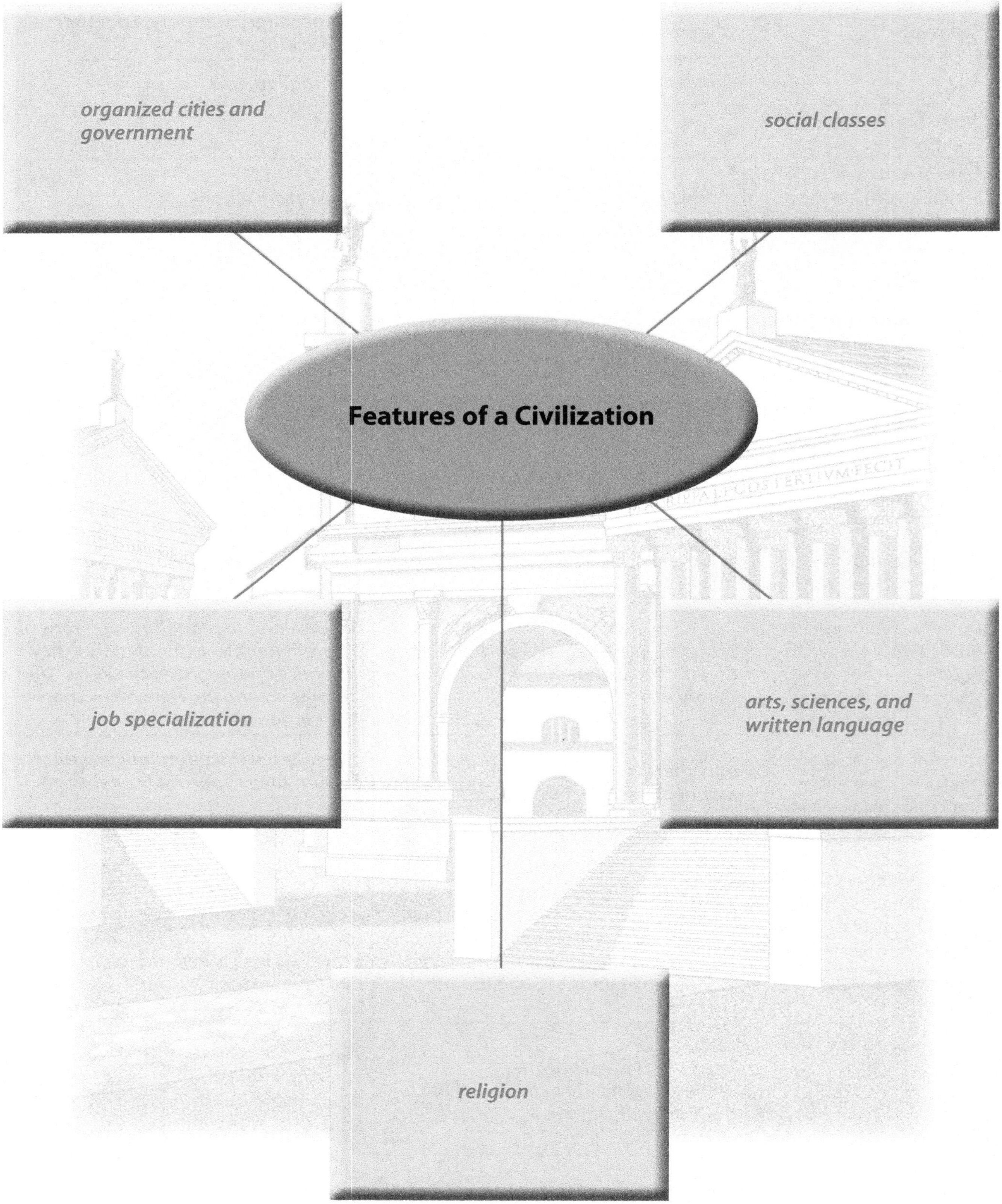

Features of a Civilization

- *organized cities and government*
- *social classes*
- *job specialization*
- *arts, sciences, and written language*
- *religion*

In the Beginning

Use with Student Text pages 10–13.

Name ______________________

A. Define the terms using the glossary and Student Text pages.

1. civilization *a group of people who have established cities, government, social classes, specialized jobs, arts, sciences, written language, and religion*
2. dominion *the authority to rule*
3. Fall *the breaking of God's law by Adam and Eve with the consequence of sin for them and all people*

B. Answer the questions.

4. What happened the first week of history? *God created everything.*
5. How did God create man? *God formed man out of soil with His own hands and breathed life into him.*
6. What job did God create man to do according to Genesis 1:28? *to have children and replenish the earth, subdue the earth, and have dominion over every living thing on the earth*
7. What are two consequences of the Fall?
   possible answers: The earth rebels against man's efforts to subdue it. Roads and cities are
   - *destroyed by floods, earthquakes, and volcanoes. Wars, diseases, and plagues kill people. People*
   - *turn away from loving and worshiping God.*
8. Why do religions exist worldwide? *People have within them the sense that there is a God and that He deserves to be worshiped and obeyed.*
9. What does the Bible tell us about false religions? *God desires for people to put away their gods and worship Him alone.*

C. Write *T* if the statement is true. If the statement is false, write the correction for the underlined words.

values	10. For a civilization to prosper, it needs people who share the same <u>religion</u> to work together.
God	11. History has shown how civilizations fall apart because of man's selfishness, pride, and rebellion toward <u>priests</u>.
T	12. <u>Adam and Eve</u> chose to break God's law and tried to become like God.
T	13. <u>Atheism</u> is a belief that there is no God.
reject	14. False religions form when people <u>accept</u> God and His Word.

Examining an Artifact

Name ______________________________

Use with Student Text page 14.

A. Examine and record your observations about both sides of the coin.

	Observations
Material made of	*Answers will vary.*
Languages	
Words	
Numbers	
Buildings	
People	
Dress	
Religion	
Other observations	

B. Draw conclusions using your observations. Be ready to explain your answers. *Possible answers are based on observations of a penny.*

1. List four things archaeologists might conclude from this coin about an unknown civilization.
   - *possible answers: The civilization existed in (date on coin). People believed in a god. People knew*
   - *how to work in metal. People knew how to construct buildings. Some men wore beards. The man*
   - *is a god. A statue of a god is inside the temple. The people spoke two languages. The building is*
   - *a temple for worshiping a god.*
2. What kinds of sources might have been in the excavation that would help test their guesses about the coin? *possible answers: books about religious beliefs, pictures that would identify who Lincoln was and what the building on the penny was, and other artifacts with inscriptions to identify the common language*

C. Make a list of ten items from your house that could be used by a future archaeologist to determine something about you.

3. *Answers will vary.*
4.
5.
6.
7.
8.
9.
10.
11.
12.

Name ______________________________

Use with Student Text pages 15–18. *Complete teaching instructions are located in the Teacher's Edition.*

Evidence

Answers will vary for this page.

STUDY SKILL

Evidence	what you already know about the subject.
Ask	what you hope to learn as you listen.
Reach	toward the source by listening carefully and picking out key information.
Sum up	the important things you learned.

A. Answer the question.

1. What do you know about God's promise of redemption?

____

____

____

____

____

Ask

B. Write two questions about what you hope to learn about redemption.

2. ______________________________

____

3. ______________________________

____

Reach

C. Listen and pick out key information as your teacher discusses redemption.

Sum Up

D. Write the important things you learned.

4. Did you learn the answers to your questions? ______________________________

5. If so, what was the answer to one of them? ______________________________

____

6. What are three important things that you learned about God's promise of redemption?

- ______________________________
- ______________________________
- ______________________________

Study Guide

Use with Student Text pages 10–18.

Name ____________________

A. Define the terms using the glossary and Student Text pages.

__B__ 1. descendants
__A__ 2. dominion
__F__ 3. Fall
__D__ 4. migrate
__C__ 5. redemption
__E__ 6. universal flood

A. the authority to rule
B. generation after generation of people who originated from a certain person or group
C. Christ's act of rescuing a person and freeing him from sin; salvation
D. move from one country or region to settle in another
E. water that covered the entire earth
F. the breaking of God's law by Adam and Eve with the consequence of sin for them and all people

B. Mark the *two best* answers.

7. A civilization is a group of people who have established ____ and ____.
   - ● cities, government, and specialized jobs
   - ● sciences, written language, and religion
   - ○ armies, roads, and parks

8. Two consequences of the Fall are ____ and ____.
   - ● people turned away from loving and worshiping God
   - ○ God created the world by speaking it into existence
   - ● the earth rebelled against man's efforts to subdue it

9. Religions exist worldwide because ____ and ____.
   - ○ people made and worshiped gods in their own image
   - ● people have within them the sense that there is a God
   - ● people know that God deserves to be worshiped and obeyed

C. Match the verse with its description.

__A__ 10. Genesis 1:28
__B__ 11. Genesis 3:15

A. Man was created by God to replenish the earth, subdue the earth, and have dominion over everything.
B. God will provide salvation through Jesus Christ, Who will defeat Satan.

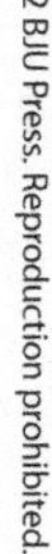

D. Fill in the blanks.

12. False religions form when people reject ____God____ and His Word.
13. God gave the task of building the ark to ____Noah____.
14. Noah's sons ____Shem____ and ____Japheth____ each received a blessing from God.
15. Noah prophesied that the descendants of Canaan, a son of ____Ham____, would be slaves.
16. A symbol of God's own goodness and promises is the ____rainbow____.

Name ______________________

E. Answer the questions.

17. What three things were brought into the world by Adam and Eve's disobedience?
   - *sin*
   - *suffering*
   - *death*

18. When did the history of redemption begin? *when God told Satan that there would be hatred between Satan and Eve and between Satan's offspring and Eve's offspring*

19. Why did God destroy the world with a universal flood? *People became so sinful and wicked that God was grieved that He had made man.*

20. How did nations develop? *God caused the people of Babel to speak different languages. They formed groups that spoke the same language. These groups scattered throughout the earth and developed into nations.*

F. Finish the map.

21–23. Choose a color for each of Noah's sons. Color the regions and the key to match.

24. Label the Mediterranean Sea.

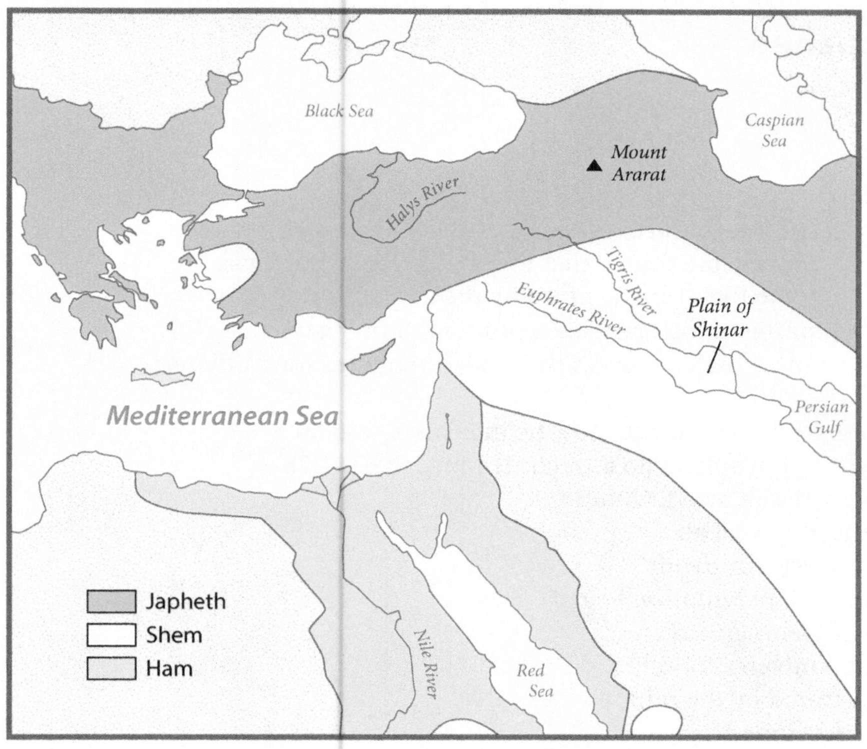

G. First, plan the essay on your own paper. Then, write it on a new sheet of paper.

25. Identify the five characteristics of a civilization.

The student's essay should include these characteristics: (1) organized cities and government, (2) social classes, (3) job specialization, (4) arts, sciences, and written language, and (5) religion.

Chapter 1 Summary

Name ______________________

Define these terms

civilization
descendant
dominion
Fall
migrate
prehistory
redemption
universal flood
worldview

Locate these places

Mediterranean Sea
regions where God directed Japheth, Ham, and Shem

Tell about these people

Ham
Japheth
Moses
Noah
Shem

Explain what happened

as a consequence of the Fall
the Flood

Be able to . . .

Write an essay analyzing the importance of studying ancient history
Identify the only completely reliable source that reveals how history began
Describe what is meant by the Bible's being given by the inspiration of God
Contrast the biblical beginning of history with evolutionary prehistory
Identify and describe the three major sources that a historian uses for studying the past
Describe how a person's worldview affects how he interprets evidence
Explain the job God created people to do as recorded in Genesis 1:28
Relate the five characteristics of a civilization
Identify the consequences of the Fall
Describe why religions exist worldwide
Identify when the history of redemption began
Describe the promise of Genesis 3:15
Explain why God sent a universal flood
Explain the promise pictured by the rainbow
Describe how nations developed

Sumerian Organizer

Name ________________________________

Use with Student Text pages 20–22.

Write the main topic in the hub of the wheel. Complete the facts about the topic on the spokes of the wheel.

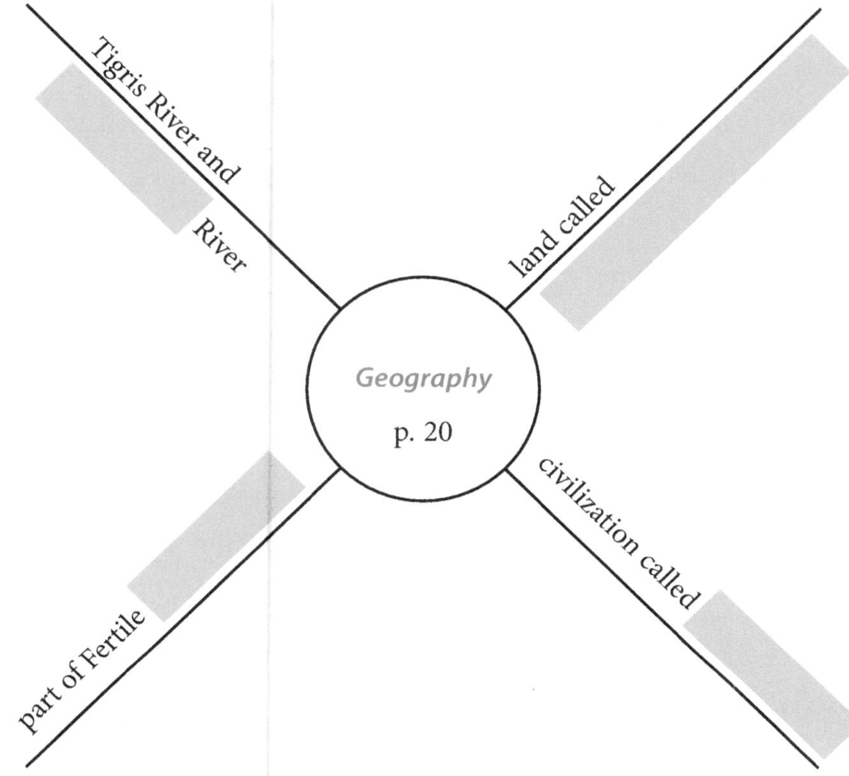

tell—mound of layered
and
earlier buildings
of
artifacts interpreted and
by experts
Archaeology
pp. 20–22
Sumerian sites excavated by
Sir Leonard
found during a dig

Sumerian Civilization

Name ______________________

Use with Student Text pages 20–22.

A. Answer the questions.

1. Whose descendants settled in the plain called Mesopotamia? *Shem's*
2. What does the Greek word for Mesopotamia mean? *between the rivers*
3. What two rivers were found in Mesopotamia? *Tigris and Euphrates*
4. What mountains did these rivers flow from? *Taurus Mountains*
5. Why was the region containing Mesopotamia called the Fertile Crescent? *It had fertile soil and was shaped like a curve or a crescent.*
6. A cradle is often a baby's first bed. Why is Mesopotamia considered the cradle of civilization? *The earliest evidence of agriculture, written language, and cities was discovered there.*
7. What was the name of the civilization that formed in Mesopotamia? *Sumer*
8. What is a tell? *a mound made up of layered dirt and the remains of earlier buildings and structures*
9. What is the significance of Sir Leonard Woolley to Mesopotamia? *He was one of the British archaeologists who excavated Ur and the land of Sumer.*

B. Identify the places on the map.

10. *Mesopotamia*
11. *Tigris River*
12. *Euphrates River*
13. *Ur*
14. *Mediterranean Sea*
15. *Persian Gulf*

C. Shade the Fertile Crescent on the map.

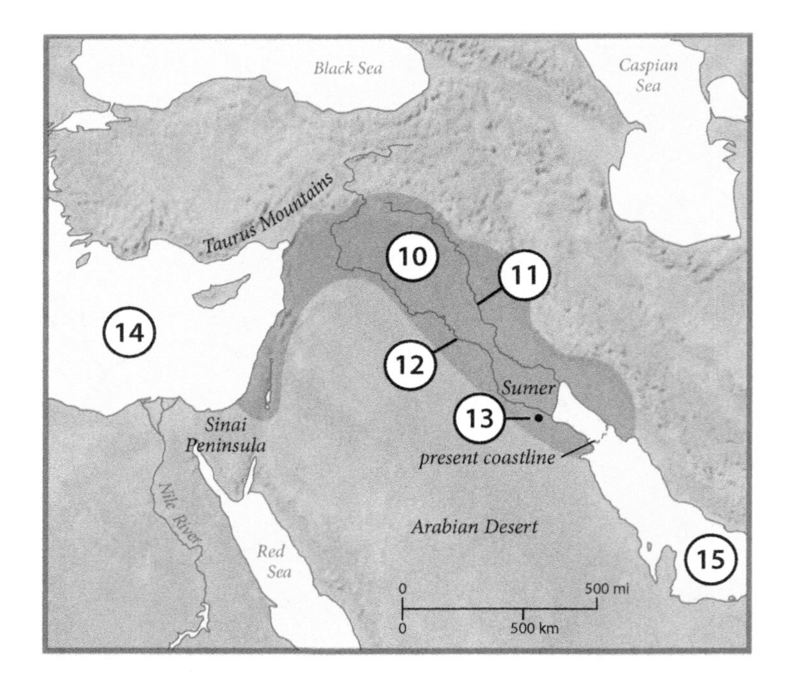

Civilization Organizer

Use with Student Text pages 23–44.

Name ______________________

Complete the web.

The Sumerian Civilization

Job Specialization
pp. 25–29

- Irrigation and the plow helped to create a food *surplus*.
- Fewer farmers were needed, so people worked at specialized *jobs* and *trades*.
- Three specialized jobs were *possible answers:* *fishermen, merchants,* and *traders, soldiers, priests, artisans (craftsmen)*.

Social Classes
p. 27

- The upper class consisted of the ruler, *governmental officials*, and *priests*.
- The middle class consisted of farmers, fishermen, merchants, *traders*, and *skilled workers*.
- The lowest class was the *slaves*.

Organized Cities and Government
pp. 25, 35–36

- Sumer was made up of several *city-states*.
- The people believed that a god chose the *king*.
- The king served as chief *lawmaker* and *judge*.

Arts, Sciences, and Written Language
pp. 39–41

- The Mesopotamians developed a twelve-month *calendar*.
- They recorded stories, proverbs, and poems using *cuneiform*.
- Their most famous works of art are *cylinder seals*.

Religion
pp. 33–35

- Sumerians practiced *polytheism* and rejected the one true *God*.
- They believed man was created to serve the *gods*.
- The priests helped the people gain the *favor of the gods*.

Study Guide

Use with Student Text pages 20–25.

Name ______________________

A. Match each term with its definition.

_D_ 1. city-state
_E_ 2. irrigation
_H_ 3. surplus
_G_ 4. tell
_A_ 5. Tigris and Euphrates
_F_ 6. Mesopotamia
_C_ 7. Sir Leonard Woolley
_B_ 8. Ur

A. flow into the Persian Gulf
B. a city-state in Sumer
C. excavated the city of Ur
D. a city and the surrounding land and villages that it controlled
E. a way of supplying water to land or crops
F. comes from a Greek word that means "between the rivers"
G. a mound made up of layered dirt and the remains of buildings
H. more than what was needed

B. Answer the questions.

9. What was the Fertile Crescent? *It was a curved area from the Persian Gulf to the Mediterranean Sea.*

10. How do we know that Sumer was not the first civilization? *The Bible tells that civilizations existed before the Flood. Sumer was settled after the Flood by Shem's descendants.*

11. What were two benefits of the Tigris and Euphrates?
- *The rivers provided fertile soil for farming.*
- *The rivers provided water for crops, animals, and people.*

12. What were two problems for farmers, and how were they solved?
- *To help control the destruction of floods, the Sumerians built levees.*
- *To help when there was no rain, the Sumerians developed irrigation, built storage basins, and dug canals.*

13. What three tools were developed to make farming easier?
- *plow*
- *yoke*
- *wheel*

14. Why was farming important to establish Sumer as a civilization? *The farmers were able to produce a food surplus, which made new occupations and job specialization possible.*

Planning a Book Jacket

Name ____________________

Use with Student Text page 26.

arch and column	medicine	potter's wheel	twelve-month calendar
cylinder seals	number system based on 60	sail	wheel
iron weapons	place value	shell inlay	writing system
irrigation	plow	system of laws	yoke

Use these steps to help you and your partner plan your book jacket. *Answers will vary.*

1. Our invention or achievement is ____________________.
2. The title of our book is ____________________.
3. The illustration or picture we want on the front cover is ____________________.
4. The main ideas for the front flap are
   - ____________________,
   - ____________________,
   - ____________________.
5. The main ideas for the back flap are
   - ____________________,
   - ____________________,
   - ____________________.
6. The main ideas for the back cover are
   - ____________________,
   - ____________________,
   - ____________________.
7. Write your name next to the parts of the project you are doing.
8. Write a rough draft for the back cover and flaps.
9. Make a neat copy of the summary and information.
10. Read the steps on Student Text page 26. Did you forget any part of the assignment?
11. Put the book jacket together.

Arches in the ancient city of Hatra, Iraq

Trade and Artisans

Name ____________________

Use with Student Text pages 27–32.

A. Write a second sentence that illustrates the first sentence and clearly shows your understanding of the bolded word. *Part A presents a new skill. Work the first one with the student.*

1. One feature of ancient civilizations was the development of **social classes**. *possible answer: The Sumerian civilization had three levels into which the people were divided.*
2. Trade among the early cities was conducted by **barter**. *possible answer: The Sumerian people would exchange their goods without the use of money.*
3. The workshop of the **artisan** was located in Ur. *possible answer: The skilled craftsman turned raw materials into finished goods.*
4. The **scribe** allowed the soft clay tablet to dry. *possible answer: The man had finished recording the information for the business deal.*
5. The merchant rolled his **cylinder seal** across the wet clay. *possible answer: The cylinder-shaped clay had carvings that identified the owner.*

B. Answer the questions.

6. Why was trade important to Sumer's city-states? *possible answers: The people traded for natural resources they did not have. Trading was essential to the growth of a civilization. Trade helped the city-states grow in wealth and power.*
7. What tools did a scribe use? *stylus and clay tablets*
8. Which Sumerian social class was the largest? *middle class*
9. What invention helped the potter? *the wheel*
10. What invention made trading to faraway places easier? *sails on boats*
11. What craft was used in making the Standard of Ur? *shell inlay*
12. Who were in the lowest class? Explain who these people were. *slaves; They were criminals, prisoners of war, or people who needed to pay off debts.*
13. How did the economies of the Mesopotamians and the American colonists differ? *The Mesopotamians turned raw materials into finished goods themselves. The colonists shipped raw materials abroad where the goods were made then shipped back to the colonists.*
14. What primary source shows that the Sumerians had chariots pulled by donkeys? *the Standard of Ur*

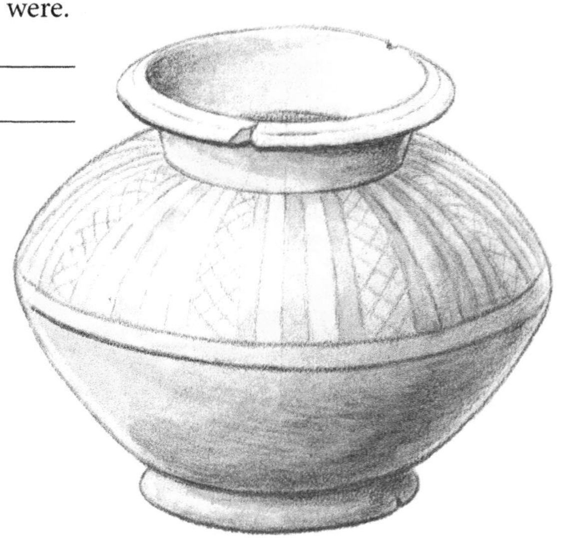

Study Guide

Use with Student Text pages 27–36.

Name ____________________

A. Complete each sentence.

polytheism 1. Mesopotamians worshiped many gods, a practice called ___.

scribe 2. A person who recorded information in writing was called a ___.

cylinder seal 3. A merchant signed his signature with a ___.

ziggurat 4. A pyramid-like temple called a ___ was built to honor the god of the city-state.

social classes 5. The Sumerian people were divided into three different levels called ___.

artisans 6. Skilled craftsmen called ___ turned raw materials into finished goods.

B. Answer the questions.

7. Why were scribes important? *They kept records of business dealings.*

8. Name three reasons that the priests were powerful people in Mesopotamia.

- *possible answers: People relied on priests to gain the favor of the gods. Priests interpreted the*
- *wishes of the gods. Only priests could communicate with the gods. Priests owned much of the land.*
-

9. How did the kings of the city-states begin? *Priests chose leaders for city-states during times of battle. Some of these leaders held on to their positions and became kings.*

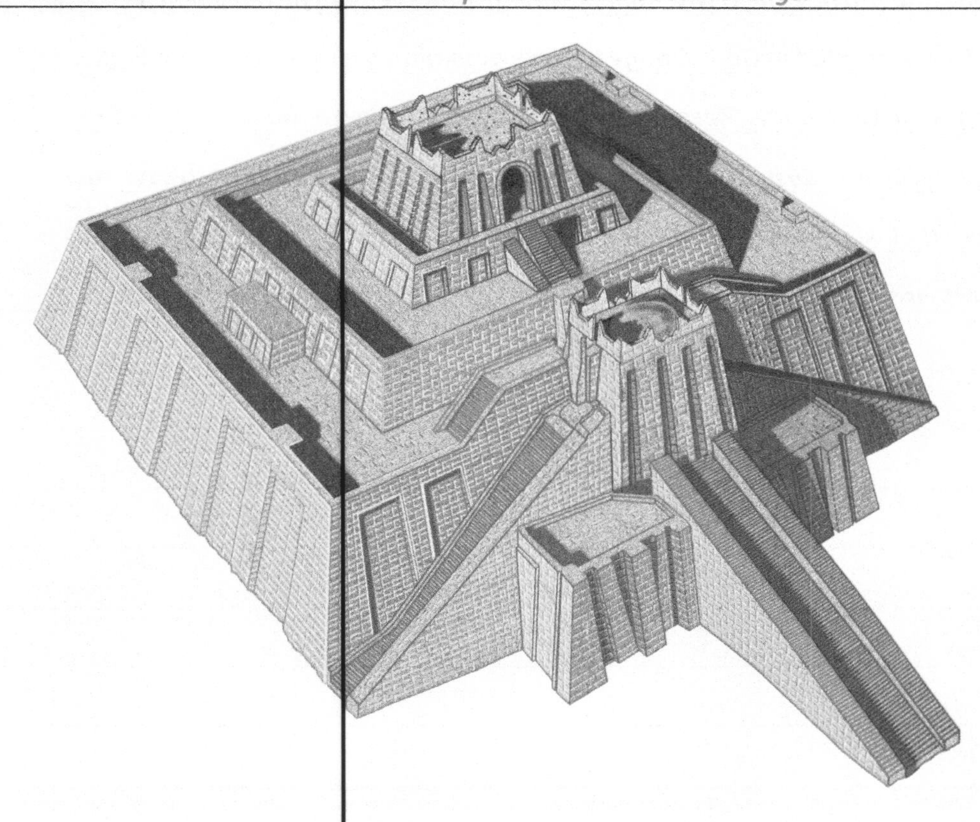

C. Write *T* if the statement is true. If the statement is false, write the correction for the underlined words.

middle 10. In Sumer the lowest class was the largest social class.

T 11. The Sumerians traded for natural resources they did not have.

ziggurat/temple 12. The Royal Cemetery was important not only as the center of religion but also as the seat of the government.

T 13. Trade helped the city-states grow in wealth and power.

D. First, plan your essay on your own paper. Then, write it below.

14. Contrast the Mesopotamian religious beliefs with the truth taught in the Bible. Include at least three differences.

The student's essay should include at least three of these differences: Mesopotamians practiced polytheism. The Bible teaches that there is only one God. Mesopotamians believed that the earth was born of the sea that surrounded it on all sides. The Bible teaches that God created the heavens and earth in six days. Mesopotamians believed that man was created to serve the gods and provide them with food, clothing, and shelter. The Bible teaches that man was created in God's image to have dominion over the earth and to glorify and serve God alone. Mesopotamians generally believed that a person's fate was decay and dust. The Bible teaches that those who trust Christ to save them from their sins will spend eternity with Him. All others will be judged eternally for their sins. See the Bible Connection on page 23 for additional differences.

Compare and Contrast

Name ___________________________

Use your Bible and Student Text pages 33–35 to complete each statement.

Mesopotamian religious beliefs	Biblical truth
The Mesopotamians practiced *polytheism*. They worshiped many gods.	The Bible teaches that there is *one God* (1 Cor. 8:6).
The Mesopotamians had *statues* of their gods. Most temple images were made from precious wood. Some were made of clay.	In the Bible, God says not to make *idols* or any graven image (Lev. 26:1).
The Mesopotamians relied on the *priests* to help gain the favor of the gods.	The Bible teaches that there is only "one God, and one *mediator* between God and men," Who is Jesus Christ (1 Tim. 2:5).
The Mesopotamians were taught that only *priests* could communicate with the gods.	The Bible teaches that God's "ears are open" to all righteous men's *prayer(s)* (1 Pet. 3:12).
Religious *rituals* and *prayers* accompanied all the Mesopotamians' activities, no matter how *ordinary*.	The Bible teaches that all should be done to the *glory* of *God* (1 Cor. 10:31).
The Mesopotamians believed that the earth was *born* of the sea that *surrounded* it on all sides.	The Bible teaches that God *created* the heavens and the earth in *six* days (Gen.1:1, 31).
The Mesopotamians believed that man was *created* to *serve* the gods and *provide* them with food, clothing, and shelter.	The Bible teaches that man was *created* in God's image to have *dominion/rule* over the earth and to glorify and serve God alone (Gen. 1:27–28).

Map and Architecture

Name ______________________

Use with Student Text pages 39–44.

A. Label the places on the map.

1. *Syria*
2. *Turkey*
3. *Jordan*
4. *Iraq*
5. *Iran*
6. *Sumer*
7. *Euphrates River*
8. *Tigris River*
9. *Mesopotamia*
10. *Persian Gulf*

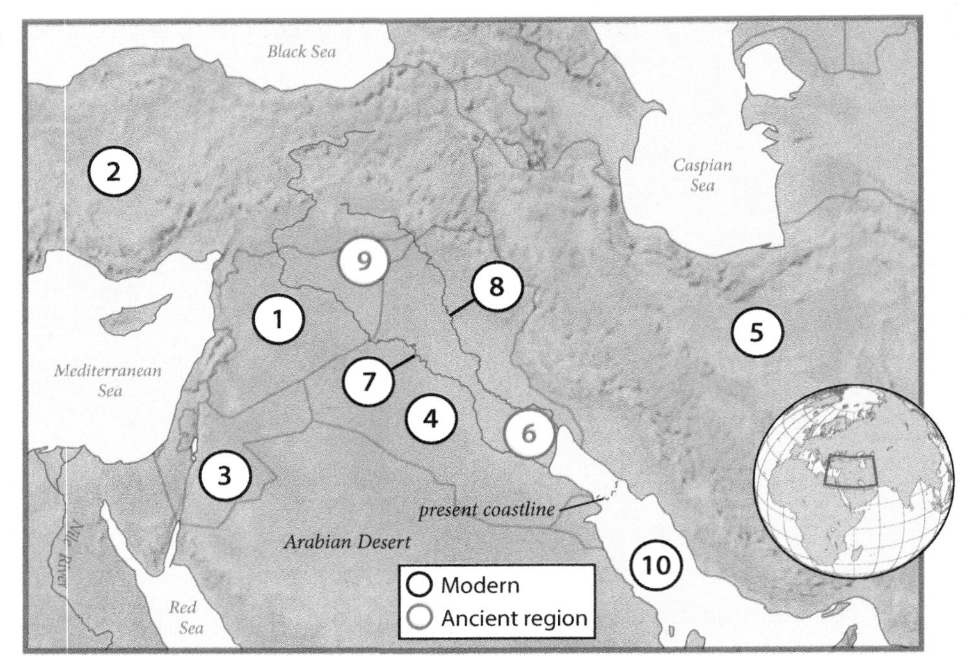

B. Compare and contrast your house with a Mesopotamian house using the Venn diagram. *Possible answers given.*

Mesopotamian house	Both	My house
mud brick	*door*	*wood*
flat roof	*rugs*	*shingled roof*
courtyard	*stairs*	*backyard*
chapel	*bedrooms*	*windows*
entertain on roof		*entertain on deck*

Study Guide

Use with Student Text pages 37–44.

Name ______________________

A. Match the term with its description.

_C_ 1. cuneiform
_E_ 2. scribe
_A_ 3. twelve-month calendar
_B_ 4. epic
_D_ 5. cylinder seals
_F_ 6. clothing
_I_ 7. mathematical advance
_J_ 8. obedience and respect
_G_ 9. architectural features
_H_ 10. wheel

A. based on the cycles of the moon
B. long poem that tells the story of a hero
C. wedge-shaped writing
D. Mesopotamians' most famous works of art
E. kept records for merchants, the temple, and the government
F. natural resources of wool and flax
G. arches, columns, and domes
H. improved transportation and the making of pottery
I. the 60-minute hour and the 60-second minute
J. taught by parents to their children

B. Answer the questions.

11. Why should a Christian not be involved in astrology? *The position of the stars and the planets do not determine what will happen. God determines what will happen.*

12. How did cuneiform benefit the Sumerians and archaeologists? *Cuneiform was used to record Sumerian literature. It helps archaeologists learn about the ancient civilization.*

13. Why were the buildings constructed of mud bricks? *Mud was the natural resource that was available.*

14. Who attended school? What did they study to become? *boys from wealthy families; The boys studied to become scribes.*

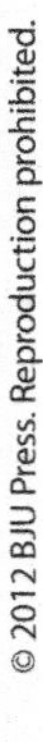

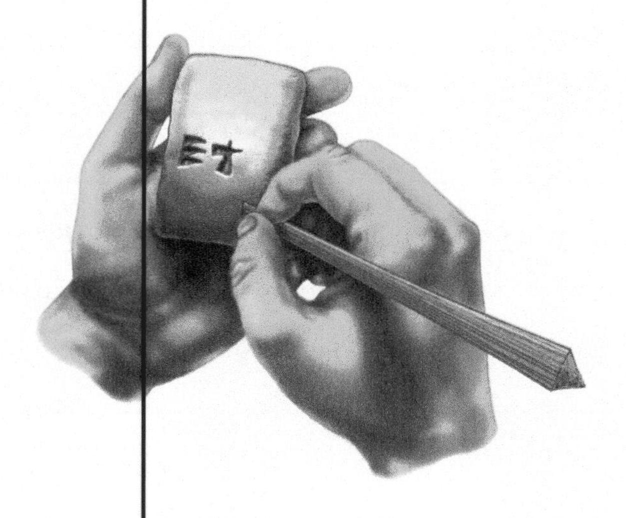

Measurement

Name ______________________

Weights and measurements were probably different from city-state to city-state. As the Sumerian civilization and government grew, some consistency became necessary. The measurements of ancient Mesopotamia can be re-created from artifacts of weights and containers and especially from economic records. One can see evidence of the number system based on the number 60 in the measurements. The human body was used for scale. The joint of a finger and the length of a forearm served as basic units. One of the most common measures of length was the cubit, the distance from the elbow to the tip of the middle finger. It would be to a customer's advantage to find a merchant with long arms when he was buying cloth or rope!

A. Follow the directions with the piece of string your teacher gives you.

1. Use the joint of one of your fingers to divide the string into 30 fingers.
2. Mark each "finger" with a black crayon.
3. Mark 1 cubit on the string with a red crayon.

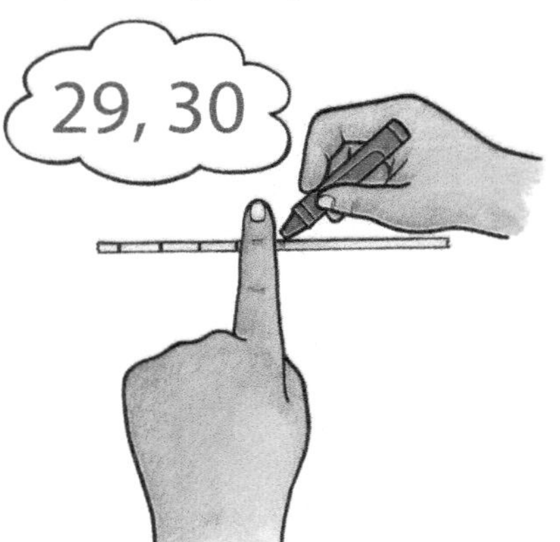

Mesopotamian measures
1 finger
30 fingers = 1 cubit or elbow
6 cubits = 1 reed or cane
30 cubits = 1 cord

B. Measure the items using the string. Record and label the measurements.

Item	Measurement
length of your elbow to the tip of your middle finger	
width of your *Heritage Studies 6* textbook	
width of your desk	
height of the teacher's desk	
width of the window	

1. Do your measurements agree with your classmates? *Answers to questions 1 and 2 will vary.*
2. Is the length from your elbow to the tip of your middle finger (forearm) the same as 1 cubit? ______
3. What would be a problem with a measurement based on a finger-joint width? *All finger joints are not the same length.*
4. What needs to happen for measurements to be the same? *an agreement on how long a "finger" is*
5. What would happen to a trader if the measurements were different between city-states or countries? *possible answer: A trader might make more or less than expected.*

Later Civilizations

Use with Student Text pages 46–54.

Name ______________________

For each civilization write its capital, its main leaders, and its main accomplishments. The accomplishments are listed below.

built city walls	cuneiform writing	Hammurabi's Code	military accomplishments
built new canals	destroyed Nineveh	Hanging Gardens	one of the best libraries
built roads	farming techniques	horse-drawn chariots	religion
built up Babylon	first known empire	iron weapons	

Civilization	Capital	Main leader(s)	Accomplishments
Akkadian Empire	*Akkad*	*Sargon I*	• *cuneiform writing* • *farming techniques* • *first known empire* • *religion*
Amorite civilization (Babylonian Empire)	*Babylon*	*Hammurabi*	• *built city walls* • *built new canals* • *Hammurabi's Code*
Hittite Empire	Hattushash	a king	• *horse-drawn chariots* • *iron weapons*
Assyrian Empire	*Nineveh*	Sargon II Sennacherib	• *built roads* • *one of the best libraries*
Chaldean Empire (New Babylonian Empire)	*Babylon*	*Nebuchadnezzar* *Belshazzar*	• *built up Babylon* • *destroyed Nineveh* • *Hanging Gardens* • *military accomplishments*

Study Guide

Name ________________________________

Use with Student Text pages 46–54.

A. Write the number of each place on the map. Shade the Fertile Crescent.

1. Asia Minor
2. Babylon
3. Euphrates River
4. Mesopotamia
5. Nineveh
6. Sumer
7. Tigris River
8. Ur

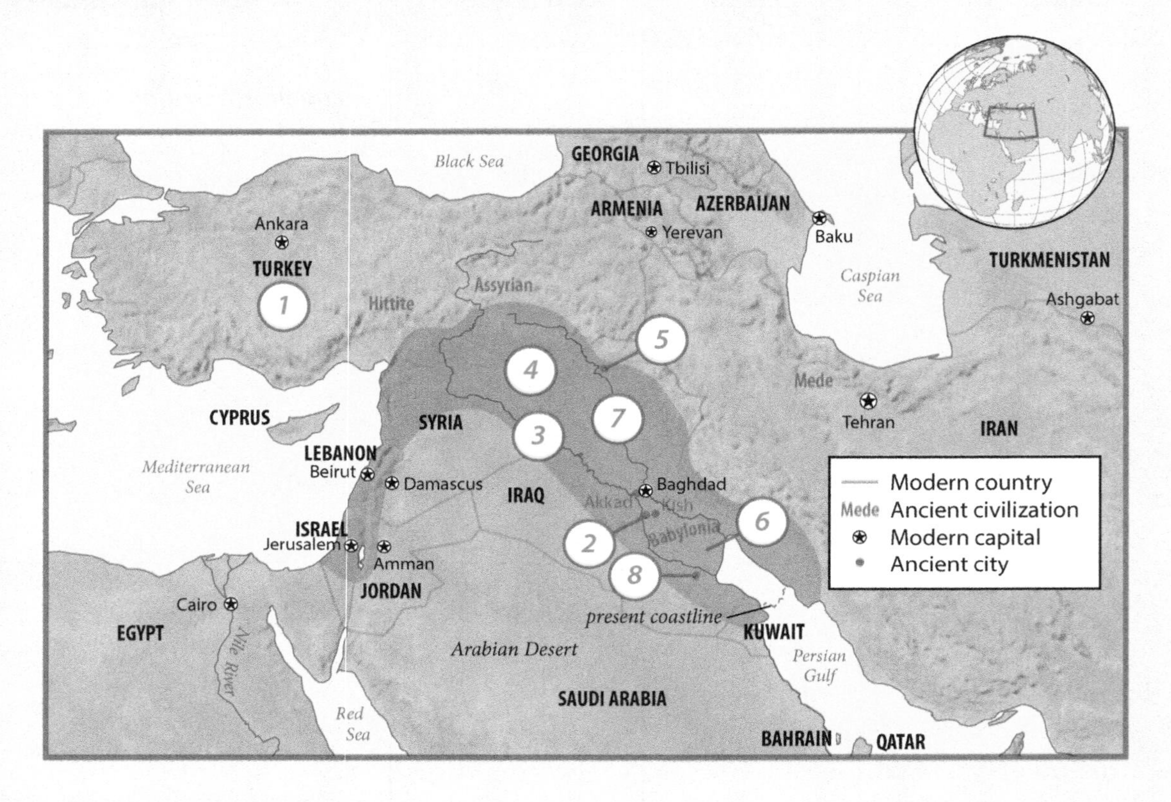

B. Write the letter of the correct answer.

__C__ 9. The abbreviation *ca.* means
- A. "before Christ."
- B. "in the year of the Lord."
- C. "around."

__A__ 10. When God called Abraham to leave Ur, He was telling Abraham
- A. to leave idolatry and the practice of polytheism.
- B. to bring his way of life with him.
- C. to leave his accomplishments and his heart of pride.

__C__ 11. Asia Minor is a peninsula between
- A. the Mediterranean Sea and the Persian Gulf.
- B. the Black Sea and the Persian Gulf.
- C. the Black Sea and the Mediterranean Sea.

Study Guide

Use with Student Text pages 46–54.

Name ______________________

C. Match the term to its description.

D 12. Hammurabi
B 13. Nebuchadnezzar
A 14. Sargon I
E 15. Babylonian Empire
C 16. Akkadian Empire

A. emperor of the Akkadian Empire
B. king of the Chaldean Empire
C. first empire
D. king of the Amorites who collected 282 laws
E. Amorite civilization

D. Answer the questions.

17. What was the result of Jonah's trip to Nineveh? *The Assyrians "turned from their evil way" (Jon. 3:10). God showed mercy on them and turned away His wrath.*

18. What happened to Nebuchadnezzar because of his pride? *God's judgment fell upon him. He lost his throne and became like a beast of the field.*

E. Complete the chart.

19–24. Contrast the Mosaic law with Hammurabi's Code.

	Mosaic law	Hammurabi's Code
Religion	*large sections on how to worship God*	*no religious section*
Treatment of wealthy people	*forbids giving special treatment*	*gives special treatment*
Crime	*sin against God*	*doing wrong to another person*

Ancient Assyrian art

Chapter 2 Summary

Name ______________________________

Define these terms

artisans
Asia Minor
ca.
city-state
cuneiform
cylinder seal
epic
Fertile Crescent
irrigation
polytheism
scribe
social classes
surplus
tell
ziggurat

Locate these places

Asia Minor
Babylon
Euphrates River
Fertile Crescent
Mesopotamia
Nineveh
Sumer
Tigris River
Ur

Tell about these people

Hammurabi
Jonah
Nebuchadnezzar
Sargon I
Sir Leonard Woolley

Explain what happened

God's call to Abraham

Be able to . . .

Write an essay contrasting the Mesopotamian religious beliefs with biblical truth
Tell why Sumer was not the first civilization
Explain the benefits of the Tigris and Euphrates to Mesopotamian civilization
Describe farming in Sumer (tools, importance, and problems and solutions)
Identify the Sumerian social classes
Tell about the trading of goods in Sumer
Explain how the Mesopotamian kings began to rule
Explain how cuneiform benefited the Mesopotamians and archaeologists
Identify Mesopotamian math and science achievements
Describe Mesopotamian architecture
Describe the education, family life, and clothing of the Mesopotamians
Identify the first empire
Identify the Amorite civilization as the Babylonian Empire
Contrast Hammurabi's Code with the Mosaic law
Describe the result of Jonah's trip to Nineveh
Describe what happened to Nebuchadnezzar because of his pride

Navigating the Nile

Use with Student Text pages 56–58.

Name ____________________

A. Fill in the blanks with the answers to the clues given.

1. T R A D E
2. N I L E
3. W A T E R
4. I N V A S I O N
5. S A H A R A
6. C A T A R A C T
7. M I Z R A I M
8. W O R S H I P E D
9. T R A N S P O R T A T I O N

1. Because the river traffic slowed, ___ settlements developed along the cataracts.
2. The longest river in the world is the ___.
3. The Egyptians depended on the Nile for food and ___.
4. The geography of Egypt helped protect the people from ___.
5. Protection in the east and the west was provided by the ___.
6. A section of river that is shallow and rocky that causes dangerous rapids is called a ___.
7. In the Bible, Egypt is often referred to as ___.
8. The Egyptians ___ the Nile as a god.
9. The Nile was also important for providing a method of ___.

B. Use the shaded letters to complete the statement.

10. The Nile River flows from south to north because the south has a higher *elevation*.

C. Color the map. *Yellow and red coloring may vary.*

11. Blue - Nile River
12. Green - Mediterranean Sea
13. Yellow - Egypt (the New Kingdom)
14. Red - Sahara

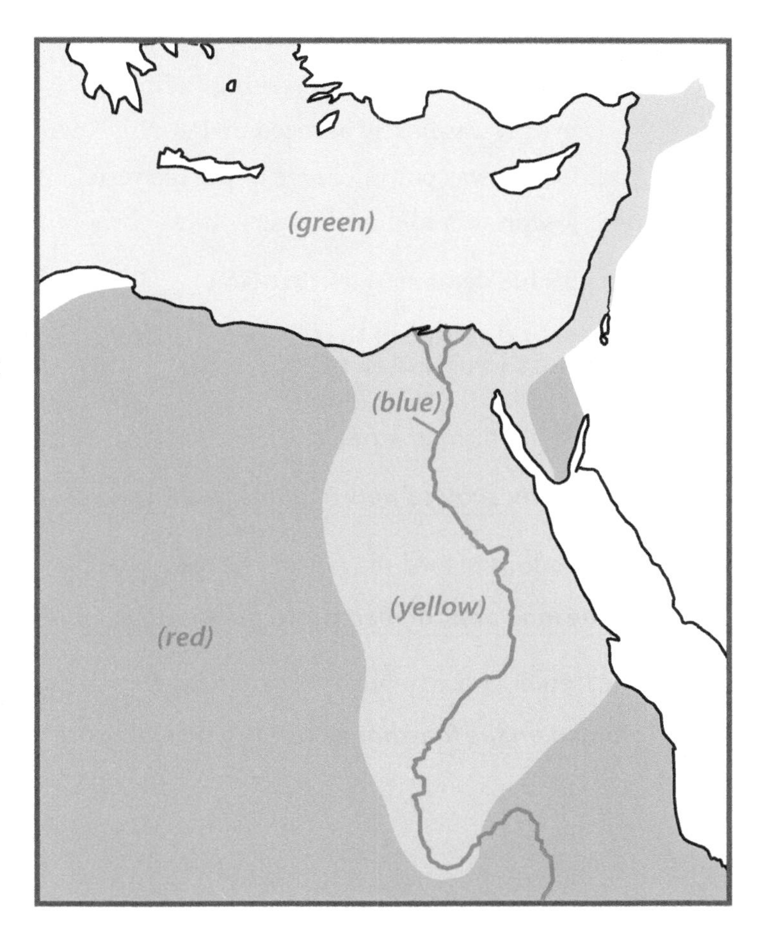

Study Guide

Name ______________________________

Use with Student Text pages 56–62.

A. Complete the section.

1. What two geographic features provided protection for Egypt against invaders?
   - *the Sahara*
   - *the cataracts of the Nile River*
2. Name three things the Nile River provided for the Egyptians.
   - *water*
   - *food*
   - *transportation*
3. What was the nickname for the Nile? What did it mean? *Hapi, meaning "well fed" or "fat"*
4. What benefit did the flooding of the Nile have? *It deposited silt on the soil, making very fertile farmland.*
5. How did the flooding of the Nile affect the taxes the people paid? *Taxes were based on how good the crops were. The more the Nile flooded, the more fertile land there was to produce crops.*
6. How did the flooding of the Nile affect the development of the calendar? *The calendar included three seasons based on the Nile's flood: Flooding, Planting, and Harvest.*

B. Number the events in Joseph's life in order. Then fill in the blanks in the last statement.

5 7. Joseph interpreted the dreams of Pharaoh.

7 8. Joseph was able to provide food and land for his family.

4 9. Joseph was faithful in his service in prison.

2 10. Joseph was faithful in serving Potiphar.

3 11. Joseph was falsely accused by Potiphar's wife and thrown into prison.

6 12. Joseph was put in charge of the harvests.

1 13. Joseph was sold into slavery.

14. Joseph's life demonstrates that God *blesses* those who *honor* Him.

C. Write a second sentence that illustrates the first sentence and clearly shows your understanding of the bolded word.

15. The Egyptians used a **nilometer** to help figure the taxes that the people would pay. *possible answer: A nilometer showed how high the Nile River was when its banks flooded.*
16. The **shadoof** helped the farmer get water to his crops. *possible answer: The farmer took the bucket on the long pole, dipped it into the Nile River, pulled it up, and then emptied it into the canal.*
17. The farmer chose to plant his crops on the **delta** of the Nile River. *possible answer: His crops were planted on the fan-shaped fertile land where the Mediterranean Sea and the Nile meet.*

Pyramid Organizer: Old Kingdom

Name ____________________

Use with Student Text pages 63–68.

A. Complete the sentences on the side of the pyramid.

1. Rulers were called *pharaohs* and were worshiped as *gods*.
2. Pyramids were built to house the body of the *pharaoh* and what he would need for the afterlife.
3. The three most famous pyramids are in the *valley* of *Giza*. The largest is called the *Great Pyramid*.
4. Egyptians wrote using *hieroglyphics*.
5. The key to unlocking the meaning of hieroglyphics was the *Rosetta stone*, which provided a *Greek* translation.
6. The first person to translate part of the Rosetta stone was *Jean-François Champollion*.
7. Egyptians used a plant readily available along the Nile, called *papyrus*, to make *paper*.
8. A dead body preserved by an embalmer of ancient Egypt is called a *mummy*.

Old Kingdom

B. First, plan the essays on your own paper. Then, write them on a new sheet of paper.

9. Describe the Egyptian pyramid. Include a description of two of the rooms inside the pyramid.
10. Describe the process of making mummies.

The answers to the essay questions are located on page 34.

Answers for essay questions on page 33

9. Describe the Egyptian pyramid. Include a description of two of the rooms inside the pyramid.

   The student's essay should include the following information: Each pyramid was constructed on a rectangular base with four sloping triangular sides. Each pyramid contained the buried body of a pharaoh (or other wealthy person), food, clothing, furniture, games and toys, and small statues. These things were to bring pleasure and ease in the afterlife. Detailed scenes of daily life were painted on the walls. The essay should also include descriptions of two of these rooms: underground chamber—possibly the pharaoh's original burial chamber or designed as a fake chamber to fool robbers; Grand Gallery—a large passageway that led upward to the pharaoh's burial chamber; queen's burial chamber—possibly the location where the pharaoh's possessions were placed for the afterlife; or pharaoh's burial chamber—the location of the pharaoh's sarcophagus.

10. Describe the process of making mummies.

    The student's essay should include the following: First, the embalmer cleaned out the body's skull. Then he cleaned out the abdominal cavities and dried the liver, stomach, lungs, and intestines. The embalmer placed each of these organs in special containers called canopic jars. He then filled the body with spices. The body was soaked for seventy days in natron. Then the body was washed and wrapped in linen strips. The embalmer returned the preserved mummy to the family for burial.

Mummies

Use with the article *Kinds of Mummies.*

Name ____________________

A. Fill in the blanks with the answers to the clues given. Unscramble the letters in the circles to answer the last question.

1. The Egyptian's heart was weighed against the *F E (A) T (H) E R O F T R (U) T H*.
2. The oldest mummies were found in *P (E) (R) U* and *C H I L (E)*.
3. The South American mummies were found in *C R O U C (H) E (D)* positions.
4. Scientists determined that the Lindow Man trimmed his beard with *(S) H E A R (S)*.
5. The Inuit mummies were found lying on *S E A L S (K) I (N) B L A (N) K E T S*.
6. As trophies for their victories, some peoples of South America would turn their conquered enemies into *S H R U N K E N H E A D S*. (**Hint:** The same letter begins the first word and ends the second word.)

B. Answer the questions.

The resurrection of Jesus from the dead guarantees that all who put their trust in Christ will also one day be raised bodily from the dead (1 Cor. 15:20).

7. Why would a person have himself frozen? *possible answers: extend his life, find a cure for his disease, live forever*
8. Read Hebrews 9:27. Write the verse in your own words. *Accept any reasonable answer. The verse states, "And as it is appointed unto men once to die, but after this the judgment."*
9. Based on this verse, what would you say is the ultimate goal of the people being frozen? *possible answers: to live forever, to avoid judgment*
10. What does the person being frozen hope that scientists in the future will give him? *possible answers: a cure for his disease, a new body*
11. What does God promise that all Christians will receive after the resurrection? (1 Cor. 15:51–52; 1 John 3:2) *a new body or to be like Christ*

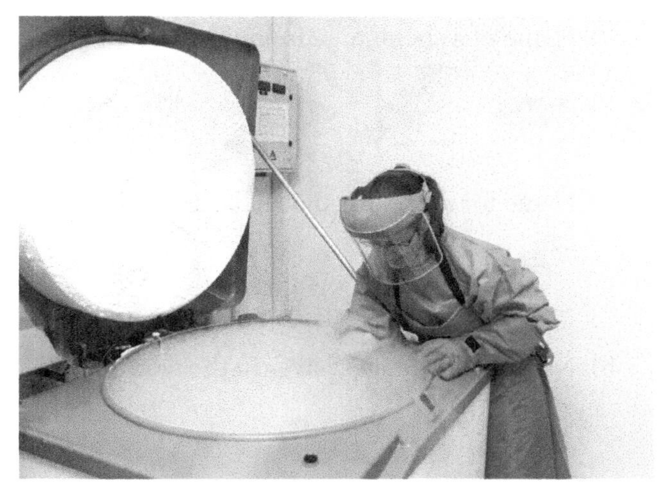

A cryogenics lab

Hieroglyphics

Name ______________________

Use with Student Text page 69.

Hieroglyphics probably began with one picture representing each word. That system soon became impractical. It changed to have each symbol representing a sound. This is slightly different from the English alphabet in which sounds can be represented by combinations of letters. For instance, "sh" as in *shop* is made in English by combining an *s* and an *h*. However, there is a symbol in hieroglyphics for the "sh" sound. Also some English letters can sound like other letters. The *c* in *cat* sounds like a *k*, and the *c* in *cent* sounds like an *s*. When reading or writing hieroglyphics, remember to think of the English sounds and not just the letters.

A. Use the key on Student Text page 69 to help you match the words.

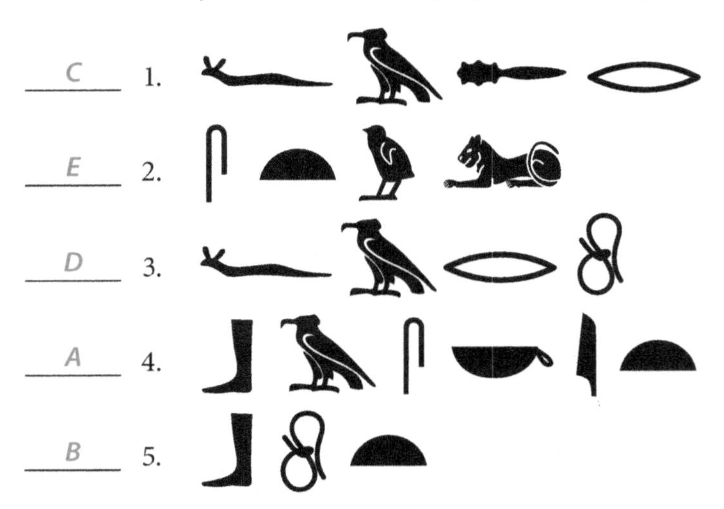

A. basket
B. boat
C. father
D. pharaoh
E. stool

B. Write the answer in hieroglyphics.

6. Name of Egyptian paper

7. Name of Egyptian tool for dipping water

8. Name of a shenu on a monument

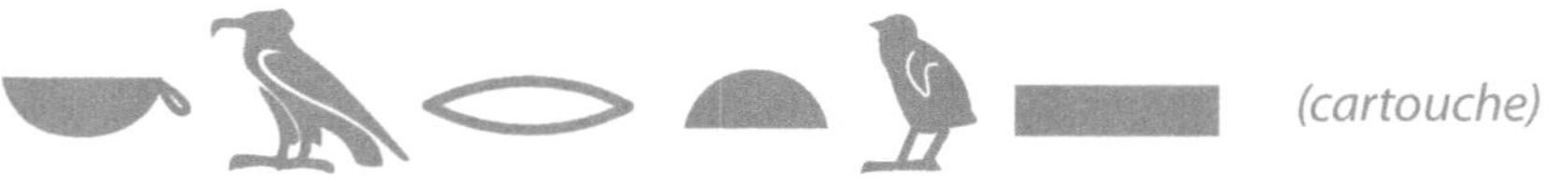

9. Name for a preserved dead body

10. Name of the longest river in the world

C. Write your name in hieroglyphics in the cartouche outline.

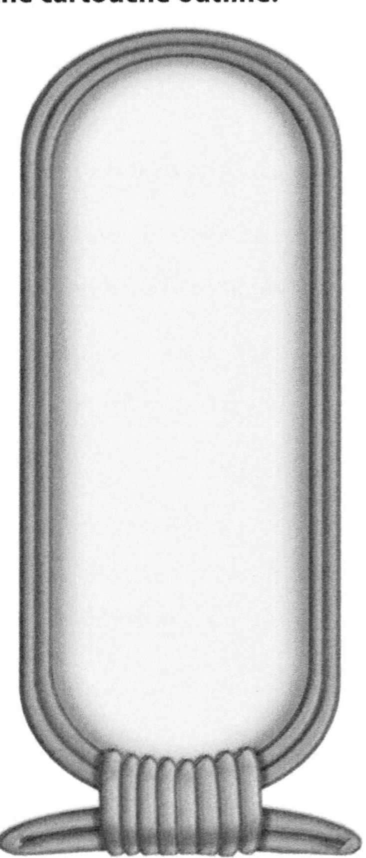

Pyramid Organizer: Middle Kingdom

Name ______________________________

Use with Student Text page 70.

A. Complete the sentences on the side of the pyramid.

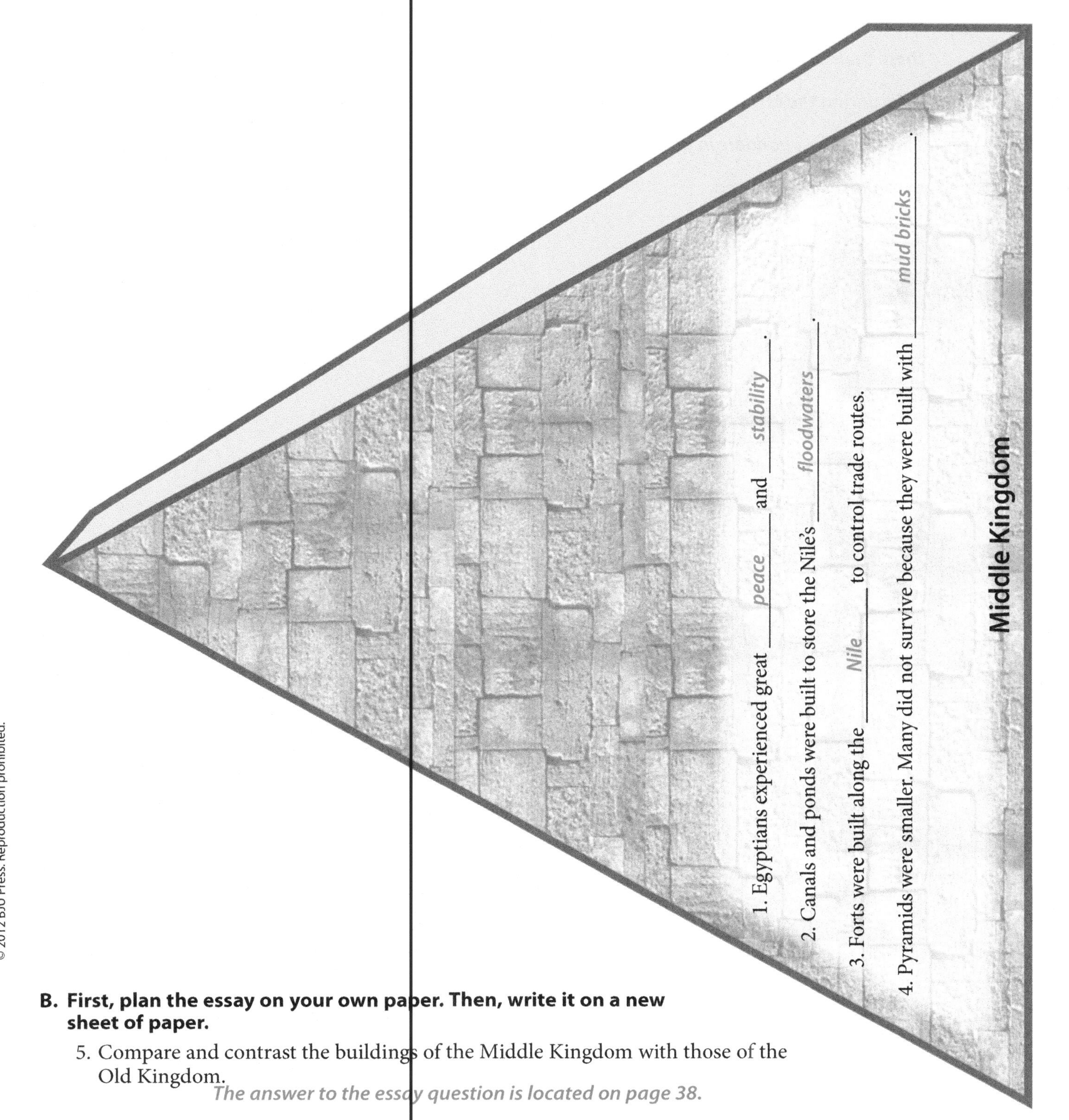

B. First, plan the essay on your own paper. Then, write it on a new sheet of paper.

5. Compare and contrast the buildings of the Middle Kingdom with those of the Old Kingdom.

The answer to the essay question is located on page 38.

Answer for essay question on page 37

5. Compare and contrast the buildings of the Middle Kingdom with those of the Old Kingdom.

   The student's essay should include the following information: Temples, pyramids, and palaces were constructed during both the Old and Middle Kingdoms. The people in the Middle Kingdom decorated these buildings with sculptures and paintings, much like those of the Old Kingdom. The pyramids built during the Middle Kingdom were smaller and less grand than those of the Old Kingdom. Instead of using stone, builders in the Middle Kingdom used mud bricks. Not many of the Middle Kingdom's pyramids have survived.

Pyramid Organizer: New Kingdom

Use with Student Text pages 71–74.

Name ______________________________

A. Complete the sentences on the side of the pyramid.

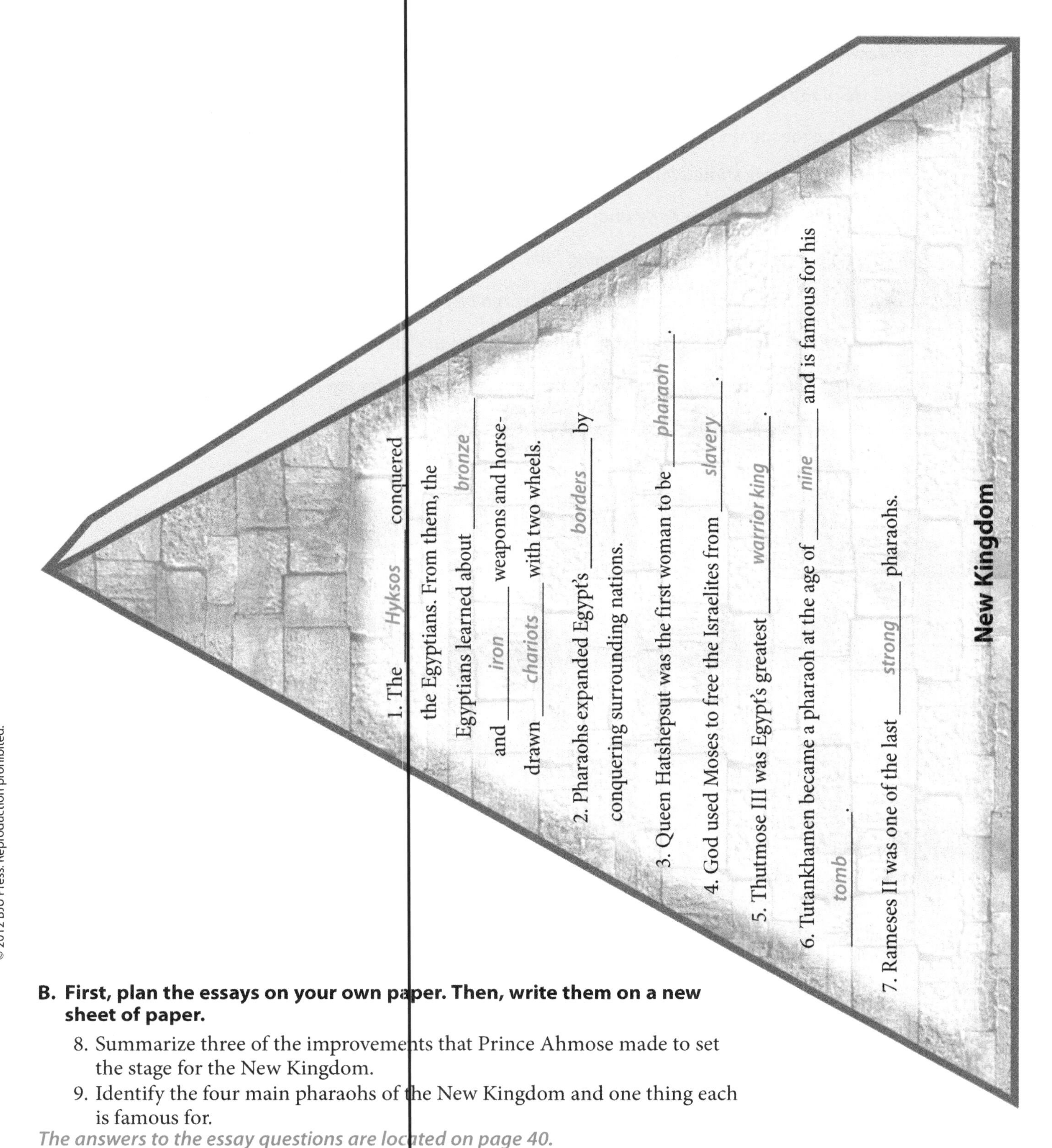

B. First, plan the essays on your own paper. Then, write them on a new sheet of paper.

8. Summarize three of the improvements that Prince Ahmose made to set the stage for the New Kingdom.
9. Identify the four main pharaohs of the New Kingdom and one thing each is famous for.

The answers to the essay questions are located on page 40.

Answers for essay questions on page 39

8. Summarize three of the improvements that Prince Ahmose made to set the stage for the New Kingdom.

   The student's essay should include three of the following: Ahmose drove out the Hyksos. He created a protective buffer south of the Upper Kingdom to prevent invasions. He expanded the kingdom farther east. He made Egypt mightier than it had ever been.

9. Identify the four main pharaohs and one thing each is famous for.

   The student's essay should include all these pharaohs and one of these facts for each pharaoh: Queen Hatshepsut was an early pharaoh and was the first woman pharaoh. Thutmose III was the greatest Egyptian warrior king, invaded Palestine and Syria, and stretched the Egyptian empire to the Euphrates River. Tutankhamen, or King Tut, was a boy ruler and is famous for his tomb. Rameses II, or Rameses the Great, had a reputation for being a wise and good pharaoh and was kind to his subjects, was the last of the great pharaohs who kept Egypt strong, defeated the Hittites, and built some of the greatest temples in Egypt.

Study Guide

Use with Student Text pages 63–74.

Name ______________________

A. Complete each sentence.

dynasty 1. A line of kings or rulers who belong to the same family is called a ___.

pharaohs 2. During the Old Kingdom, rulers of Egypt became known as ___.

Moses 3. God sent ___ to Pharaoh to ask him to let the Israelites go.

plagues 4. God sent ten ___ to the Egyptians when Pharaoh refused to free the Israelites.

B. Write *T* if the statement is true. If the statement is false, write the correction for the underlined words.

Lower 5. The plain around the Nile delta was called ~~Upper~~ Egypt.

T 6. The Great Pyramid is the largest of the pyramids located in the valley of Giza.

bronze 7. From the Hyksos the Egyptians learned to use weapons of ~~steel~~ and iron.

C. Match the description to the correct person or term.

E 8. famous for his tomb

B 9. first woman to be a ruler in Egypt

A 10. first to translate a portion of the hieroglyphics on the Rosetta stone

C 11. the last of the strong pharaohs

D 12. the greatest Egyptian warrior king

A. Jean-François Champollion
B. Hatshepsut
C. Rameses II
D. Thutmose III
E. Tutankhamen

J 13. paper made from the soft sponge-like center of a stem of a plant growing along the Nile

L 14. a stone coffin

H 15. Egyptian writing or picture writing

G 16. hieroglyphs of a name written inside an oval shape

F 17. special containers for the organs of a dead body

I 18. a dead body that has been preserved from decaying

K 19. a large tomb

F. canopic jars
G. cartouche
H. hieroglyphics
I. mummy
J. papyrus
K. pyramid
L. sarcophagus

D. Complete the section.

20. Who had the Great Pyramid built? *Khufu*

21. How did the Rosetta stone unlock the Egyptian language? *Answer should include that Greek was a known language and that the Greek portion was used to translate the Egyptian symbols on the other portion of the stone.*

22. Name three uses the Egyptians had for papyrus. *possible answers: record keeping, writing letters, telling stories, basket weaving, making boats, forming ropes*

- ______
- ______
- ______

23. How is the Hyksos invasion of Egypt described? *The Hyksos brutally attacked and seized whatever they wanted.*

24. Besides weapons, what did the Hyksos bring to the Egyptians that changed their warfare? *the horse-drawn chariot with two wheels*

E. Number the steps of the mummy-making process in order.

2 25. The skull and then the abdominal cavity were cleaned out.

5 26. The body was washed and wrapped in linen strips.

1 27. The embalmer dressed in a jackal-headed costume of Anubis.

4 28. The body was filled with spices and soaked for seventy days in a salt solution called natron.

6 29. The body was returned to the family for burial.

3 30. The organs were dried and placed in special containers called canopic jars.

F. First, plan the essay on your own paper. Then, write it below.

31. Describe the Egyptian pyramid. Include a description of two of the rooms inside the pyramid.

The student's essay should include the following: Each pyramid was constructed on a rectangular base with four sloping triangular sides. Each pyramid contained the buried body of a pharaoh, food, clothing, furniture, games and toys, and small statues. These things were to bring pleasure and ease in the afterlife. Detailed scenes of daily life were painted on the walls. The essay should also include two of these room descriptions: underground chamber—possibly the pharaoh's original burial chamber or designed as a fake chamber to fool robbers; Grand Gallery—a large passageway that led upward to the pharaoh's burial chamber; queen's burial chamber—possibly the location where the pharaoh's possessions were placed for the afterlife (the queen was actually buried in a smaller pyramid nearby); and pharaoh's burial chamber—the location of the pharaoh's sarcophagus.

What's in a Name?

Name ___________________________

In ancient times, names were very important. They told something about the character of the person bearing the name. Amenhotep II changed his name to Akhenaton when he changed his religion. He wanted everyone to know that he worshiped one god and that his loyalty was to Aton.

People gave names to certain places to preserve the memory of an event that took place there. Parents often named their children for a certain trait they demonstrated or for the circumstances of their birth.

God communicates through the names He is given in His Word. Each name for God reveals a part of His character. His names help Christians to understand more about Who He is and how they can be more like Him.

Read the passage. Write a sentence or two describing what each listed name of God reveals about the character of God.

Accept all reasonable answers. A summary of the passage has been given.

1. Genesis 22—Jehovah-jireh (the Lord provides) *This passage speaks of taking Isaac up the mountain to be sacrificed. God provided a ram as a sacrifice.*

2. Exodus 17:8–16—Jehovah-nissi (the Lord is my banner) *This passage describes the battle where Aaron and Hur held Moses' hands up until the Israelites had won the battle. Moses built an altar and called the place Jehovah-nissi (the Lord is my banner).*

3. Judges 6:1–24—Jehovah-shalom (the Lord is peace) *This passage speaks of God's calling Gideon to be His servant in the battle. In spite of Gideon's initial fear and doubt, he built an altar and called it Jehovah-shalom (the Lord is peace) because it is only God Who can give true peace.*

4. Psalm 23—Jehovah-rohi (the Lord is my shepherd) *This passage is the well-known reference to the Lord's tender care for His sheep.*

Egyptian Culture

Name ________________________

Use with Student Text pages 75–79.

Complete the crossword puzzle.

Across

6. the god of the underworld
9. the pharaoh who changed his name to show he worshiped one god
10. the person everyone worked for
11. a black cosmetic powder
12. one of the main themes in Egyptian music
13. a triangle-shaped diagram of social classes (2 words)
16. the god who weighed the dead person's heart against the feather of justice, order, and truth
17. a Hebrew slave who became the second-most-powerful man in Egypt

Down

1. a part of Egyptian everyday life as well as celebrations
2. a large ornament thought to protect the wearer from evil spirits
3. a scroll buried with every person (4 words)
4. an Egyptian's main food made from wheat or barley
5. people at the top of the social pyramid (2 words)
7. a plant woven into cloth
8. the type of religion the Egyptians had
12. an article worn by both men and women and made of gold and beads
14. the goddess who protected children
15. an article worn by both men and women and made of beeswax

Study Guide

Use with Student Text pages 75–79.

Name ______________________

A. Fill in the blanks.

amulets 1. To provide protection from evil spirits, Egyptians wore ___ as large ornaments on necklaces.

Akhenaton 2. Amenhotep IV changed his name to ___ to show that he worshiped one god, Aton.

B. Complete the social pyramid by writing the correct occupations on each level. Then answer the questions about social classes.

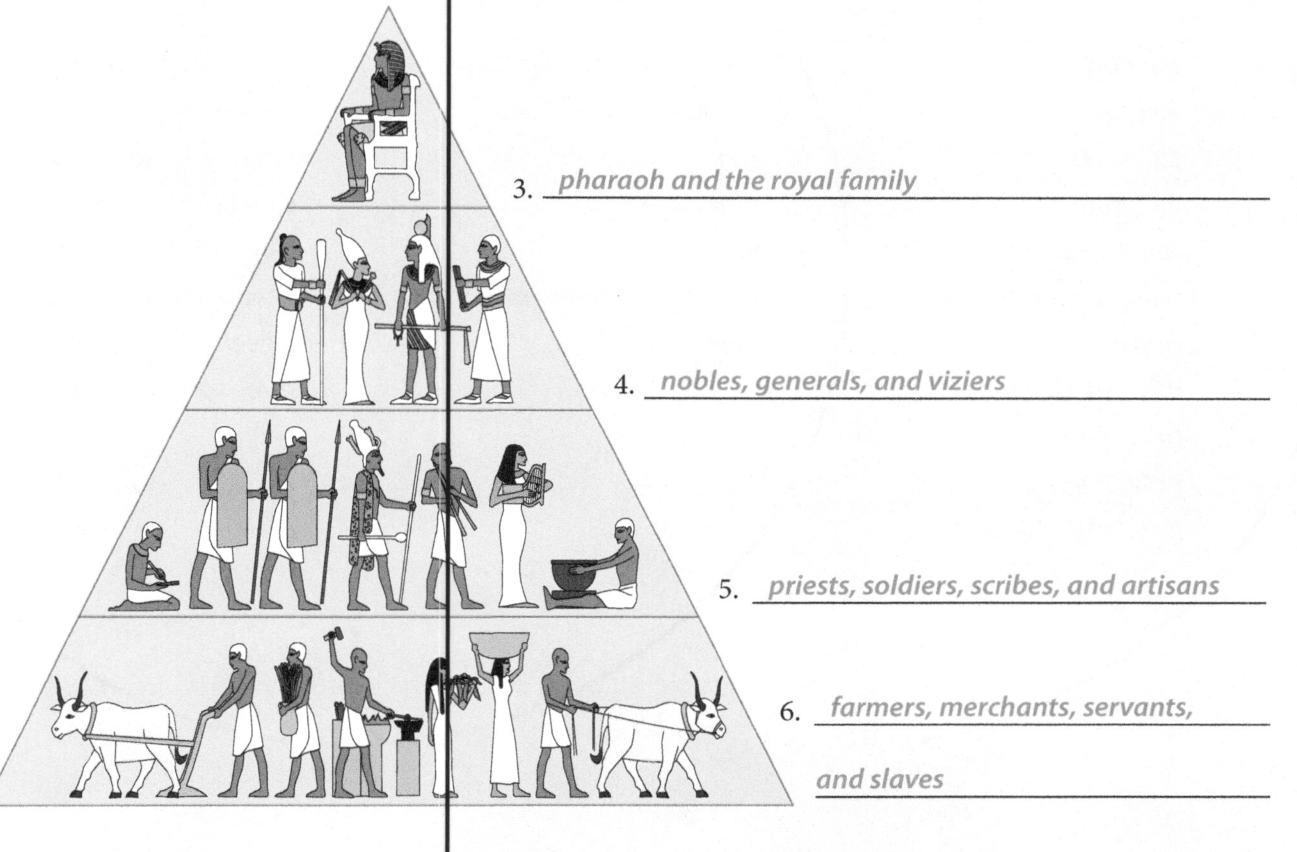

7. What determined someone's position in the social classes? wealth or power

8. How could someone rise to a higher social class? by gaining the pharaoh's favor

9. What was different about the roles that women played in Egyptian society from most ancient civilizations? possible answers: They were able to buy and sell property. They could work as farmers or merchants or hold other jobs usually held by men. Some served in the temple.

C. First, plan the essay on your own paper. Then, write it on a new sheet of paper.

10. Contrast the Egyptian religion with biblical truth. Include at least three differences.

Suggested answer is on page 48.

Comparing and Contrasting

Name ____________________

Use with Student Text page 81.

Use the Venn diagram to compare and contrast Egypt with Mesopotamia. *Possible answers have been given.*

Egypt	Both	Mesopotamia
mud brick	*fertile soil from river floods*	*Tigris and Euphrates*
Nile	*farming*	*city-states*
cataracts	*trade*	*ruled by kings*
kingdoms	*pottery*	*cuneiform writing*
ruled by pharaohs	*metal products*	*clay tablets*
hieroglyphic writing	*hot and dry summers*	*12-month calendar*
papyrus	*polytheism*	*wheel, plow, and sail*
365-day calendar		*three social classes*
mummies		
pyramids		
four social classes		

Statue of Rameses II in the court of Rameses II, Luxor Temple, Egypt

Pyramid Organizer: Kush

Name ______________________________

Use with Student Text pages 82–86.

Complete the sentences on the side of the pyramid. Then put the pyramid organizer together by gluing or taping the tabs.

1. Like the Egyptians, the Kushites depended on the *Nile* for food, water, transportation, and trade.
2. They used an *irrigation* *system* to be able to farm or raise cattle.
3. The Kushites had an abundance of *natural* *resources*.
4. They developed two systems of written language, a form of *hieroglyphics* and later a script called *Meroitic*.
5. Kush began as a strong *village*. The Egyptians feared its growing *power* and conquered the Kushites.
6. The Kushites began to adopt Egyptian *culture*.
7. Kush grew in power and conquered *Egypt*. Soon Kush was conquered by the *Assyrians* and driven out of Egypt.
8. The Kushites exhausted their ______________ and were conquered by the *Aksum*.

Kush

Answer for essay question on page 45

10. Contrast the Egyptian religion with biblical truth. Include at least three differences.
The student's essay should include the following points: (1) The Egyptians were polytheistic. Their gods were false and were invented by man. The Bible teaches that there is only one true God. (2) The Egyptians believed that after death they would be judged according to their works. If their works were good enough, they would spend the afterlife in a place of peace. The Bible teaches that where man will spend eternity depends on his relationship with Jesus Christ. (3) The Egyptians believed that they could preserve their souls and provide for them in the afterlife. Their burial practices were based on this belief. They believed it was important to preserve the deceased body to preserve that person's soul, but they did not believe that body would ever live again. The Bible teaches differently. The resurrection of Jesus from the dead guarantees that all who put their trust in Him will also one day be raised bodily from the dead.

Answer for essay question on page 49

14. Compare and contrast Kush with Egypt. Include at least two similarities and one difference.
The student's essay should include two of these similarities: Kush and Egypt are similar in that they used an irrigation system to increase farmland. Women held a variety of roles but were the primary caregivers in the household. Both Kush and Egypt used hieroglyphics, developed similar architecture, depended on the Nile for survival, and were polytheistic. The essay should include one of these differences: The Egyptians had more farmland, which provided more variety in their diet. Kushites added the Meroitic script to the Egyptian hieroglyphics and depleted their nation's natural resources.

Study Guide

Use with Student Text pages 82–86.

Name ______________________

A. Complete the section.

1. What were the two forms of writing that the Kushites used?
   - *hieroglyphics*
   - *Meroitic*
2. What happened to the Kushites when the Egyptians conquered them? *They adopted Egyptian culture, began dressing like the Egyptians, worshiping Egyptian gods, and changed Egyptian hieroglyphics to fit their own language.*
3. What gave the Assyrians the advantage to conquer the Kushites? *iron weapons*
4. What did the Kushites discover around the capital at Meroë? *iron ore deposits*
5. Why did the Kushite civilization decline? *They used all their natural resources.*
6. Name two advantages and two disadvantages of the Aswan High Dam.

Advantages	Disadvantages
Controls the flooding of the river	*Covered many artifacts with Lake Nasser*
Provides hydroelectric energy	*Traps silt behind the dam leaving no nutrients in the soil beyond the dam; affected the fishing*

7. How did archaeologists save the Temples at Abu Simbel? *They moved them to higher ground where the water would not reach.*

B. Write the names of the numbered places on the map.

8. *Egypt*
9. *Lake Nasser*
10. *Kush*
11. *Mediterranean Sea*
12. *Nile River*
13. *Sahara*

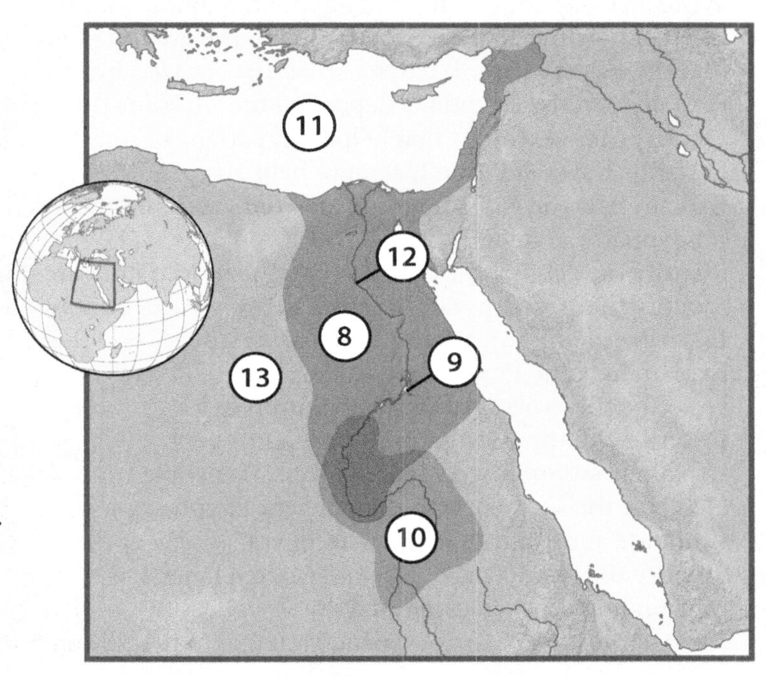

C. First, plan the essay on your own paper. Then, write it on a new sheet of paper.

14. Compare and contrast Kush with Egypt. Include at least two similarities and one difference.

Suggested answer is on page 48.

Chapter 3 Summary

Name ______________________

Define these terms

amulet
canopic jars
cartouche
delta
dynasty
hieroglyphics
mummy
nilometer
papyrus
pharaoh
pyramid
sarcophagus
shadoof

Locate these places

Egypt
Kush
Lake Nasser
Mediterranean Sea
Nile River
Sahara

Tell about these people

Akhenaton
Jean-François Champollion
Queen Hatshepsut
Ramses II
Thutmose III
Tutankhamen

Explain what happened

the Hyksos invasion of Egypt

Be able to . . .

Write an essay contrasting the Egyptian religion with biblical truth
Explain how the Nile's geography led to the growth of the Egyptian civilization
Identify Egypt's natural barriers that discouraged invasions
Explain how the Egyptians depended on the Nile's floodwaters for survival
Identify the two things that helped Egyptians become successful farmers
Describe how God used Joseph to help His people
Explain how the Nile's flooding affected taxes and the development of the Egyptian calendar
Identify the geographic regions that united into one kingdom
Identify the largest pyramid in the valley of Giza built by Khufu
Describe the significance of the Rosetta stone
Explain how the Egyptians used papyrus
Describe the process of making mummies
Describe the three kingdoms of ancient Egypt
Explain how God used Moses to free His people from slavery
Describe the social pyramid of ancient Egypt
Compare and contrast Kush with Egypt
Identify the two forms of Kushite written language
Explain how Kush became wealthy
Explain the advantages and disadvantages of the Aswan High Dam

Chapter 4 Organizer

Use with Student Text pages 88–116.

Name ____________________

Complete the two-column organizer as you study the chapter.

pp. 88–91	What is the Abrahamic Covenant?	God promised Abraham that his offspring would become a great nation. God would bring a great blessing to all the families of the earth. Jesus fulfilled this last promise.
	The name of the nation is . . .	Israel because that was a special name that God had given Jacob.
	Joseph oversaw the building of storehouses to prepare . . .	for a famine in Egypt.
	Joseph's father and brother and their families came to Egypt for . . .	food.
	The Egyptian pharaoh made the Israelites . . .	slaves.
	To deliver the Israelites, God called . . .	Moses.
	Because of the pharaoh's stubbornness, God unleashed . . .	ten plagues.
	God instructed the Israelites to spread . . .	the blood of a sacrificed lamb on each doorpost and lintel to protect them from death.
	The Jews remember their deliverance from the death of the firstborn and from slavery in Egypt as . . .	the Passover.
	The Israelites' leaving Egypt is known as the . . .	Exodus, which took place ca. 1446 BC.
	At Mount Sinai God gave Israel . . .	His law through Moses.
	What is the Mosaic Covenant?	God gave Israel laws that told the people how to live to please Him. If they obeyed these laws, the nations around Israel would see the great and true God, and He promised to bless Israel. If the Israelites disobeyed, God promised to punish them.
	Israel's history under the Mosaic Covenant shows that it is . . .	impossible to please God with one's own efforts.
	One of the reasons God gave the Israelites the Ten Commandments was . . .	so other nations could see the wisdom and righteousness of God.
p. 92	God told the Israelites to build a place for worship called . . .	the tabernacle.
	The tabernacle was a symbol of God's . . .	presence with His people.
	The materials and furnishings of the tabernacle symbolized God's . . .	holiness, justice, and other attributes.

pp. 94–95	The belief in one god is called . . .	monotheism.
	The Hebrew name for the one true God is . . .	Yahweh.
	The capital city of Israel was . . .	Jerusalem.
	The restoration of the broken relationship between God and man is called . . .	atonement.
	True atonement was made possible by . . .	Christ's sacrificial death on the cross.
	The Hebrew religious calendar is a . . .	lunar calendar.
	Jesus celebrated Passover with . . .	His disciples in an upper room.
	When Jesus broke bread and took the cup of wine, He established . . .	the Lord's Supper, which is observed by Christians.
pp. 96–100	Because the Israelites did not trust God to help them take Canaan, . . .	they wandered for forty years in the desert.
	God helped the Israelites by parting . . .	the Jordan River.
	God punished the Israelites for disobedience by sending . . .	other nations to rule over parts of Israel.
	The Israelites asked Samuel to give them . . .	a king like other nations.
	Samuel anointed . . .	Saul as Israel's first king.
	Because Saul disobeyed God, . . .	David was chosen by God to replace Saul.
	Two important products of the Phoenicians were . . .	a purple dye and the famous cedars of Lebanon.
	The Phoenicians' greatest achievement was . . .	the development of one of the first alphabets.
	What is the Davidic Covenant?	God promised David that he would always have a legitimate heir to his throne. God would establish David's throne forever. Jesus, David's descendant, will rule from David's throne forever, fulfilling this promise.
	God gave Solomon . . .	wisdom and understanding that no other man has ever known.
	Solomon's most impressive building project was . . .	the temple in Jerusalem.
pp. 102–5	The Northern Kingdom kept the name . . .	Israel and was ruled by Jeroboam.
	Israel's capital was at . . .	Samaria.
	God sent judgment to Israel, and it was . . .	conquered by the Assyrian Empire.
	The Southern Kingdom took the name . . .	Judah and was ruled by Rehoboam.
	Judah's capital remained at . . .	Jerusalem.
	Nebuchadnezzar of the Chaldean Empire . . .	conquered Judah.
	The Babylonian captivity took place in . . .	586 BC.

Chapter 4 Organizer

Name ______________________

Use with Student Text pages 88–116.

Complete the two-column organizer as you study the chapter.

Pages		
pp. 102–5	The scattering of the Israelites into many other nations is known as the . . .	Diaspora. It fulfilled the Mosaic Covenant.
	The Israelites became known as . . .	the Jews.
	What is the New Covenant?	God promised to restore Israel and Judah from exile. He promised Jews and Gentiles that those who are part of this covenant would receive the Holy Spirit. God promised that He would forgive His people of all their sins.
	Assimilate means . . .	"to absorb."
	The descendants of Israelites who intermarried with other conquered peoples that were moved into the Northern Kingdom . . .	were called Samaritans.
	The name given to the former Southern Kingdom of Judah was . . .	Judea.
	The queen who risked her life to plead with King Xerxes to save the Jews was . . .	Esther.
	The Jews celebrated their deliverance from destruction by Haman with a feast . . .	that became known as the holiday Purim.
pp. 106–9	The Greek translation of the Old Testament Scriptures is called . . .	the Septuagint.
	The people who were not Jews were called . . .	Gentiles.
	The king who placed idols in the temple and sacrificed pigs on the altar of God was . . .	Antiochus IV.
	The son of Mattathias who took leadership of the revolt against the Syrians was . . .	Judas Maccabeus.
	Judas and his army cleansed and rededicated the temple 2,300 days . . .	after the first pagan sacrifice was offered, just as the prophet Daniel prophesied.
	The Jews who stressed purity of life and obedience to the Torah and opposed the current rulers were called . . .	the Pharisees.
	The Jews who supported the current rulers were called . . .	the Sadducees.
	The cleansing and rededication of the temple is celebrated . . .	every year by the Jews as the holiday Hanukkah.
	A symbol of Hanukkah is . . .	the menorah.
pp. 110–13	Jesus was born during the reign of . . .	King Herod.
	Jesus identified Himself as . . .	the Messiah, or the Christ.
	Jesus preached about the need for . . .	repentance.

pp. 110–13	The death and resurrection of Jesus made possible . . .	the ___salvation___ of all people who repent and trust Him for eternal life.
	The Jews preached the gospel to the people of Israel and to people all over the world . . .	and proved to be a blessing to all the nations, just as God had promised ___Abraham___.
	The final fulfillment of the Davidic Covenant will be . . .	when Jesus returns to earth to rule from ___Jerusalem___.
	Judaism is . . .	a ___monotheistic___ religion.
	When the Israelites had no temple, . . .	the ___synagogue___ became the center of Jewish worship.
	The synagogue was . . .	a place where the Jews could gather for ___prayer___ and Scripture reading.
	In rabbinic Judaism the focus is . . .	on careful obedience to the ___law___.
	The Jews were so focused on keeping the law . . .	that they did not recognize Jesus as the ___Messiah___.
	A rabbi is . . .	a Jewish religious ___teacher___.
	The Talmud is . . .	the collection of Jewish law and tradition known as the Mishnah and the ___Gemara___.
	A port city located about sixty miles northwest of Jerusalem was . . .	___Caesarea Maritima___.
	Roman engineers built the city and harbor, which had . . .	loading ___docks___, storage areas, an inner harbor, and an outer harbor with a lighthouse.
	Caesarea Maritima had been constructed over . . .	a geological ___fault line___ that runs along the coast of Israel.
	The destruction of Caesarea Maritima may have been caused by . . .	an unstable foundation and a ___tsunami___ that struck between the first and second centuries AD.
pp. 114–16	The Jews yearned for freedom from . . .	extortion by the Roman ___governors___ and the brutality of the Romans.
	Jews that plotted the overthrow of Rome by military action were known . . .	as ___Zealots___.
	A legion consisted of . . .	three to six ___thousand___ men.
	In AD 70 Titus and the Roman army surrounded Jerusalem and brought . . .	about the ___destruction___ of Jerusalem.
	Josephus was a . . .	Jewish ___historian___.
	The Jewish stronghold at a mountaintop fortress was called . . .	___Masada___.
	The Romans worked to reach Masada . . .	for ___three___ years.
	When the Jews saw that the Romans would break through, . . .	they committed mass ___suicide___.

Cause and Effect

Use with Student Text pages 88–91.

Name ____________________

A. Match the cause with its effect.

Causes

C 1. Because Abraham believed God,

B 2. Because God enabled Joseph to interpret the pharaoh's dream,

E 3. Because the famine struck,

A 4. Because God moved Joseph to Egypt,

D 5. Because the Egyptians feared that the Israelites would become too powerful,

Effects

A. Joseph was able to provide for his family.
B. Joseph was made the second-highest ruler in Egypt.
C. God considered this former idolater to be a righteous man.
D. the pharaoh made the Israelites slaves.
E. people from many nations went to Egypt for food.

Causes

F 6. Because the Israelites continued to grow in number,

I 7. Because the people of Israel cried out to God,

K 8. Because Moses killed the Egyptian taskmaster,

G 9. Because the pharaoh refused to release the Israelites,

H 10. Because the Israelites put the blood on the doorposts and lintel,

J 11. Because of the death of the pharaoh's firstborn,

Effects

F. the pharaoh commanded that all the Israelite male babies be killed.
G. God unleashed ten plagues on Egypt.
H. the Israelites' firstborn sons were spared from death.
I. God called Moses to deliver the Israelites.
J. the ruler agreed to let the Israelites leave Egypt.
K. Moses fled from Egypt.

B. Define the terms and tell what took place on the date.

12. covenant *binding agreement*

13. Canaan *the land where God told Abraham to go*

14. lintel *the beam above the door*

15. Passover *the day the Jews remember the Lord's passing over homes with blood of a sacrificed lamb on the doorposts and lintel*

16. Exodus *the Israelites' leaving Egypt*

17. ca. 1446 BC *the Exodus*

Tabernacle Furnishings

Name ____________________

Use with Student Text pages 92–93.

A. Choose a tabernacle furnishing from the chart below. Write its name in the chart title in Part B.

Furnishing	Altar of burnt offering	Altar of incense	Ark of the covenant	Golden lampstand	Laver	Table of showbread
Bible verses	Exodus 27:1–8 38:1–7 40:29	Exodus 30:1–10 37:25–28	Exodus 25:10–22 26:33–34 37:1–9	Exodus 25:31–40 26:35 37:17–24	Exodus 30:18 38:8 40:7	Exodus 25:23–30 26:35 37:10–16

B. Write notes about the tabernacle furnishing. Use your notes as you make your model.

Tabernacle Furnishing:			
Appearance	Dimensions (cubit = 20.4 in.)	Purpose	Location (court, holy place, or holy of holies)

C. Format your report like a museum identification card. Include the categories in Part B. Write the rough draft of the report below. Then, write the final version on an index card. Display the card with your model.

____

____

____

____

____

____

____

____

____

____

Culture in Ancient Israel

Name ______________________________

God gave laws to the Jews that influenced all aspects of their lives, even their education, diet, and clothing.

Family Life

The Jews placed great importance on family. During Old Testament times the family included not only the parents and children but also aunts, uncles, cousins, and the servants and their families. The father was the ruler. He was to be obeyed and shown respect and honor. Children were to obey and respect their mother as well.

Education

Mothers were responsible for both boys' and girls' education for the first years of their lives. Mothers continued to teach the girls their domestic duties throughout their childhood.

Fathers were responsible for teaching the boys about the law. They also taught their sons a trade. At the age of five, Jewish boys attended the "house of the book," which was connected to the synagogue. They learned Jewish law and read the writings of prophets like Isaiah and Jeremiah. They also studied other biblical books like Chronicles.

A Jewish boy was recognized as entering manhood at thirteen years of age. Today Jewish boys celebrate their bar mitzvahs at this age.

Food

The Jewish law instructed the people on acceptable and unacceptable foods. For example, they could eat beef and lamb but not pork. They could eat scaly fish but not smooth-skinned fish. Bread made from wheat or barley was their main food. The people also ate vegetables, such as beans and lentils, and fruits, such as figs, olives, and grapes. Honey was used for sweetening.

Today food that is prepared according to Jewish dietary laws is called *kosher*. A symbol similar to one of these can be found on packaged foods that have been certified by the proper people.

Jewish Clothing

Men, women, and children all wore tunics. A tunic was much like a cloth sack with slits made in the corners for the arms and a V-shaped opening cut for the head. Sometimes a woman's tunic had embroidered edges around the neck opening. A tunic was tied around the waist with a girdle, which was a wide strip of leather or coarse cloth. When a man or woman needed freedom to run, to work, or to carry things, the hem of the tunic was lifted and tucked into the girdle. This was called "girding up the loins." When a person could afford it, a mantle or cloak was worn on top of the tunic. Simple sandals made out of leather were worn on the feet. Everyone wore a head covering, but a woman's head covering was longer than a man's and covered her hair.

Searching for Culture

Name ___________________________

Search for more about the Jewish culture by answering these questions.

1. Children were considered a blessing. How many children does the man in Psalm 127:5 have?
   a quiver full or many children
2. From an early age what were children taught to do (Exod. 20:12)? *honor their father and mother*
3. What were parents supposed to do with a rebellious child who would not obey (Deut. 21:18–21)?
   They were to take him to the elders of the city, and then he would be stoned to death by the men of the city.
4. What time of day did Abraham get up (Gen. 22:3)? *early in the morning* The Jews got up at this time of day so they could take advantage of the daylight hours.
5. In the summer afternoons it was very hot in Israel. The Jews rested until it was cool enough to work again. Where did Abraham rest in the heat of the day (Gen. 18:1)? *in the tent door or entrance*
6. Music was important to the Jewish people. It was always part of the celebration of *winning a battle/victory* (1 Sam. 18:6) and the coronation of the *king* (2 Chron. 23:13). Music was played to help a person *feel/get better* (1 Sam. 16:16). James said that the singing of psalms shows a person is *happy/cheerful/merry* (James 5:13).
7. "Eating bread" was the same as saying "having a meal." Jesus taught His disciples to pray for their daily *bread*, meaning their food for the day (Luke 11:3). Bread was so important that Jesus referred to Himself as the "*bread of life*" (John 6:35).

Today in Israel this Bedouin cooks over a fire similarly to the way the Israelites did.

Study Guide

Use with Student Text pages 88–100.

Name ____________________

A. Match the characteristic to the correct covenant.

A. Abrahamic Covenant
B. Davidic Covenant
C. Mosaic Covenant

__A__ 1. God would bring a great blessing to all the families of the earth.
__C__ 2. God gave Israel laws that told the people how to live to please Him.
__B__ 3. God promised a man that he would always have a legitimate heir to his throne.
__C__ 4. If the Israelites obeyed these laws, the nations around them would see the great and true God.
__A__ 5. God promised a man that his offspring would become a great nation.
__B__ 6. Jesus will rule forever, fulfilling this promise.

B. Match the cause with its effect.

Causes

__A__ 7. Because the famine struck,
__C__ 8. Because the Israelites continued to grow in number,
__D__ 9. Because the pharaoh refused to release the Israelites,
__B__ 10. Because of the death of the pharaoh's firstborn,

Effects

A. people from many nations went to Egypt for food.
B. the ruler agreed to let the Israelites leave Egypt.
C. the pharaoh made the Israelites slaves.
D. God unleashed ten plagues on Egypt.

Causes

__E__ 11. Because the Egyptians feared that the Israelites would become too powerful,
__I__ 12. Because the Israelites did not trust God to help them take the land from the Canaanites,
__F__ 13. Because the people of Israel cried out to God from Egypt,
__H__ 14. Because the Israelites chose to disobey God's laws,
__G__ 15. Because Saul disobeyed God,

Effects

E. the pharaoh commanded that all the Israelite male babies be killed.
F. God called Moses to deliver the Israelites.
G. David was chosen by God to be the new king.
H. other nations ruled over parts of Israel.
I. the people wandered for forty years in the desert.

C. Define the terms and tell what happened on the date.

16. atonement *the restoration of the broken relationship between God and man*
17. monotheism *the belief in one god*
18. ca. 1446 BC *the Exodus*

D. Match each description to the correct person.

A. David
B. Samuel
C. Saul

__C__ 19. Israel's first king
__B__ 20. Israel's last judge
__A__ 21. king of God's special choosing

E. Write *T* if the statement is true. If the statement is false, write the correction for the underlined words.

T 22. The nation of twelve tribes was called Israel because it was the special name that God had given Jacob.

temple 23. Solomon's most impressive building project was the ~~tabernacle~~.

T 24. God gave the Israelites the Ten Commandments so other nations could see the wisdom and righteousness of God.

T 25. The tabernacle was a symbol of God's presence with His people.

Yahweh 26. The Hebrew name for the one true God is ~~Shema~~.

alphabets 27. The Phoenicians' greatest achievement was the development of one of the first ~~hieroglyphs~~.

Abraham 28. ~~Moses~~ moved his family from Ur of the Chaldeans to Canaan as God instructed him to.

F. Answer the questions.

29. Why do the Jews observe Passover?

to remember their deliverance from the death of the firstborn and from slavery in Egypt

30. Why do Christians observe the Lord's Supper?

to remember that Jesus is the Passover lamb because He shed His blood on the cross

G. Label the places on the map. Be sure to mark the location of any cities.

31. Egypt
32. Israel
33. Jerusalem
34. Jordan River
35. Mediterranean Sea

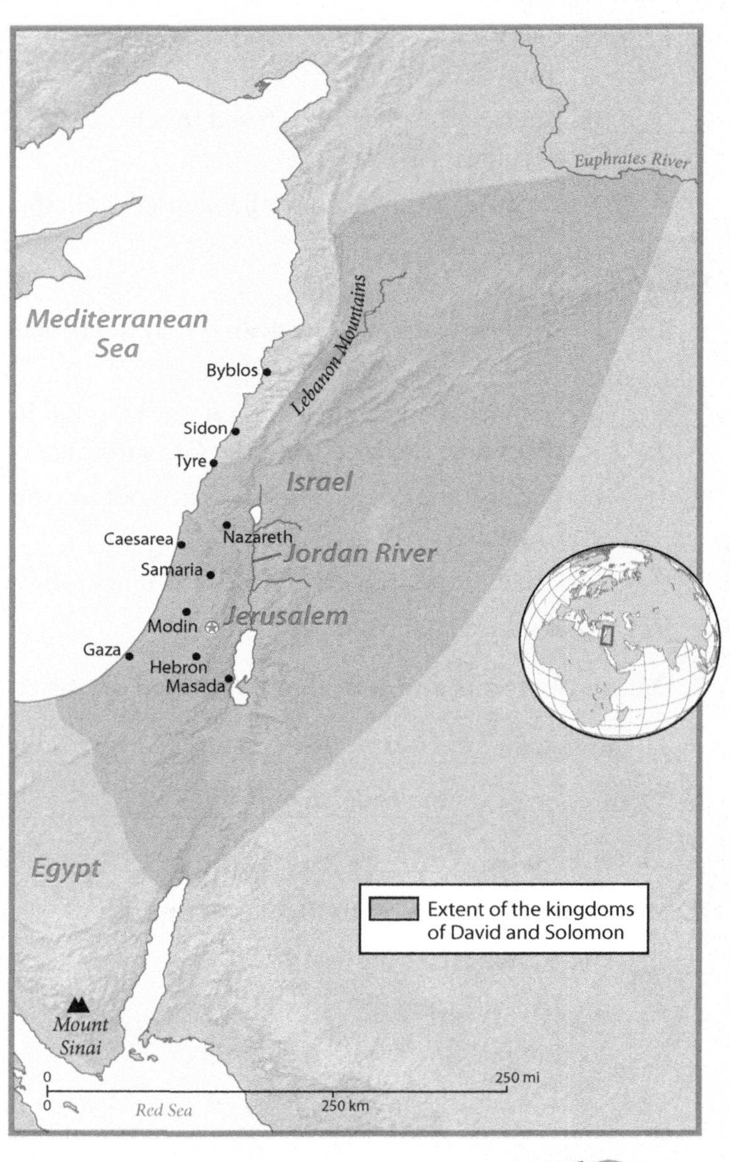

Costs and Benefits

Name ___________________________

Use with Student Text page 101.

A. Circle the account you and your partner choose.

Israelites ask for a king 1 Samuel 8:4–22	Fiery furnace Daniel 3:1–30	Daniel in the lions' den Daniel 6:1–28

B. Identify the people and the choice that was made.

People involved

king: Israelites, Samuel

furnace: King Nebuchadnezzar, Shadrach, Meshach, Abednego, Chaldeans, fourth man (Jesus)

Daniel: King Darius, Daniel, angel, presidents, satraps, prefects, counselors, governors, accusers' families

Choice that was made

king: The Israelites asked for a king.

furnace: Shadrach, Meshach, and Abednego chose not to bow down and worship the golden image of Nebuchadnezzar.

Daniel: Daniel chose to pray to God even though King Darius had signed an injunction (decree/document) against making a petition to any god or man except the king.

C. Complete the chart. *Possible answers are given.*

Costs	Benefits
king: The king would take sons for soldiers and daughters to work in his house. He would take a tenth of the grains, olive orchards, flocks, and donkeys to take care of his household.	*king: Israel would be like other nations. The king would judge the people. The king would go before them in battle.*
furnace: Shadrach, Meshach, and Abednego were thrown into the fiery furnace.	*furnace: Shadrach, Meshach, and Abednego were protected in the fiery furnace by God. Shadrach, Meshach, and Abednego showed their loyalty to God. Nebuchadnezzar promoted Shadrach, Meshach, and Abednego in the province of Babylon. Nebuchadnezzar and the Chaldeans saw the power of God.*
Daniel: Daniel was put in the lions' den.	*Daniel: Daniel was protected from the lions by God. Daniel showed his loyalty to God. King Darius and the people saw the power of God. Daniel prospered during the reign of Darius and Cyrus.*

D. Write a paragraph summarizing the decision that was made. Include an application to your own life.

Kingdom Divided

Name ______________________

Use with Student Text pages 102–5.

A. Write the event for each date on the timeline.

1. Assyria conquers Israel. 2. Babylonian captivity 3. Kingdom divides. 4. Persia conquers Babylon.

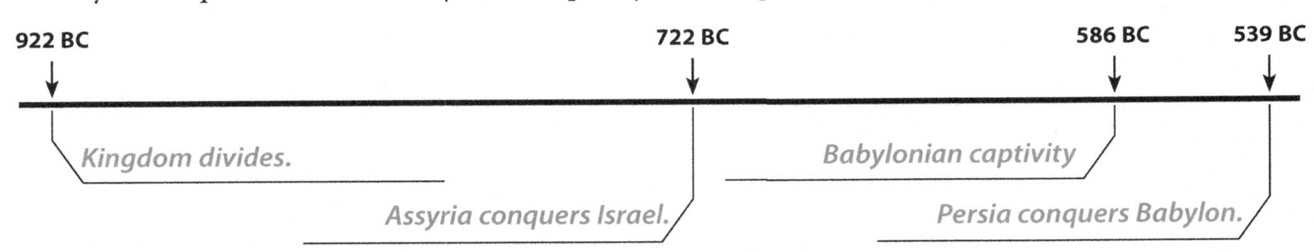

B. Write a sentence that shows how the pair of terms are related. *Possible answers are given.*

5. Northern Kingdom ◆ Southern Kingdom

The ten northern tribes formed the Northern Kingdom, and the two southern tribes formed the Southern Kingdom.

6. Jeroboam ◆ Rehoboam

While Jeroboam ruled the Northern Kingdom, Rehoboam ruled the Southern Kingdom.

7. Samaria ◆ Israel

The northern tribes kept the name Israel and established their capital at Samaria.

8. Judah ◆ Jerusalem

The southern tribes took the name Judah and kept the capital at Jerusalem.

9. Israel ◆ Assyrian Empire

God's judgment came to Israel when the Assyrian Empire conquered the nation.

10. Mosaic Covenant ◆ Diaspora

Because the Israelites did not keep the Mosaic Covenant, they were scattered among the nations in the Diaspora.

11. Israelites ◆ Samaritans

The descendants of Israelites who married people from other conquered nations in the Northern Kingdom were known as Samaritans.

12. Queen Esther ◆ King Xerxes

Queen Esther pleaded with King Xerxes to save the Jews from destruction.

Study Guide

Use with Student Text pages 102–9.

Name ______________________________

A. Complete each sentence in a way that shows that you understand the bolded term. *Possible answers are given.*

1. The **Diaspora** took place when the Israelites did not keep the Mosaic Covenant and as God promised they were *scattered among other nations*.
2. The Jews celebrated the holiday **Purim** to commemorate the deliverance *of the Jews from destruction by Haman*.
3. The **Septuagint** made it possible for the Jews who did not know Hebrew to read *the Old Testament in Greek*.
4. God made the New Covenant with Israel and Judah and later with the **Gentiles**, which was the name *given to people who were not Jewish*.
5. The menorah is lit on each night of **Hanukkah** to commemorate *the cleansing and rededication of the temple in Jerusalem*.

B. First, plan the essay on your own paper. Then, write it below.

6. Describe what happened to Israel after Solomon's death.

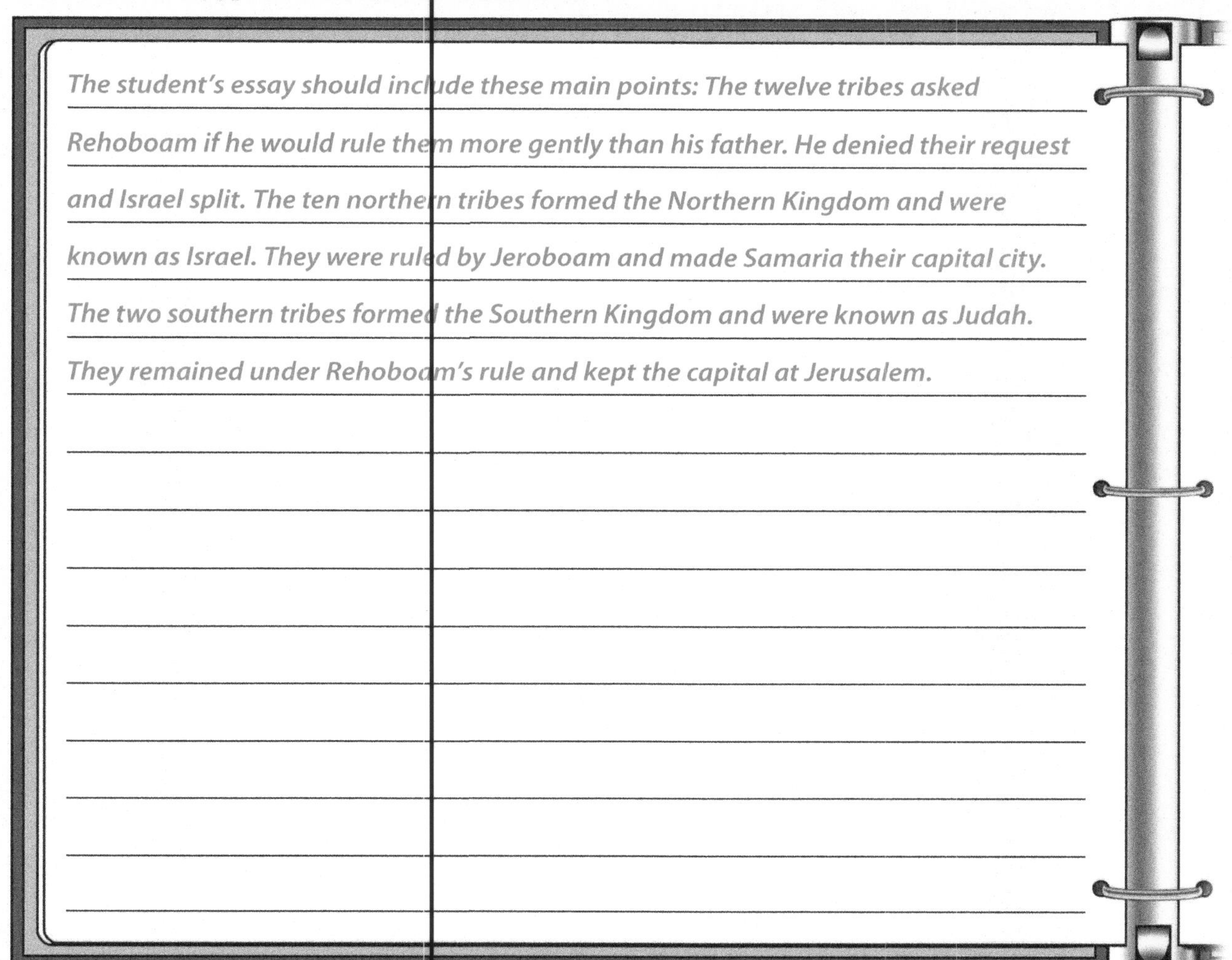

The student's essay should include these main points: The twelve tribes asked Rehoboam if he would rule them more gently than his father. He denied their request and Israel split. The ten northern tribes formed the Northern Kingdom and were known as Israel. They were ruled by Jeroboam and made Samaria their capital city. The two southern tribes formed the Southern Kingdom and were known as Judah. They remained under Rehoboam's rule and kept the capital at Jerusalem.

C. Answer the questions.

7. What happened to the Israelites in 586 BC? *The Babylonian captivity began.*
8. What did God promise Israel and Judah in the New Covenant? *He would restore Israel and Judah from exile, those who are part of this covenant would receive the Holy Spirit, and He would forgive His people of all their sins.*
9. What does the word *assimilate* mean? *to absorb*
10. Who were the Samaritans? *the descendants of Israelites in the Northern Kingdom who intermarried with people from conquered nations*
11. What was one difference between the Pharisees and the Sadducees? *possible answer: The Pharisees opposed the current rulers, and the Sadducees supported the current rulers.*
12. What did Antiochus IV do to Jerusalem and the temple? *He tore down the city's walls, placed idols in the temple, and sacrificed pigs on the altar of God.*
13. As Daniel prophesied, what did Judas Maccabeus and his army accomplish? *They cleansed and rededicated the temple 2,300 days after the first pagan sacrifice.*

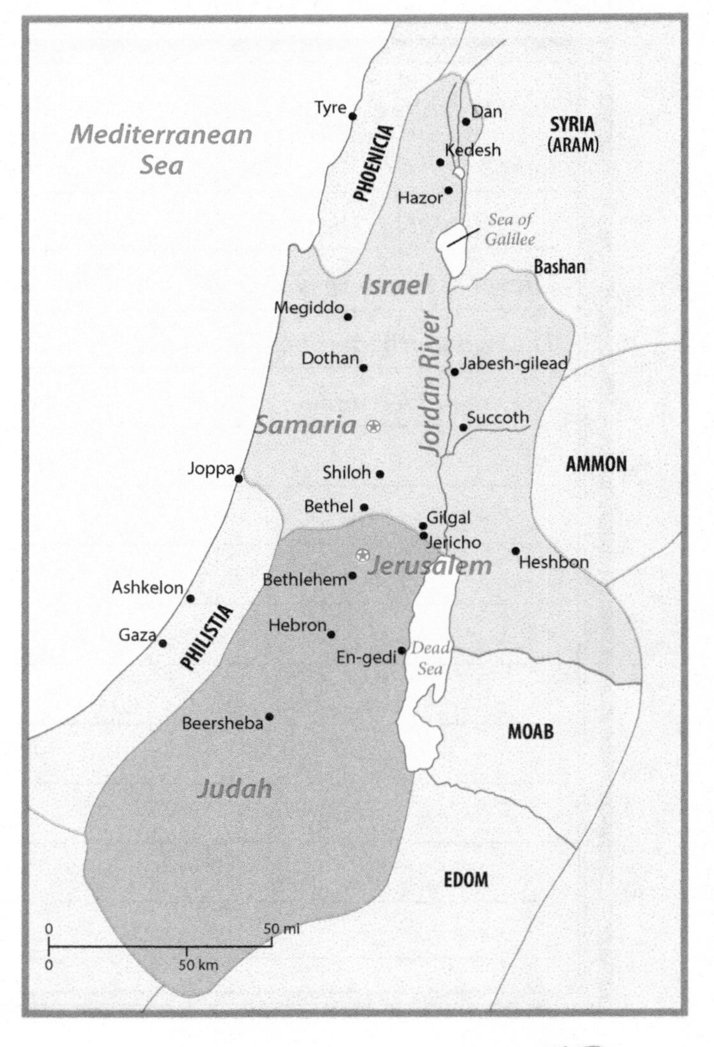

D. Label the map. Be sure to mark the location of any cities.

14. Israel
15. Judah
16. Samaria
17. Jerusalem
18. Jordan River
19. Mediterranean Sea

Roman Rule

Use with Student Text pages 110–13.

Name ______________________

A. Answer the questions.

1. Who was king of Judea when Jesus was born? *Herod*
2. Who did Jesus identify Himself as? *the Messiah or the Christ*
3. What did Jesus tell the people was the root of all their problems? *their sin*
4. What was the purpose of the death and resurrection of Jesus? *the salvation of all people who repent and trust Him for eternal life*
5. How were all the nations blessed as God promised Abraham? *The gospel was preached to people all over the world.*
6. What will be the final fulfillment of the Davidic Covenant? *the return of Jesus to earth to rule from Jerusalem*

B. Complete the comparison table.

7–14. Compare the tabernacle, the temple, and the synagogue.

	Tabernacle	Temple	Synagogue
Purpose	*worship* (p. 92)	*worship* (p. 94)	*worship, prayer, and Scripture reading* (p. 112)
Building instructions given by God to	*Moses* (Exod. 25:1, 8–9)	*David* (1 Chron. 28:11, 19–20)	No instructions were given.
Movable or unmovable	*movable*	*unmovable*	*unmovable*

Synagogue in Capernaum

Modern synagogue in Munich, Germany

C. First, plan the essay on your own paper. Then, write it on a new sheet of paper.

15. Describe the construction of Caesarea Maritima and two things that may have contributed to its destruction.

The student's essay should include these main points: Caesarea Maritima was a port city and harbor constructed by Roman engineers for King Herod. It had loading docks, storage areas, an inner harbor, and an outer harbor with a lighthouse. The harbor was constructed over a geological fault line. Seismic action and the sandy ocean floor caused the foundation to be unstable. There is evidence that a tsunami struck the area. The unstable foundation and a tsunami may have contributed to the destruction of Caesarea Maritima.

Ancient Trade Routes

Name ____________________

Israel was on two of the great trade routes of the ancient world. The King's Highway was the main caravan route from southern Arabia. The Via Maris (Way of the Sea) connected Egypt with Asia. These roads linked the two great civilizations, Egypt and Mesopotamia. Because of Israel's position on the roads, it was expected that Israel would become a trading nation. Mules and camels were used as beasts of burden to carry goods. Food for the animals was available along the route, making travel easier for the traders. The downside of Israel's position was that it also lay on the path of armies from Egypt or Mesopotamia. Any invading army knew it was necessary to acquire Israel before it moved on to its real target. Israel often had to pay huge amounts to buy its safety. Sometimes even money failed to keep Israel safe.

Answer the questions.

1. Which ancient world trade route is named in Isaiah 9:1? *Way of the Sea (Via Maris)*
2. Which ancient trade route is named in Numbers 20:17? *King's Highway*
3. What direction would a merchant travel when going from Aleppo to Gaza?
   - ○ south
   - ● southwest
   - ○ southeast
4. From which of these cities could a merchant ship travel to Cyprus?
   - ○ Ezion-geber
   - ● Tyre
   - ○ Damascus
5. Solomon made a naval base at Ezion-geber. What body of water was the base on?
   - ○ Great Sea
   - ○ Euphrates River
   - ● Red Sea
6. What is the approximate distance between Damascus and Ezion-geber?
   - ○ 175 kilometers
   - ● 425 kilometers
   - ○ 575 kilometers
7. Which items might be on a merchant ship from Ezion-geber?
   - ● peacocks
   - ○ purple dye
   - ● ivory

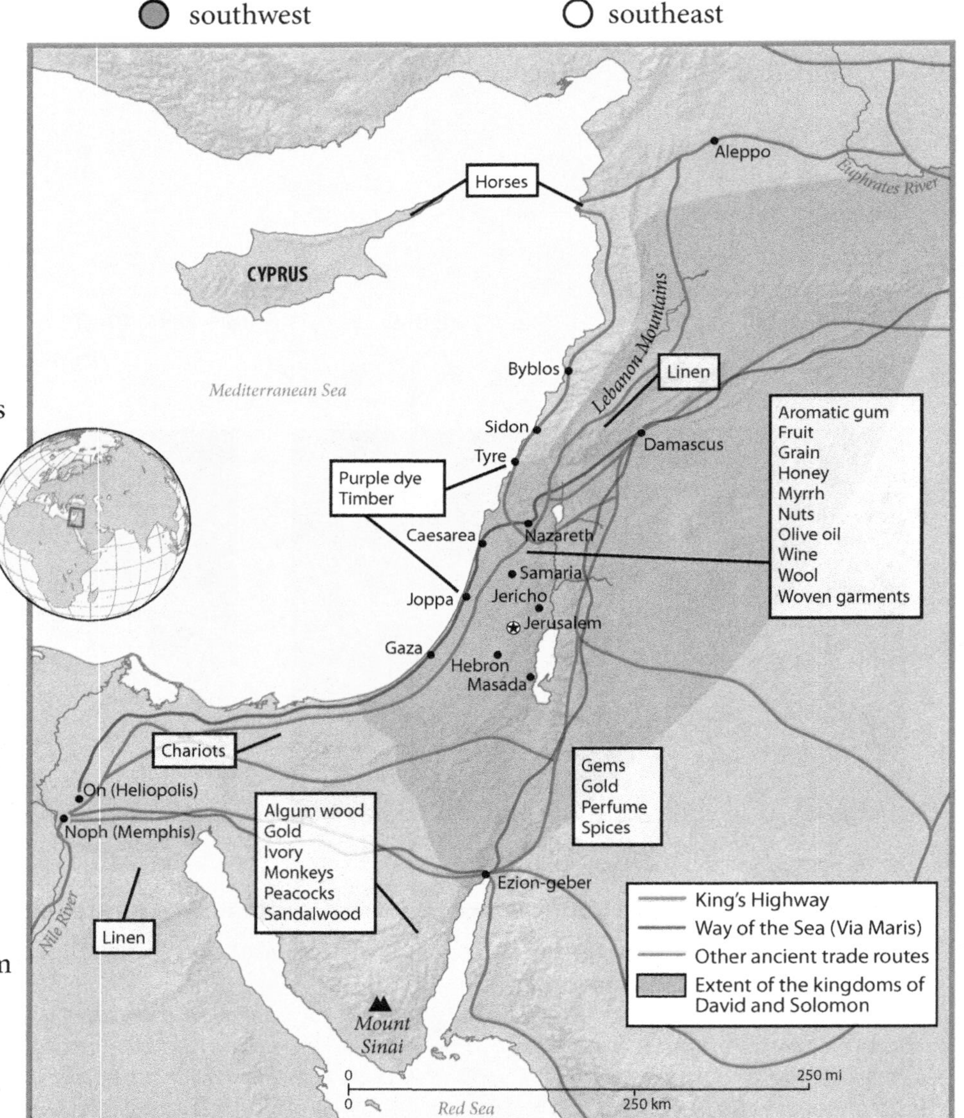

Study Guide

Use with Student Text pages 110–16.

Name ________________

A. Match the term with its description.

C 1. AD 70
A 2. Josephus
F 3. legion
D 4. Messiah
E 5. rabbi
B 6. Talmud

A. a Jewish historian
B. the Mishnah and the Gemara, which are the collection of Jewish law and tradition
C. the destruction of Jerusalem by the Romans
D. the Christ Who was anointed to save His people
E. a Jewish religious teacher
F. three to six thousand men

B. Mark the correct answer or answers.

7. All nations are blessed as God promised Abraham by ___.
   - ○ their obedience to the law
   - ○ the Messiah's return to rule
   - ● the preaching of the gospel to all people

8. Judaism is ___.
   - ● the monotheistic religion of the Jews
   - ○ the Jewish polytheistic religion
   - ○ the philosophy of the Talmud

9. Rabbinic Judaism focuses on ___.
   - ○ Jesus Christ as the Messiah
   - ○ obedience to the law and Jewish tradition
   - ○ the teachings of the Sadducees

10. The purpose of the death and resurrection of Jesus is ___.
   - ● the salvation of all who repent and trust Him for eternal life
   - ○ to be a blessing to all people
   - ○ to spread the message of salvation

11. When the Jews at Masada saw that the Romans would break through, they ___.
   - ● committed mass suicide
   - ○ built a huge ramp
   - ○ attacked from the mountaintop

12. The purpose of the tabernacle, the temple, and the synagogue was ___.
   - ● worship
   - ○ money changing
   - ○ spreading the gospel

13. Caesarea Maritima was constructed by ___.
   - ○ Pontius Pilate
   - ○ Israelite slaves
   - ● Roman engineers

14. Two possible reasons for the destruction of Caesarea Maritima were ___ and ___.
   - ● an unstable foundation
   - ● a tsunami that struck the area
   - ○ crumbling limestone blocks

15. The Zealots were Jews who ___.
   - ○ focused on the law
   - ● plotted to overthrow Rome by military action
   - ○ focused on sacrifices to atone for their sins

16. Two causes that led to Jerusalem's destruction were that ___ and ___.
   - ○ Vespasian became emperor
   - ● the governors took money from the people
   - ● the Romans were brutal

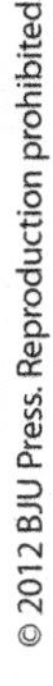

Chapter 4 Summary

Name ____________________

Define these terms

assimilate
atonement
Diaspora
legion
monotheism
rabbi
Septuagint

The Israeli flag was adopted in 1948. In the center is the Star of David, a symbol often associated with the Jewish people.

Locate these places

Egypt
Israel
Jerusalem
Jordan River
Judah
Mediterranean Sea
Samaria

Tell about these people

Abraham
Antiochus IV
David
Gentiles
Josephus
Judas Maccabeus
Messiah
Moses
Queen Esther
Samaritans
Samuel
Saul
Yahweh

Explain what happened

ca. 1446 BC—Exodus
586 BC—start of the Babylonian captivity
AD 70—destruction of Jerusalem by the Romans

Be able to . . .

Write an essay describing what happened to Israel after Solomon's death
Identify characteristics of these covenants: Abrahamic, Mosaic, Davidic, and New
Summarize the time the Israelites spent in Egypt
Identify one of the reasons God gave the Israelites the Ten Commandments
Compare the temple, tabernacle, and synagogue
Describe the Lord's Supper
Describe these three Jewish holidays: Passover, Hanukkah, and Purim
Explain what happened when the Israelites did not trust God to help them take the land of Canaan
Explain why God sent other nations to rule over Israel
Identify the greatest achievement of the Phoenicians
Describe Solomon's most impressive building project
Contrast the Pharisees with the Sadducees
Describe the Maccabean revolt
Explain the purpose of the death and resurrection of Jesus Christ
Explain how God's promise to Abraham was fulfilled
Explain Judaism, rabbinic Judaism, and the Talmud
Describe the construction and destruction of Caesarea Maritima
Identify the causes that led to the destruction of Jerusalem
Describe the Zealots and what happened at Masada

Harappan Civilization Organizer

Name ______________________

Use with Student Text pages 118–23.

A. Complete the web.

Organized Cities and Government
pp. 119, 121

- The two main cities, ___Harappa___ and ___Mohenjo-Daro___, were settled along the ___Indus River___.
- Archaeologists have found the Harappan cities to be very ___organized___.
- Mohenjo-Daro appeared to have had ___two main___ streets.

Social Classes
p. 121

- Many buildings along the main streets appeared to be ___middle-class___ houses.
- The unearthed houses showed that the middle class was probably made up of ___merchants___ and ___craftsmen___.

The Harappan Civilization

Religion
pp. 119, 123

- Many historians believe that the ___Great Bath___ was used for religious ceremonies.
- Historians can make guesses about the Harappans' religious beliefs and customs by looking at the ___pictographs___, but they cannot conclude anything definite.

Job Specialization
p. 119

- The fertile Indus Valley was good for ___farming___ and ___raising animals___.
- Artifacts showed that the Indus people were ___artistic___ and ___skilled___ craftsmen.

Arts, Sciences, and Written Language
pp. 121, 123

- Harappans developed technology that allowed them to have running ___water___, indoor ___plumbing___, and an advanced ___sewage system___.
- Many artifacts display writings in ___pictographs___, which ___linguists___ have been unable to decipher.

B. Answer the question.

How did the Harappan civilization end? *Evidence suggests that the civilization came to a sudden halt. Possible reasons for its disappearance are an invasion, a flood, or a famine.*

India's Landforms

Name ______________________________

Use with Student Text pages 118–21.

Label and color the map according to the instructions given.

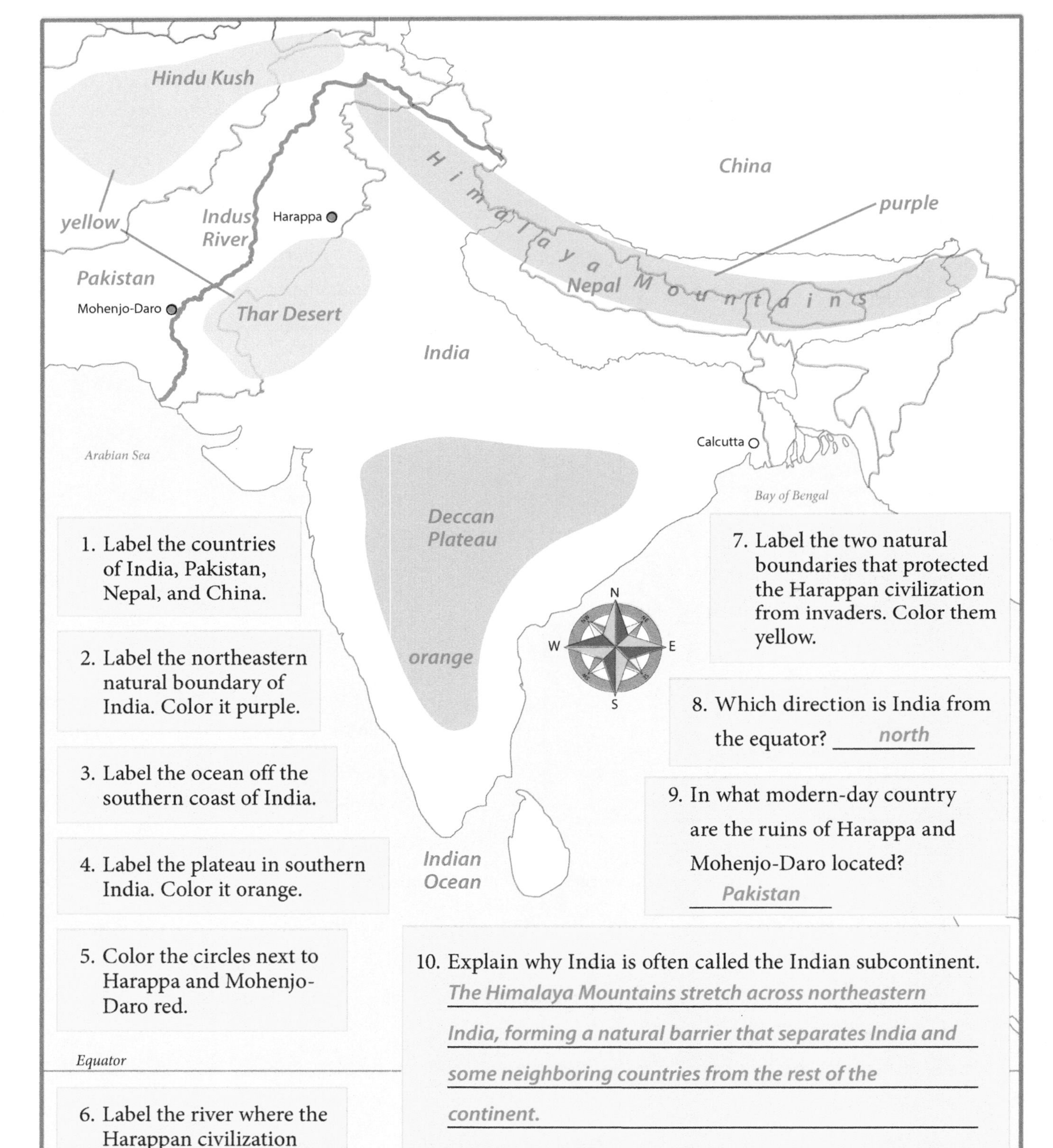

1. Label the countries of India, Pakistan, Nepal, and China.
2. Label the northeastern natural boundary of India. Color it purple.
3. Label the ocean off the southern coast of India.
4. Label the plateau in southern India. Color it orange.
5. Color the circles next to Harappa and Mohenjo-Daro red.
6. Label the river where the Harappan civilization began. Trace it in red.
7. Label the two natural boundaries that protected the Harappan civilization from invaders. Color them yellow.
8. Which direction is India from the equator? *north*
9. In what modern-day country are the ruins of Harappa and Mohenjo-Daro located? *Pakistan*
10. Explain why India is often called the Indian subcontinent. *The Himalaya Mountains stretch across northeastern India, forming a natural barrier that separates India and some neighboring countries from the rest of the continent.*

Site Map

Use with Student Text page 122.

Name ______________________________

Label the sections of your artifact pan to match this site map.
Draw each artifact at the location in which it was found.
Number each artifact on the map.

A	B
C	D

Catalog for Artifacts

Name ______________________

Use with Student Text page 122.

Complete the chart about the artifacts.

Collection of ______________________

Date ______________________

Number	Description	Material	Dimensions	Weight	Remarks

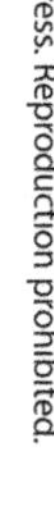

Aryan Civilization Organizer

Name ______________________________

Use with Student Text pages 124–34.

Complete the web.

Organized Cities and Government
p. 124

- The Aryans spread across northern India and settled into ___villages___.
- The Aryans did not form a strong ___central___ government.
- Each village was governed by a council of leading men and a ___headman___.

Social Classes
pp. 129–30

- Since the rise of Hinduism, the two basic social groups in India have been the ___family___ and the ___caste___, or social class.
- The oldest man in the family had complete ___authority___ over the other members.
- There were four main caste divisions: (1) priests, (2) warriors and ___rulers___, (3) farmers, traders, and ___artisans___, and (4) laborers and ___servants___.

The Aryan Civilization

Religion
pp. 126, 132–33

- The Aryans developed a religion called ___Hinduism___, which is polytheistic.
- The belief that everything in the universe is part of a supreme being is called ___pantheism___.
- Siddhartha Gautama changed his name to ___Buddha___, and his religion became known as ___Buddhism___.

Job Specialization
p. 124

- The craftsmen made tools and ___household___ items for the villagers.
- The farmers' success depended upon the annual rains of the summer ___monsoon___ season.

Arts, Sciences, and Written Language
p. 124

- The written language of the Aryans is called ___Sanskrit___.
- Much of the Aryans' art reflected their ___religious___ beliefs.
- Sculptures of gods and goddesses were very common and were probably used in ___worship___.

Study Guide

Use with Student Text pages 118–25.

Name ______________________

A. Identify the name of the civilization that began on each date.

1. 2300 BC *Harappan*
2. 1500 BC *Aryan*

B. Complete each statement.

3. Archaeologists believe the Harappan civilization was an advanced society because *it had organized cities, indoor plumbing, running water, and an advanced sewage system.*
4. India is often called the Indian subcontinent because *the Himalaya Mountains stretch across northeastern India, forming a natural barrier that separates India and neighboring countries from the rest of the continent.*
5. The reason that archaeologists have been unable to unravel the mysteries of the Harappan civilization is *they do not know the Harappan people's language.*
6. Three possible explanations why the Harappan civilization suddenly disappeared are *an invasion*, *a flood*, and *a famine*.

C. Match the description with the term.

C 7. a wind that reverses direction with the change of season
D 8. the written language of the Aryans
E 9. archaeologist who discovered Harappa and Mohenjo-Daro
B 10. a scholar who studies languages

A. Jean-François Champollion
B. linguist
C. monsoon
D. Sanskrit
E. Sir John Hubert Marshall

D. Write *H* if the statement describes the Harappan civilization. If the statement describes the Aryan civilization, write *A*.

A 11. They were warlike people.
A 12. Their way of life became the characteristic culture of ancient and modern India.
H 13. They had well-organized cities.
A 14. Each village was governed by a council of leading men and a headman.
H 15. They had indoor plumbing, running water, and a sewage system.

E. Sequence the events to show how the term *Aryan* has echoed through history.

1 16. The Aryans were the nomadic warriors who invaded India from the north.
3 17. Hitler used the term *Aryan* to describe the people of his Germany.
2 18. Some of the Aryans migrated to the area that is now Iran.

Hinduism

Name ______________________

Use with Student Text pages 126–30.

A. Fill in the blanks.

1. The three most important gods in Hinduism are *Brahma*, *Shiva*, and *Vishnu*.
2. These three gods are forms of the great god *Brahman*.
3. The Rig-Veda is a collection of *hymns*, *prayers*, and *poems*.
4. The two basic groups in India since the rise of Hinduism have been the *family* and the *caste*.

B. Match each term with its correct description.

C 5. caste
B 6. karma
G 7. dharma
E 8. Vedas
H 9. Brahman
A 10. reincarnation
F 11. pantheism
D 12. Hinduism
I 13. untouchables

A. the belief that a person lives more than once in different bodies
B. the result of a person's good and bad deeds
C. a social class of Indian society
D. the religion that the Aryans developed in India
E. the sacred books of Hinduism
F. the belief that everything is part of Brahman, including plants, animals, and gods
G. the duty that a Hindu must follow to become part of Brahman
H. name of the great soul or world soul
I. those outside the caste system, including anyone who is not a Hindu, who works with meat, or who has been expelled from his own caste

C. Write the occupations for each level of the Indian social pyramid. *Answer to essay question on page 76*

priests

warriors and rulers

farmers, traders, and artisans

laborers and servants

non-Hindus, those who work with meat, those expelled from their castes

The student's essay should include three of these differences: Hinduism teaches that there are many gods. The Bible tells that the one true God is the Creator and Lord over all. Hinduism teaches people to obey the Hindu rules and do good works to have a better state in the next life. The Bible teaches that Jesus Christ is the Savior of the world and that salvation does not depend on good works. Hindus believe that a person lives many different lives through reincarnation. The Bible teaches that each person dies once and then must face judgment. Hindus believe that each person eventually becomes part of a world soul called Brahman. The Bible teaches that a person will spend eternity with God if he has confessed his sin and asked Jesus to save him.

Study Guide

Use with Student Text pages 126–34.

Name ______________________

A. Match the description to the correct term.

Term
A. Brahman
B. caste
C. dharma
D. enlightened
E. karma
F. nirvana
G. pantheism
H. reincarnation
I. untouchable
J. Vedas

__B__ 1. a social class

__A__ 2. the great god called the great soul or world soul

__F__ 3. a state of complete enlightenment

__E__ 4. the result of a person's good and bad deeds

__J__ 5. the sacred books of Hinduism

__C__ 6. the duty that a Hindu must follow to become part of Brahman

__D__ 7. gained understanding

__H__ 8. the belief that a person lives more than once in different bodies

__G__ 9. the idea that everything in the universe is part of a supreme being

__I__ 10. outcasts; rejected by others and excluded from normal life

B. Write *T* if the statement is true. If the statement is false, write the correction for the underlined words.

__Hinduism__ 11. The Aryans developed a religion called ~~Buddhism~~.

__T__ 12. The hope of many untouchables is to do their duty, die, and have a better life in a reincarnated state.

__caste__ 13. The two basic social groups in India are the family and the ~~untouchables~~.

__T__ 14. Siddhartha Gautama changed his name to Buddha.

__Eightfold Path__ 15. Buddha's list of good works was the ~~Four Noble Truths~~.

__T__ 16. The caste dictated whom one married, one's job, and one's clothing.

__Buddhism__ 17. Siddhartha Gautama began the religion called ~~Hinduism~~.

__four__ 18. There were ~~five~~ main caste divisions in Indian society.

C. Complete the chart.

19–24. Contrast Buddhism with biblical truth.

Buddhism	Biblical truth
Buddhism teaches that a person's salvation, or enlightenment, depends on his good __works__ and right thinking.	Salvation from sin comes only through __Jesus Christ__ and His payment of sin's penalty on the cross.
Buddhism teaches that suffering can be overcome by getting rid of __desires__ and __wants__.	Suffering is the result of man's __sin__. Christians can view suffering as an opportunity to see God's __faithfulness__.
Buddhism requires its followers to meditate on __riddles__ or pleasant thoughts to find peace.	Christians are to meditate on God's __Word__ to experience His blessings.

D. First, plan the essay on your own paper. Then, write it on a new sheet of paper.

25. Contrast Hinduism with biblical truth. Include at least three differences.

The answer to the essay question is located on page 75.

Comparing Religions

Name ______________________

Complete the chart.

	Hinduism	Buddhism	Christianity
Key person or founder	Hinduism was founded by the ancient ___Aryan___ civilization.	Buddhism was founded by a man named ___Siddhartha___ ___Gautama___.	Christianity was founded by ___Jesus___ Christ.
God(s)	There are many gods. The most important are ___Brahma___, ___Shiva___, and ___Vishnu___. The universe is part of Brahman.	There is no god. Some Buddhists believe that Buddha was a god.	The Bible teaches that there is ___one God___ (1 Cor. 8:6).
How a person is saved	To have a better state in the next life, people should obey the Hindu ___rules___ and do ___good works___.	A person's salvation, or enlightenment, depends on his ___good works___ and ___right thinking___. A person's ultimate goal or salvation is to reach ___nirvana___.	Salvation is received by trusting in ___Jesus___, Who paid the penalty for ___sin___ through His death and ___resurrection___ (Rom. 6:23; Phil. 3:9–10).
After death	Hindus believe in ___reincarnation___, the belief that a person lives more than once in different bodies. Each person eventually becomes part of ___Brahman___.	Buddhists believe in ___reincarnation___, the belief that a person lives more than once in different bodies.	A person will spend ___eternity___ in a resurrected body with Jesus Christ if he has ___confessed___ his sin and asked the Son of God to save him (John 3:16; 1 John 1:9).
Sacred writings	Hindu scriptures include the ___Vedas___, the oldest being the Rig-Veda; the Upanishads; and the Bhagavad-Gita.	Buddhist scriptures include the Mahavastu, the Jataka Tales, the Tripitaka, and the Tantras. Its followers meditate on ___riddles___ or pleasant thoughts to find peace.	The Bible is God's ___Word___ (2 Tim. 3:16). It is divided into the Old Testament and the ___New Testament___.
Beliefs about family	Hinduism teaches that obedience in the family is an important duty for becoming part of ___Brahman___.	Two of its six relationships are between parents and children or between husband and wife. By fulfilling responsibilities, one can achieve harmony, security, and prosperity both within the family and in society.	The most important relationship is between man and ___God___. Children should ___honor___ their parents (Exod. 20:12). Christ said that loyalty to Him may demand sacrificing loyalty to family (Matt. 10:37–38).

Etymology

Name ______________________________

Use with Student Text page 135.

A. Complete the chart. *Answers may vary slightly according to the dictionary used.*

English word	Sanskrit word	English definition	Sanskrit definition
bandanna	*bandhati*	*a large square colorful cloth*	*he ties*
guru	*guruh*	*Hindu teacher*	*heavy*
jungle	*jangalam*	*place grown over with dense vegetation*	*desert, wasteland, uncultivated area*
loot	*loptram, lotram*	*things of value taken during a war*	*plunder*
mantra	*mantrah*	*a word or phrase repeated verbally in meditation*	*Hindu prayer*
orange	*narangah*	*a color, a fruit*	*orange tree*
shawl	*sati*	*a large piece of cloth worn around the shoulders, head, or neck for warmth or decoration*	*cloth, sari*
sugar	*sarkara*	*a sweet substance that comes from sugar cane or sugar beets*	*grit, ground sugar*
yoga	*yogah*	*a Hindu system of training exercises to control the mind and body*	*union, joining*

B. Read step 4 on Student Text page 135. Write a paragraph about your findings.

____
____
____
____
____
____
____
____
____
____
____

Identifying Cause and Effect

Name ______________________

Use with Student Text page 136.

Record six cause-and-effect relationships. The first two have been started for you.

1. **Choose an event or circumstance.**
2. **Decide whether it represents a cause or an effect.**
3. **Record it in the correct column in the chart below. If it is a cause, go to step 4. If it is an effect, skip to step 6.**
4. **Identify one of its effects. Think through these questions. What did this event lead to? What was the result? Look at the clue words for effects to help you.**
5. **Record the effect in the chart below.**
6. **Identify the event or circumstance that caused it. Think through these questions. Why did this happen? What led to this? Look at the clue words for causes to help you.**
7. **Record the cause in the chart below.**

Clue Words

Sometimes a writer will use words that signal a *cause* or an *effect*.

cause—as, basis, because, motivated, reason

effect—as a result, brought about, for that reason, led to, so, therefore

Possible answers are given.

Cause	Effect
Because the Indus Valley was close to the river,	*the land was good for farming and raising animals.* (p. 119)
Because no one has found an artifact with a translation of Harappan writing, (p. 123)	linguists cannot decipher the Harappan language.
Because the Aryan's language has been translated,	*more is known about them than about the Harappans. (p. 124)*
Because the rains during the summer monsoon season were on time and heavy enough,	*the farmers had success with their crops. (p. 124)*
Because the rains were light or late during the summer monsoon season,	*drought and famine occurred. (p. 124)*
Because Hitler believed that races other than the Aryans, particularly the Jews, did not deserve to live,	*he executed them. (p. 125)*

Because Hindus believe they can make their souls purer for Brahman by disciplining their bodies, they seclude, starve, and inflict pain on themselves. (p.127) Because Hindus believe in reincarnation, many of them seek to improve their karma through good works. (p. 127) Because the untouchables were rejected and excluded from normal life, their only hope was to do their duty, die, and have a better life in a reincarnated state. (p. 131) Because Buddhism was not based on a caste system (gave everyone an equal opportunity to be enlightened), the lower classes were attracted to Buddhism. (p. 134) Because Chandragupta did not trust his subjects, he set up a network of spies. (p. 137) Because Buddhism emphasizes doing good works and relieving suffering, Asoka made many improvements to give his people better lives. (p. 138) Because Asoka sent Buddhist missionaries into other countries, many other Asian countries adopted Buddhism. (p. 138) Because Asoka tolerated opponents to Buddhism and allowed them to practice other religions, Buddhism is not a major force in India today. (p. 140)

Mauryan Empire Organizer

Name ________________

Use with Student Text pages 137–40.

Complete the web. Not all the characteristics of a civilization are discussed regarding the Mauryan Empire in the Student Text.

Organized Cities and Government

- The first ruler of the empire was *Chandragupta Maurya*.
- The capital city was *Pataliputra*.
- The empire had a *centralized* government.
- One of the greatest rulers of the empire was *Asoka*, who united most of the Indian *subcontinent* under his leadership.

Job Specialization

- Many improvements were made to give the people better *lives*.
- The people dug *wells*, planted *trees*, and constructed *hospitals* throughout the empire.

The Mauryan Empire

Religion

- Asoka worked diligently to promote *Buddhism* in his empire.
- Thousands of dome-shaped shrines called *stupas* were built. The most well-known of these structures is the *Great Stupa*.
- Asoka sent Buddhist *missionaries* into areas outside the empire's borders.

India's Golden Age

Name ______________________________

The term *golden age* is used to describe the time when a country reaches its peak. India's golden age began during the rule of the Gupta dynasty under Chandragupta II. It lasted from about AD 320 to 550 and was a time of wealth, achievement, peace, and learning.

Education

A Hindu boy began his schooling at home, where he learned the alphabet and Sanskrit. Once he reached a certain age, his family held a special ceremony. A priest placed a sacred cord on the boy's left shoulder and fastened it under his right arm. The cord had three strands, each one woven from nine threads. Throughout the rest of his life, the boy would wear the sacred cord as the symbol of his place in Hindu society. He then went to live with a *guru*, his teacher. The guru taught the Vedas and how to follow all the important Hindu rituals. Every activity, from cooking a meal to fighting a battle, followed a ritual to please the Hindu gods.

Number System

The Gupta age was the golden age of mathematics. What we call *arabic* numerals were really invented by the Hindus. Arabic numerals are the numerals we use every day, such as *1, 2, 3,* and *4*. The people of India were one of the first to use a zero. They discovered it independently of other ancient civilizations. It is the zero invented in India that spread into Europe in the 1400s. They also used the decimal system, place values, and positive and negative numbers. In more-advanced mathematics the Indians learned how to find square and cubic roots, figured an accurate value for *pi*, and used elementary algebra.

Science

During the Gupta period, scholars studied chemistry, physics, and astronomy. They described the principle of gravity. They even had an idea of how atoms make up all matter. Indian astronomers discovered that the earth and all the planets are spheres and that the earth rotates.

Art

The art of this period appeared peaceful and happy. The wealthy enjoyed painting. Most gentlemen and ladies knew how to paint. The best examples of known Gupta paintings are found in the caves at Ajanta. These paintings were done by Buddhist artists. Although they primarily show scenes from the life of Buddha, we can learn something of how the people lived, such as what they wore and what plants and animals they raised.

Music

Most music from this time was not written down. A performer began with a familiar tune and then improvised and made changes in the melody as he played. The main instrument that the Indians used was called a *vina*. The vina was a type of lute similar to a guitar. Other common instruments were flutes, drums, bells, cymbals, and gongs.

Literature

Many excellent writers lived during the golden age. Two popular types of literature were the fable and the fairy tale. Trade played a big part in spreading stories that Indian writers created, and fables and fairy tales were popular in other countries. Some stories we have today are based on early Indian fables. One such story is that of Sinbad the Sailor from *The Thousand and One Nights*. Indian poetry was complex and did not spread like the fables. The ability to write poetry was very important. Competitions were often held to see who could write the best and most complicated poem.

An Indian playing a vina

Golden Age Puzzle

Name ______________________________

Complete the puzzle.

Across

3. language learned at school
10. men who found out the earth rotates
11. caves where wall art was found
12. name of our numerals
13. dynasty of the golden age
15. cave paintings about ___
17. a civilization's peak (two words)
19. type of math used (elementary ___)

Down

1. writings taught by the guru
2. ruler of the Gupta dynasty
4. a ___ for every activity
5. story of ___ the Sailor
6. art form that was improvised
7. rituals to please the ___ gods
8. the main musical instrument
9. scientific principle described by scholars
14. golden age of ___
16. a popular type of literature
17. a boy's teacher
18. one of the first civilizations to use ___

Study Guide

Use with Student Text pages 137–40.

Name ___________________________

A. Fill in the blanks.

1. Chandragupta Maurya was the first emperor of the ___Mauryan Empire___.
2. Chandragupta chose Pataliputra as his ___capital city___ and established a centralized ___government___.
3. Chandragupta did not trust his people, so he set up a ___network of spies___ throughout the empire.
4. Under his leadership Asoka united most of the ___Indian subcontinent___.
5. Asoka lost his desire to conquer countries, so he devoted his time to ___Buddhism___ and its teachings.
6. Asoka built thousands of dome-shaped shrines called ___stupas___.
7. Asoka made improvements to give his people better lives, because Buddhism emphasizes doing ___good works___ and relieving ___suffering___.
8. Asoka spread Buddhism by sending ___missionaries___ into areas outside his country.
9. Sir John Hubert Marshall was a British archaeologist who organized ___excavations___, recorded data, established ___museums___, and helped restore the ___Great Stupa___.
10. Most people living in modern India claim ___Hinduism___ as their religion.
11. One of the greatest rulers of the Mauryan Empire was ___Asoka___.

B. Label the map.

12. Ganges River
13. Harappa
14. Himalaya Mountains
15. India
16. Indus River
17. Mohenjo-Daro
18. Pataliputra

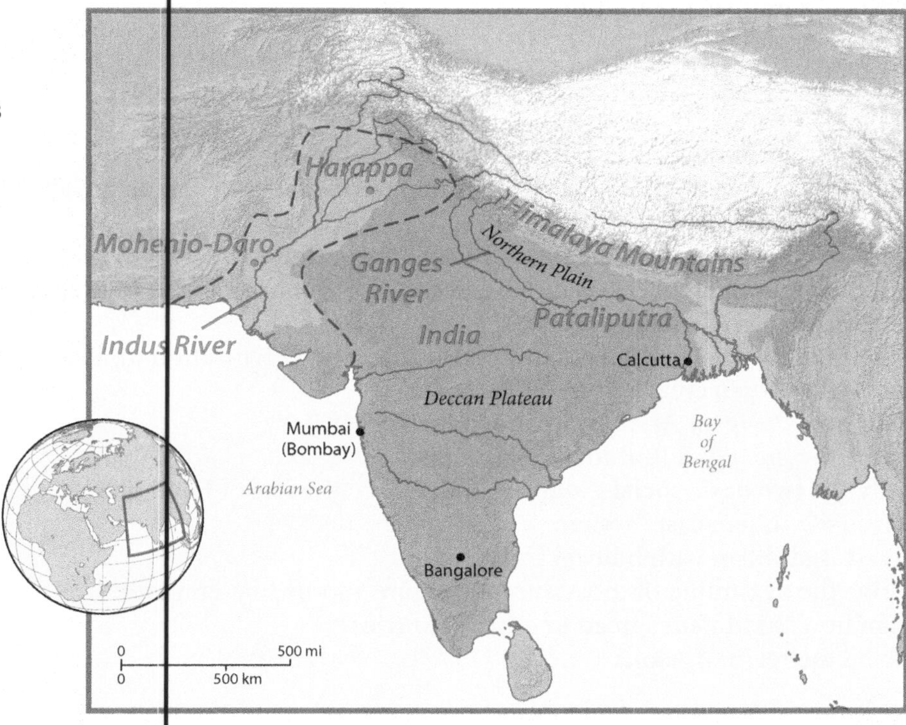

Chapter 5 Summary

Name ____________________

Define these terms

caste
dharma
enlightened
karma
linguist
monsoon
nirvana
pantheism
reincarnation
Sanskrit
stupa
untouchable
Vedas

Locate these places

Ganges River
Harappa
Himalaya Mountains
India
Indus River
Mohenjo-Daro
Pataliputra

Key Gompa, a Tibetan Buddhist monastery in India

Tell about these people

Asoka
Buddha
Chandragupta Maurya
Siddhartha Gautama
Sir John Marshall

Explain what happened

2300 BC—Harappan civilization
1500 BC—Aryan civilization

Be able to . . .

Write an essay contrasting Hinduism with biblical truth
Explain why archaeologists believe the Harappan civilization was an advanced society
Explain why India is often called the Indian subcontinent
Identify the reason archaeologists have been unable to unravel the mysteries of the Harappan civilization
Identify possible explanations as to why the Harappan civilization disappeared
Describe the Aryan civilization
Explain how the term *Aryan* has echoed through history
Describe the great god Brahman of Hinduism
Identify the two basic social groups in India since the rise of Hinduism
Describe the Indian caste system
Contrast Buddhism with biblical truth
Describe the beginning of the Mauryan Empire and its first emperor
Explain how Buddhism spread to other countries
Describe the reign of Asoka

Shang Dynasty Organizer

Name ______________________________

Use with Student Text pages 144–48.

Complete the fishbone organizer as you read about the Shang dynasty.

The **Shang dynasty** settled along the *Huang He*, called "China's Sorrow."

Religion (pp. 144–45)
- practiced *ancestor* worship
- punished or helped by ancestors' *magical* *powers*
- cooked meat for sacrifices in a *ting*
- centered on rituals and *superstition*

Oracle Bones (pp. 145, 148)
- animal *bones* or turtle *shells*
- wrote *questions* on bones
- heated bone and interpreted *cracks*
- showed a system of *writing*

Arts (pp. 147–48)
- developed a process of *bronze* casting
- produced *silk* to make colorful clothes
- carved jade *statues*
- first dynasty to use *chopsticks*

Tombs (p. 148)
- buried rulers with valuables and *pottery*
- deep cross-shaped *pits*

Government (pp. 145, 148)
- priests as *governmental* officials
- rule passed from *eldest* brother to *youngest* brother

End of Dynasty (p. 148)
- lasted about *600* years
- weakened and was *conquered*

China Then and Now

Name ______________________

Use with Student Text pages 142–45.

A. Answer the questions.

1. What benefit did China's natural boundaries provide? *They protected the Chinese people from foreign invasions.*
2. How do the advanced skills of the ancient Chinese support biblical truth? *Man, created in God's image, has always been intelligent.*
3. What did the Chinese name their land? Why? *the Middle Kingdom; They thought that it was in the center of the earth.*

B. Fill in the blanks.

4. China is the *third*-largest country in the world today.
5. China is located in East Asia, also known as the *Far East*.
6. Modern China shares its borders with *fourteen* countries.
7. China has a climate that is affected by yearly *monsoons*.
8. Modern China is the world's largest producer of *iron ore*.
9. Ancient China was ruled by several *dynasties*.
10. A dynasty is a line of kings or rulers who belong to the same *family*.

C. Match the region of China with its topography.

C 11. eastern region
D 12. central region
B 13. western region
A 14. southwest region

A. some of the highest mountain peaks
B. hilly and mountainous
C. lowlands
D. rolling hills

Cattle graze in Guilin, China. The limestone mountains in the background often appear in clusters.

Study Guide

Use with Student Text pages 141–48.

Name ______________________

A. Define the terms using the glossary and Student Text pages.

1. ting *an ornate bronze vessel used to cook meat for sacrifice*

2. oracle bone *animal bone or turtle shell used to predict the future*

B. Complete the chart.

3–6. Contrast ancestor worship with biblical truth.

Ancestor worship	Biblical truth
The Chinese believed that their *ancestors* had the power to influence the *affairs* of the *living*.	The Bible teaches that only God has *control* over all things. Daniel 4:34 says that God's "dominion is an everlasting *dominion*."
Many Chinese still believe that descendants must perform proper *rites* to give their ancestors the proper *afterlife*. These rites show honor to the *family*.	The Bible teaches that children should honor their *father* and *mother* (Exod. 20:12), but Jesus said that honoring parents cannot be placed above honoring *God* (Luke 14:26).

C. Complete the statements.

7. The Huang He was called "China's Sorrow" because *it had many floods that killed people and ruined harvests*.
8. The Chinese people were protected from foreign invaders by the natural boundaries of *mountains, jungles, a desert, and an ocean*.
9. The Chinese named their land the Middle Kingdom because *they thought it was in the center of the earth*.
10. The oracle bones show that the Shang had a system of *writing*.
11. The Shang made advances in other arts but are best known for their works of *bronze*.
12. Farmers produced silk, which weavers made into colorful *clothes/cloth*.
13. The Shang achievement used for eating was *chopsticks*.
14. The discovery of the royal tombs at Anyang was important because *much of what we know about the Shang dynasty comes from them*.

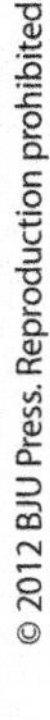

Chou Dynasty Organizer

Name ____________________

Use with Student Text pages 149–56.

Complete the fishbone organizer as you study about the Chou dynasty.

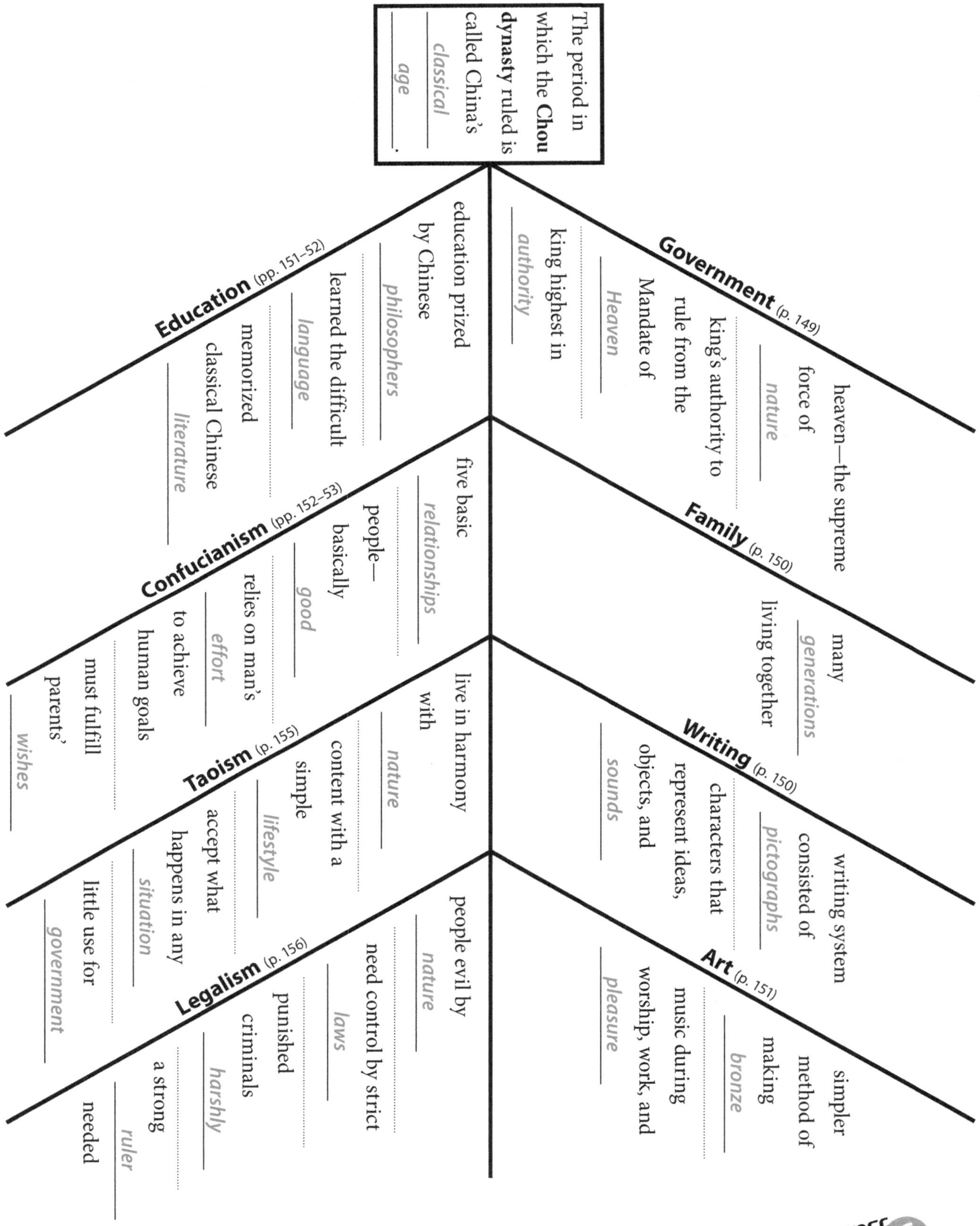

The period in which the **Chou dynasty** ruled is called China's *classical* *age*.

Government (p. 149)

- heaven—the supreme force of *nature*
- king's authority to rule from the Mandate of *Heaven*
- king highest in *authority*

Family (p. 150)

- many *generations* living together

Writing (p. 150)

- writing system consisted of *pictographs*
- characters that represent ideas, objects, and *sounds*

Art (p. 151)

- simpler method of making *bronze*
- music during worship, work, and *pleasure*

Education (pp. 151–52)

- education prized by Chinese *philosophers*
- learned the difficult *language*
- memorized classical Chinese *literature*

Confucianism (pp. 152–53)

- five basic *relationships*
- people—basically *good*
- relies on man's *effort* to achieve human goals
- must fulfill parents' *wishes*

Taoism (p. 155)

- live in harmony with *nature*
- content with a simple *lifestyle*
- accept what happens in any *situation*
- little use for *government*

Legalism (p. 156)

- people evil by *nature*
- need control by strict *laws*
- punished criminals *harshly*
- a strong *ruler* needed

Classical Age

Use with Student Text pages 151–53.

Name ______________________

A. Define the terms using the glossary and Student Text pages.

1. philosopher *a scholar who dedicates himself to the pursuit of earthly wisdom*
2. proverb *a wise saying that expresses a simple truth*

B. Answer the questions.

3. How was the making of bronze in the Chou dynasty different from in the Shang dynasty? *The Chou developed a simpler method of making bronze.*
4. How was the use of bronze similar in both the Chou and Shang dynasties? *They both used bronze in religious ceremonies.*
5. What books are considered the classics of Chinese literature? *the books written by scholars during the Chou dynasty*
6. What proverb expresses Confucius's belief about human relationships? *"What you do not want done to yourself, do not do to others."*
7. Read Luke 6:31. How does the proverb in the previous question compare to this Bible verse? *Answers will vary but should include that the proverb and the verse express similar thoughts.*

C. Write *T* if the statement is true. If the statement is false, draw a line through the incorrect part and write the correction in the blank.

T 8. Education was important during the Chou dynasty.

everyday 9. Confucius wrote many proverbs about ~~religious~~ life.

T 10. Confucius made education available to all social classes.

difficult 11. Students spent many years learning the ~~easy~~ Chinese language.

scholars 12. Throughout much of Chinese history, no one exceeded the influence of the ~~kings.~~

T 13. Confucius taught that proper behavior would allow man to live in happiness.

five 14. Confucius believed in ~~four~~ basic human relationships.

T 15. Confucianism leaves out the most important relationship of all—man and God.

good 16. Confucianism assumes that people are basically ~~evil.~~

man 17. Confucianism is ~~God~~-centered.

T 18. Christ said that loyalty to Him may demand sacrificing loyalty to family.

What the Bible Says

Name ______________________________

Complete the charts using Student Text pages 152–55 and your Bible.

Confucianism	Biblical truth
Confucianism identifies ___five___ basic ___human___ relationships.	The Bible teaches that the most important relationship is between ___man___ and ___God___. The greatest commandment is to love God with all of one's ___heart___, ___soul___, and ___mind___ (Matt. 22:37).
Confucianism teaches that people simply need to choose to act ___rightly___ in every relationship.	The Bible teaches that since unsaved people are slaves to sin, they are unable to ___please___ God (Rom. 8:7–8).
Confucianism assumes that people are basically ___good___.	The Bible teaches that everyone has ___sinned___ (Rom. 3:23) and must depend on God's ___grace___ for salvation (Eph. 2:8).
Confucianism is ___man-centered___ and relies on man's ___effort___ to achieve human goals.	The Bible teaches that a Christian can do all things through the ___strength___ of Christ (Phil. 4:13).
Confucianism does not teach that there is a ___divine___ being.	The Bible teaches that there is ___one___ ___God___ (1 Cor. 8:6).
Confucianism teaches that children must fulfill their ___parents'___ wishes, even if those wishes are wrong.	In the Bible, Christ said that loyalty to Him may demand ___sacrificing___ loyalty to family (Matt. 10:37–38).
Taoism	**Biblical truth**
Taoism teaches that people should not try to make things ___better___ for themselves or be motivated by ___desires___.	The Bible teaches that Christians should have the right desires to ___love___ God and others (Matt. 22:36–40) and try to improve the world to glorify God and for other people's ___good___ (Gal. 6:10).
Taoism teaches that people should not ___plan___ but simply ___accept___ what happens in any situation.	The Bible teaches that Christians should trust God to ___direct___ their lives as they live in ___obedience___ to Him (Prov. 3:6).
Taoism teaches that man should be in harmony with ___nature___.	The Bible teaches that man is given ___dominion/rule___ over creation (Gen. 1:28).

Study Guide

Use with Student Text pages 149–56.

Name ______________________________

A. Match the terms with the correct definitions.

B 1. classical age

D 2. Mandate of Heaven

C 3. philosopher

A 4. proverb

A. a wise saying that expresses a simple truth
B. a time of cultural development and achievement in a civilization
C. a scholar who dedicates himself to the pursuit of earthly wisdom
D. a belief that the supreme force of nature gave the king his right to rule

B. Complete the cultural aspects and achievements that made the Chou dynasty China's classical age.

5. China's culture was built around strong *family ties*.
6. The family included many *generations* that lived together.
7. The Chinese firmly established their *writing* system.
8. Chinese writing became a form of *art*.
9. The Chou developed a simpler method of *making bronze*.
10. Music was played during times of *worship*, *work*, and *pleasure*.
11. A good education was highly prized by Chinese *philosophers*.
12. Scholars wrote many books that are considered the *classics* of Chinese literature.
13. Students learned the difficult Chinese *language* and memorized classical Chinese *literature*.

C. Name the philosopher.

Confucius 14. He taught that man could solve the problems of society through proper behavior.

Lao Tzu 15. He taught that people should live in harmony with nature.

D. Complete the section.

16. What did the Chou leaders believe justified their rebellion against the Shang? *the Mandate of Heaven*

17. List the two duties that Confucius taught as part of the five basic relationships.
   - *to set a good example of proper behavior*
   - *to show respect and obedience*

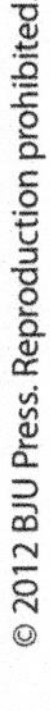

E. Match the philosophies with their teaching.

C. Confucianism   T. Taoism   L. Legalism

C 18. If proper relationships in five areas are kept, society will have harmony and order.
L 19. People are evil by nature and should be controlled by strict laws.
T 20. Men can find peace and happiness by living in harmony with nature.
L 21. A strong ruler is needed to maintain order.
T 22. This philosophy is the basis for many superstitious and magical beliefs in Chinese culture.
C 23. Children must fulfill their parents' wishes, even if those wishes are wrong.
C 24. Man is basically good, and he simply needs to choose to act rightly in every relationship.
T 25. People should not plan but simply accept what happens in any situation.

F. Complete the T-chart.

26–27. Contrast Confucianism and Taoism. List two differences. *Possible answers are given.*

Confucianism	Taoism
• *active lifestyle / fulfillment of social obligations*	• *passive lifestyle / freedom from responsibility*
• *improvement of government, laws, and education / focus on the human world*	• *minimizing of governmental authority and involvement in society / focus on the natural world*

G. First, plan the essay on your own paper. Then, write it below.

28. Contrast Confucianism with biblical truth. Include at least three differences.

The student should include at least three of these contrasts: Confucianism identifies five basic human relationships, but it leaves out the most important relationship of all—man and God. Confucianism teaches that people simply need to choose to act rightly in every relationship and assumes that people are basically good. The Bible teaches that since unsaved people are slaves to sin, they are unable to simply choose to do right. Confucianism is man-centered and relies on man's effort to achieve human goals. It does not teach that there is a divine being. Christians know that God exists and that sinful man has to depend on God's grace for salvation. Confucianism teaches that children must fulfill their parents' wishes, even if those wishes are wrong. Christ said that loyalty to Him may demand sacrificing loyalty to family.

Qin Dynasty Organizer

Use with Student Text pages 156–60.

Name ______________________

Complete the fishbone organizer as you read about the Qin dynasty.

The **Qin dynasty** was founded by the emperor *Qin Shi Huang Ti*.

Government (p. 156)

- established a *Legalist* government
- set up a *bureaucracy*
- put a *governor* in charge of each district

Changes (pp. 156–57)

- often cruel and *harsh* changes
- more *unified* China
- built a *network* of roads

Great Wall (p. 158)

- accomplishment of *Qin Shi Huang Ti*
- ______________
- linking a series of existing *fortifications*
- construction work to keep *discontented* citizens busy

Censorship (p. 158)

- governmental control of *scholars'* influence
- no education for the *common* man
- documents that *contradicted* the emperor's thinking destroyed

Terra-Cotta Army (p. 159)

- silent guard at the tomb of *Qin Shi Huang Ti*
- ______________
- built to protect the emperor in the *next* world
- life-sized *statues*

Currency (p. 160)

- *cowry shells* earliest known currency
- coins, small knives, and *spades* used as currency
- became *standardized* or consistent in Qin dynasty

Lasting Monument

Name ______________________

Use with Student Text pages 156–61.

A. Define the terms using the glossary and Student Text pages.

1. bureaucracy *the managing of government through bureaus, or departments, with appointed officials*

2. currency *money; any material of value that is exchanged for goods or services*

B. Mark the cost for each benefit.

3. Qin Shi Huang Ti "brought order to the mass of beings."
   - ● Those who did not agree with Qin Shi Huang Ti faced severe punishment that included hard labor or death.
   - ○ Qin Shi Huang Ti standardized weights, measurements, and the money system.

4. Qin Shi Huang Ti's power allowed him to make changes to unify China.
   - ○ The Chinese built a network of roads.
   - ● Qin Shi Huang Ti's methods were often cruel and harsh.

5. The Great Wall kept out invaders from the north, and the construction work kept discontented citizens busy.
   - ● It was better for a thousand people to die so that a million people could live.
   - ○ Hundreds of thousands of men used stone, dirt, or whatever natural materials were available.

C. Match the change made during Qin Shi Huang Ti's rule with how it benefited China.

B 6. standardized weights, measurements, and the money system

C 7. required the use of the same writing system

A 8. built roads that were a standard width

F 9. built canals to connect the rivers

D 10. built an irrigation system

G 11. built a wall in the north

E 12. established the same laws and taxes for everyone

A. made traveling easier for the people
B. made judging the worth of items and services easier
C. made communication easier
D. made more land available for farming
E. treated the nobles and common people the same
F. made it easier to ship goods from the north to the south
G. helped protect the people

The terra-cotta soldiers of the Qin dynasty protect their emperor.

Study Guide

Use with Student Text pages 156–60.

Name ______________________

A. Match the description with the correct term. The terms may be used more than once.

A. bureaucracy
B. common man
C. currency
D. Great Wall
E. Qin Shi Huang Ti
F. scholars
G. terra-cotta army
H. the name China

E 1. was "First Emperor"
G 2. carved to protect Qin Shi Huang Ti as he lived in the next world
F 3. buried alive or sent to work on the wall for not burning their books
E 4. disliked the teachings of Confucius
D 5. project that kept discontented citizens busy
H 6. lasting tribute to the Qin dynasty
G 7. lifelike statues
C 8. money; any material of value that is exchanged for goods or services
E 9. standardized weights, measurements, and the money system
D 10. kept out invaders from the north
D 11. one of the best-remembered accomplishments of Qin Shi Huang Ti
F 12. persecuted by Qin Shi Huang Ti because he thought they were breaking up his empire
B 13. should not waste time with education but instead grow food
A 14. the managing of government through departments with appointed officials
E 15. established the same laws and taxes for everyone

B. Identify the places on the map.

16. China
17. Gobi Desert
18. Great Wall
19. Himalaya Mountains
20. Huang He
21. Pacific Ocean
22. Yangtze River

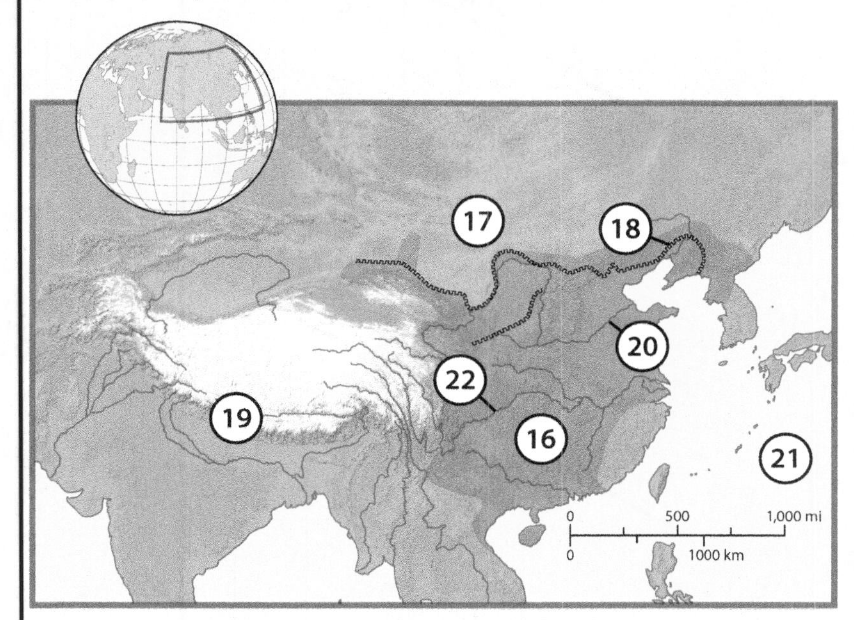

Han Dynasty Organizer

Name ____________________

Use with Student Text pages 161–68.

Complete the fishbone organizer as you read about the Han dynasty.

The **Han dynasty** had a strong and fair *central* *government*.

Government (p. 161)

- the supply of *grain* under governmental control
- Confucianism—government's official *philosophy*
- developed a *civil* *service* system

Medicine & Manufacturing (p. 162)

- special *herbs* and acupuncture as medicine
- used *rudder* to change the ship's direction
- used foot-powered *looms* to weave silk

Science & Literature (pp. 163–64)

- a complete history of all the Chinese *dynasties*
- used a *seismoscope* to detect earthquakes
- made paper from *hemp* or tree *bark*

Trade Routes (pp. 166–67)

- main route called the *Silk Road*
- traveled in groups for *protection*
- exchanged *ideas* and *inventions*

Religion (p. 167)

- branch of Buddhism in China—*Mahayana*
- duty to help others reach *nirvana*
- person who delays nirvana to help others—*bodhisattva*

Society (p. 168)

- time of social *change*
- rigid *social* *classes*
- honored dead parents with *offerings* and *ceremonies*

China's Golden Age

Name ______________________________

For the four hundred years after the Han dynasty, China suffered from internal wars and barbarian invasions. Then under the Tang and Song dynasties, the Chinese people enjoyed a time when their country was at its best. These six hundred years are called China's golden age (AD 618–1279).

Trade

During both of these dynasties, trade was an important part of China's economy. Through the Silk Road the Chinese traded their famous silk, spices, and fine pottery. The Chinese not only traded their goods but also shared their ideas and inventions.

Literature and Poetry

All scholars had to be good writers of both poetry and prose. Their poems spoke of life, nature, home, friendship, and romance. Other golden-age literature included philosophy, religion, politics, stories, and fables. Writers produced many how-to books, giving instruction in painting, handwriting, and gardening. The Tang rulers began a tradition in which each new dynasty wrote the official history of the last dynasty.

Printing

The Tang dynasty developed *block printing*. The printer carved a whole page of characters into a block of wood. The characters had to be backward, much like those on a rubber stamp. The oldest known printed book is a block-printed scroll dating back to AD 868. It is the *Diamond Sutra*, a book sacred to Buddhists.

The Song dynasty began to use movable-type printing. Each character was carved onto an individual wood block. The printer then arranged these characters to form a whole page. The major problem was organizing the more than forty thousand characters of the written Chinese language.

Inventions

Chinese scholars put their minds to work on several other practical matters. Did you know that gunpowder was first used by the Chinese? They did not use gunpowder in warfare until the Song dynasty. But earlier, they used it in firecrackers in social, religious, and victory celebrations.

The Chinese invented a way of making *porcelain*, a thin, but strong, translucent pottery. Porcelain, or "china," is made from a mixture of white clay and the mineral feldspar. Once the pottery dried, it was decorated with paint, carvings, or a glaze of liquid glass.

The Chinese produced other practical devices too. They discovered the magnetic compass and built highly accurate clocks run by water. The Chinese made rain and snow gauges that helped with flood control.

Architecture

The Chinese believed their buildings should blend into the landscape. Wooden pillars and beams supported the roofs of the houses, while the walls were simply screens decorated with carvings, paintings, or lacquer. Another Chinese building style begun during this age was the pagoda. Pagodas were first used as Buddhist temples. Soon, however, the pagoda was just another type of building used for many purposes.

Golden Age Puzzle

Name ______________________________

Complete the crossword puzzle using Activity Manual page 97.

									1 G		2 W				
						3 P	A	G	O	D	A				
						O			L		T				
		4 S	I	L	K	R	O	A	D		E				
						C			E		R		5 D		6 L
						E			N				I		A
	7 S	O	N	8 G		L		9 T	A	N	G		A		N
				U		A			G				M		D
				N		10 I	N	V	E	N	T	I	O	N	S
				P		N							N		C
				O									D		A
11 B	A	C	K	W	A	R	D						S		P
L				D									U		E
O				E									T		
C			12 A	R	C	H	I	T	E	C	T	U	R	E	
K													A		

A Chinese pagoda

Across

3. a building first used as a Buddhist temple
4. made sharing ideas and inventions possible (two words)
7. the second dynasty in the golden age
9. the first dynasty in the golden age
10. for example, the magnetic compass and rain and snow gauges
11. the position of the characters in block printing
12. art involving construction of buildings

Down

1. a time when a country is at its best (two words)
2. what the Chinese clocks were run by
3. a thin, strong, translucent pottery
5. the oldest block-printed book (two words)
6. what the Chinese buildings blended into
8. used in religious and social celebrations before being used in war
11. the method of printing developed by the Tang

Study Guide

Use with Student Text pages 161–68.

Name ______________________

A. Match the description with the correct term. The terms may be used more than once.

A. acupuncture
B. bodhisattva
C. Chang Heng
D. paper
E. seismoscope
F. Silk Road
G. Wu Ti

C 1. invented the seismoscope

G 2. provided a strong and fair central government

A 3. method to relieve pain or cure sickness

F 4. helped the exchange of ideas and inventions between countries

A 5. poking needles through the skin at specific points on the body

G 6. expanded China's borders from North Korea to central Asia

E 7. detected earthquakes

D 8. made from hemp or tree bark

F 9. the main trade route between China and other regions

B 10. a person who has reached enlightenment but delays nirvana to help others reach enlightenment

F 11. needed armed guards to protect the merchants from bandits along the way

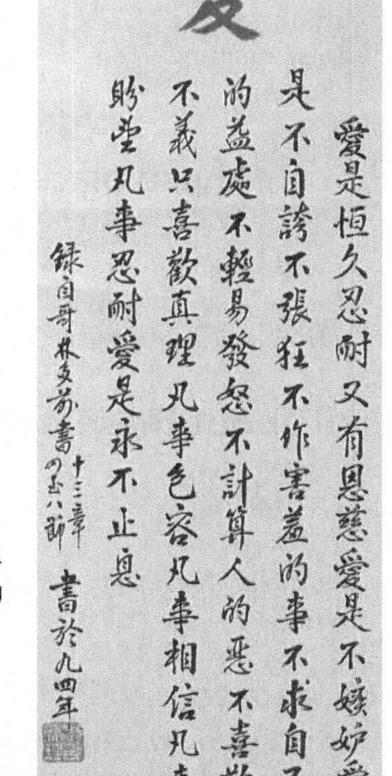

1 Corinthians 13:4 in Chinese writing

H. civil service system
I. literary achievement
J. manufacturing achievement
K. medical achievement
L. science achievement

H 12. trained people for governmental service

J 13. use of the iron plow and wheelbarrow to increase production on farms

H 14. required a recommendation to begin

K 15. use of special herbs

J 16. swords and armor, which made the army more powerful

I 17. a complete history of China's dynasties through early Han

H 18. included three public exams

J 19. the rudder, which allowed ships to travel farther and establish trade connections

L 20. the seismoscope

K 21. acupuncture

J 22. foot-powered looms to weave silk

B. First, plan the essay on your own paper. Then, write it on a new sheet of paper.

23. Contrast Mahayana Buddhism with biblical truth.

The student's essay should include these two differences: Mahayana Buddhism teaches that everything that people see is an illusion. The Bible teaches that God's creation is very good but cursed as a result of the Fall. Buddhism teaches that the ultimate goal for people is the state of nirvana. The Bible teaches that people will not be completely delivered from sin and suffering until they are reunited with Christ. The Christian looks forward to a glorified body and a new creation.

Chapter 6 Summary

Name ____________________

Define these terms

- acupuncture
- bodhisattva
- bureaucracy
- currency
- oracle bone
- philosopher
- proverb
- ting

Locate these places

- China
- Gobi Desert
- Great Wall
- Himalaya Mountains
- Huang He
- Pacific Ocean
- Yangtze River

This temple of Confucius is a pagoda.

Tell about these people

- Chang Heng
- Confucius
- Lao Tzu
- Qin Shi Huang Ti
- Wu Ti

Be able to . . .

- Write an essay contrasting Confucianism with biblical truth
- Explain why the Huang He was called "China's Sorrow"
- Describe China's natural boundaries
- Tell why the Chinese called their land the Middle Kingdom
- Contrast ancestor worship with biblical truth
- Describe the Shang dynasty's achievements in the arts
- Identify why the Shang's tombs are important
- Explain how the Chou used the Mandate of Heaven to justify rebellion against the Shang
- Explain what made the Chou dynasty China's classical age
- Describe the traditional Chinese family
- Identify the importance of education during the Chou dynasty
- Contrast Confucianism with Taoism
- Describe the philosophy of Legalism
- Describe the changes made during the Qin dynasty
- Describe the purpose of the Great Wall
- Explain how Qin Shi Huang Ti felt about philosophers and education
- Describe the terra-cotta army and its purpose
- Identify the lasting monument of the Qin dynasty
- Describe the civil service system of the Han dynasty
- Describe achievements of the Han dynasty in medicine, manufacturing, science, and literature
- Identify the purpose of the seismoscope
- Identify the importance of the invention of paper during the Han dynasty
- Describe the benefits and problems of the Silk Road
- Contrast Mahayana Buddhism with biblical truth

Cyrus the Great

Use with Student Text pages 170–73.

Name ______________________

A. Mark the correct answer.

1. What two tribes of nomads settled south of the Caspian Sea in the area that is now Iran?
   - ● Medes and Persians
   - ○ Chaldeans and Medes
   - ○ Chaldeans and Persians
2. After Cyrus defeated Croesus and captured Sardis, how far west did the Persian Empire extend?
   - ● the Aegean Sea
   - ○ the Mediterranean Sea
   - ○ the Black Sea
3. Who was the last ruler of the Chaldean Empire?
   - ● Belshazzar
   - ○ Nebuchadnezzar
   - ○ Marduk
4. What is another name for the Chaldean Empire?
   - ○ Assyrian Empire
   - ○ Mauryan Empire
   - ● New Babylonian Empire
5. Who interpreted the message that the hand wrote on the Chaldean palace wall?
   - ○ Ezra
   - ● Daniel
   - ○ Isaiah
6. Where was the Persian capital city under Cyrus?
   - ○ Persepolis
   - ● Pasargadae
   - ○ Babylon
7. Who foretold that God would use Cyrus to free the Israelites from slavery in Babylon?
   - ○ Ezra
   - ○ Daniel
   - ● Isaiah
8. When God allowed the Cyrus Cylinder to be found, what was it a testimony to?
   - ● the truth of God's Word
   - ○ the numbering of days left in the Chaldean kingdom by God
   - ○ the tolerant attitude of Cyrus the Great

B. First, plan your essay on your own paper. Then, write it below.

9. Describe four ways that Cyrus showed tolerance toward his subjects. Include at least one way he showed tolerance to the Israelites.

The student's essay should include three of these points: Cyrus let the people help make their own rules. He let them speak their own languages. He let them keep their own customs and religious beliefs. Cyrus freed some of his conquered peoples. He let them return to their homelands and make sanctuaries for their gods. The essay should include one of these points: Cyrus allowed the Israelites to return to Judah and rebuild God's house in Jerusalem. Cyrus returned the temple treasures that the Chaldeans had taken from the Israelites.

Chapter 7 Organizer

Name ____________________

Use with Student Text pages 174–91.

Complete the PERSIA organizer as you read the chapter.

Political Influences (pp. 174, 185, 190–91)

- Cyrus II defeated the Medes and began the *Achaemenid* period of Persia.
- A province was known as a *satrapy*, and a governor was a *satrap*.
- A Greek traitor helped the Persians win the Battle of *Thermopylae*.
- King Artaxerxes I allowed some Jews to return to *Jerusalem* to rebuild the wall.
- The Persian Empire finally fell to the armies of *Alexander the Great*.

Economic Influences (pp. 175–76)

- Darius's system of roads kept the empire connected. The longest one was the *Royal Road*.
- A common currency encouraged trade; Darius issued a gold coin called a *daric* and a silver coin called a *shekel*.

Religious Influences (p. 181)

- Zoroaster founded the main religion of Persia, called *Zoroastrianism*.
- The god of Zoroastrianism is *Ahura Mazda*, who struggles with an equally powerful evil being.
- The holy writings of Zoroastrianism are called the *Avesta*.

Social Influences (p. 191)

- When the Seleucids took control of Persia, *Hellenistic* culture spread throughout Asia.

Intellectual Influences / Arts (pp. 178–80)

- The Father of History was *Herodotus*; he recorded the history of the Persian Empire.
- The common language spoken in the empire was *Aramaic*.
- The Behistun carving was one of the sources used to decipher Persian *cuneiform*.

Area/Geographic Influences (pp. 174, 185)

- Darius moved the capital from *Pasargadae* to the city of *Susa* and then later to *Persepolis*.
- The strait between Asia Minor and Greece is called the *Hellespont*.

Political Influences
Economic Influences
Religious Influences
Social Influences
Intellectual Influences / Arts
Area/Geographic Influences

Study Guide

Use with Student Text pages 170–78.

Name ____________________

A. Fill in the blanks.

1. After Cyrus rose to power among the Persians, he led a rebellion against the *Medes*.
2. Under Cyrus the Persian Empire reached as far as the *Aegean* Sea in the west.
3. The dynasty that Cyrus II began is known as the *Achaemenid* period of Persia.
4. The Persian Empire reached its greatest size and power under *Darius* the Great.
5. Every Persian family lived in a province called a *satrapy*.
6. Darius named a governor, or *satrap*, to collect tribute in each province.
7. Darius moved the capital from *Pasargadae* to the city of *Susa* and then later to *Persepolis*.
8. A famous Greek historian named *Herodotus* described the Royal Road.
9. Darius's image was stamped on a gold coin called a *daric*.
10. Darius had royal messengers stationed along the *Royal Road* to carry messages in relay style.
11. The king's own special military force was called the *Immortals*.

B. Complete the chart.

12–14. Explain how Darius solved the problems his large empire faced.

Challenges Darius faced	Solutions Darius used
How to govern the whole empire	*He set up a centralized government.*
How to keep the empire connected	*He built and maintained a good road system.*
How to keep control of the empire	*He paid soldiers who were professionally trained and kept a well-trained cavalry.*

Persian soldiers on a relief

C. Answer the questions.

15. What two nations did Cyrus II conquer?
    - Lydia
    - Chaldean Empire

16. What was Daniel's interpretation of the handwriting on the Chaldean palace wall? The words meant that God had numbered the days left in the Chaldean kingdom and it had come to an end.

17. What are two ways that Cyrus showed tolerance to his subjects? possible answers: Cyrus let the people
    - help make their own rules. He let them speak their own languages. He let them keep their own customs and religious beliefs. Cyrus freed some of his conquered peoples. He let them return to their
    - homelands and make sanctuaries for their gods. Cyrus allowed the Israelites to return to Judah and rebuild God's house in Jerusalem. Cyrus returned the temple treasures that the Chaldeans had taken from the Israelites.

18. How did the Cyrus Cylinder become an important testimony to the truth of God's Word? The cylinder describes how Cyrus allowed the Israelites to return to Judah and rebuild God's house in Jerusalem and also how Cyrus returned the temple treasures that the Chaldeans had taken from the Israelites.

19. What two things encouraged trade during the rule of Darius?
    - the road system
    - a common currency or coin system

20. "Neither snow nor rain nor heat nor gloom of night stays these couriers from the swift completion of their appointed rounds." Who wrote this quotation, which is sometimes used to describe the United States Postal Service? Herodotus

A courier along the Royal Road

Immortals

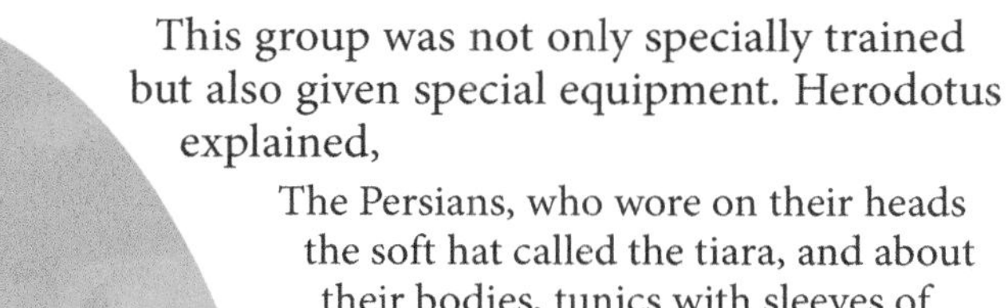

Name ______________________________

Besides having a formidable fleet of ships on the sea, the Persians developed an elite fighting force on land. Herodotus described this army of ten thousand as the Immortals. It seems that Herodotus was the first to come up with this name although many have used it since. If one of the soldiers was killed or sick, then he was immediately replaced with a warrior that was already trained to fill his rank. Therefore, the army was never more or less than ten thousand strong. Herodotus described these soldiers as being a highly trained, dangerous fighting force. During times of peace, these men served as bodyguards to the king.

This group was not only specially trained but also given special equipment. Herodotus explained,

> The Persians, who wore on their heads the soft hat called the tiara, and about their bodies, tunics with sleeves of divers colours, having iron scales upon them like the scales of a fish. Their legs were protected by trousers; and they bore wicker shields for bucklers; their quivers hanging at their backs, and their arms being a short spear, a bow of uncommon size, and arrows of reed. They had likewise daggers suspended from their girdles along their right thighs.

The soldier would often wear a brightly colored tunic over a leather vest that was covered with metal plates. These plates were designed to stop arrows shot by the enemy. They were not strong enough, however, to stop a spear or a sword. This fighting force was key to the Persians' victory in the Battle of Thermopylae and many other battles.

Answer the questions by writing two or more complete sentences. *Accept all reasonable answers.*

1. Why do you think Herodotus named this group of soldiers the Immortals? *possible answer: The number of soldiers was always the same. Whenever one of them became unable to fight, he was immediately replaced. Therefore, it seemed as if the soldiers never died, that they were immortal.*

2. Taking into consideration the dress that the Immortals wore, what attack strategies would the Greeks have had to use to defeat them? *possible answer: The Greeks would have needed to use hand-to-hand combat rather than long-range warfare since their arrows would not have been effective. Swords and spears would have been necessary to pass through the metal plating.*

3. Why do you think the Immortals were given the job of protecting the king? *possible answer: They were highly trained and were the most qualified for the job. This job would have helped them keep up their skills during times of peace.*

Cliffs of Behistun

Name ______________________

Use with Student Text pages 179–82.

A. Fill in the blanks with the answers to the clues given.

1. The Persian people spoke a common language called A (R) A M A I C.
2. Darius built the glorious city of P E R S E P (O) L I S to display the great wealth of the Persian Empire.
3. Darius had a carving done in B E H (I) S T U N that told of his rise to power.
4. The main religion of Persia was founded by Z O R O A S T (E) R.
5. The god of Zoroastrianism is called A H (U) R A M A Z D A.
6. Zoroastrianism was different from most other ancient religions because it was a form of M O (N) O T H E I S M.
7. Darius's decree that let the Jews rebuild their temple was upheld by (C) Y R U S.
8. The Zoroastrians believed that their god was represented by (F) I R E.
9. The priests in the Persian Empire were called (M) A G I.

B. Unscramble the letters in the circles to find the answer to the last clue.

10. The Persians' wedge-shaped symbols look similar to the ancient Sumerians' C U N E I F O R M.

C. Pretend you are Henry Rawlinson. Describe one of your days climbing on the cliffs at Behistun.

Answers will vary.

Behistun cliff-face inscription

Study Guide

Use with Student Text pages 179–86.

Name ______________________

A. Write a second sentence that illustrates the first sentence and clearly shows your understanding of the bolded word. *Possible answers are given.*

1. The Persian put the **rhyton** to his lips. *He took a drink from the vessel.*
2. The Persian read from the **Avesta**. *He studied the holy writings of Zoroastrianism.*
3. The **magi** kept a fire burning on the altar in the temple. *The priests in the Persian Empire believed that Ahura Mazda was represented by fire.*
4. My mother entered the **marathon**. *She ran a race of 26.2 miles.*

B. Answer the questions.

5. How did God use two kings who did not worship Him as part of His plan to rebuild the temple? *Cyrus allowed the Israelites to return to Judah to rebuild the temple. Darius ordered that the Jews be allowed to continue rebuilding, that help be given with their expenses, and that anyone that changed his orders would die.*
6. What events led to the Persian Wars? *The Greek city-states in Asia Minor rebelled against the Persians. Athens and a few other city-states on the Greek mainland sent an army to help the Greeks in Asia Minor. Darius was angry that the Greeks had banded together and rebelled against him.*

C. Identify the nation that won each battle of the Persian Wars.

7. Marathon *Greece* 8. Thermopylae *Persia* 9. Salamis *Greece*

D. First, plan your essay on your own paper. Then, write it below.

10. Compare and contrast Zoroastrianism with biblical truth.

The student's essay should include the following points: Zoroastrianism recognizes only one god, but not the God of the Bible. Zoroastrianism's god is equal with the evil being he battles against. The true God rules over all. Satan is a rebellious angel who can do nothing unless God permits it. Zoroastrianism teaches that what man does in this life determines what his eternity will be like. The Bible teaches that where man spends eternity depends on his relationship with Jesus Christ. Zoroastrianism teaches that a battle rages between good and evil. People must choose which side they are on. The Bible teaches that all people are born sinful and need God to save them from their sins. Salvation is only through Jesus Christ, Who paid the penalty for sin through His death and resurrection.

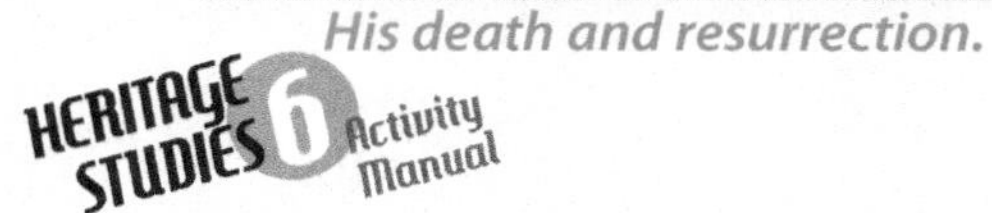

E. Write the correct answer.

B 11. What was the common language in the Persian Empire?
A. Greek
B. Aramaic
C. Hebrew

A 12. What was the architecture and art like in the Persian Empire?
A. splendid palaces, ornate carvings, elaborate headdresses
B. ornate carvings, large ziggurats, perfumed cones
C. splendid palaces, bronze tings, Great Wall

B 13. What is the importance of the Behistun cliff inscription?
A. Henry Rawlinson risked his life to climb the cliffs and copy the script.
B. Interpreting the script resulted in understanding ancient civilizations and reading other cuneiform scripts.
C. The Old Persian language was written in cuneiform similar to that of the Sumerians and was solved with the Rosetta stone.

C 14. Who founded the main religion of ancient Persia?
A. Darius
B. Xerxes
C. Zoroaster

C 15. What made Zoroastrianism different from most other religions in the ancient world?
A. It was the worship of idols.
B. It had temples.
C. It was monotheistic.

A 16. What did Zoroaster teach was the way to eternal happiness?
A. to do more good than evil in this life
B. to read the Avesta, the holy writings
C. to believe in a good god, Ahura Mazda

B 17. Who ordered his soldiers to beat the waters of the Hellespont?
A. Pheidippides
B. Xerxes
C. Themistocles

F. Label the map.

18. Aegean Sea
19. Black Sea
20. Caspian Sea
21. Hellespont
22. Pasargadae
23. Persepolis
24. Persia
25. Susa

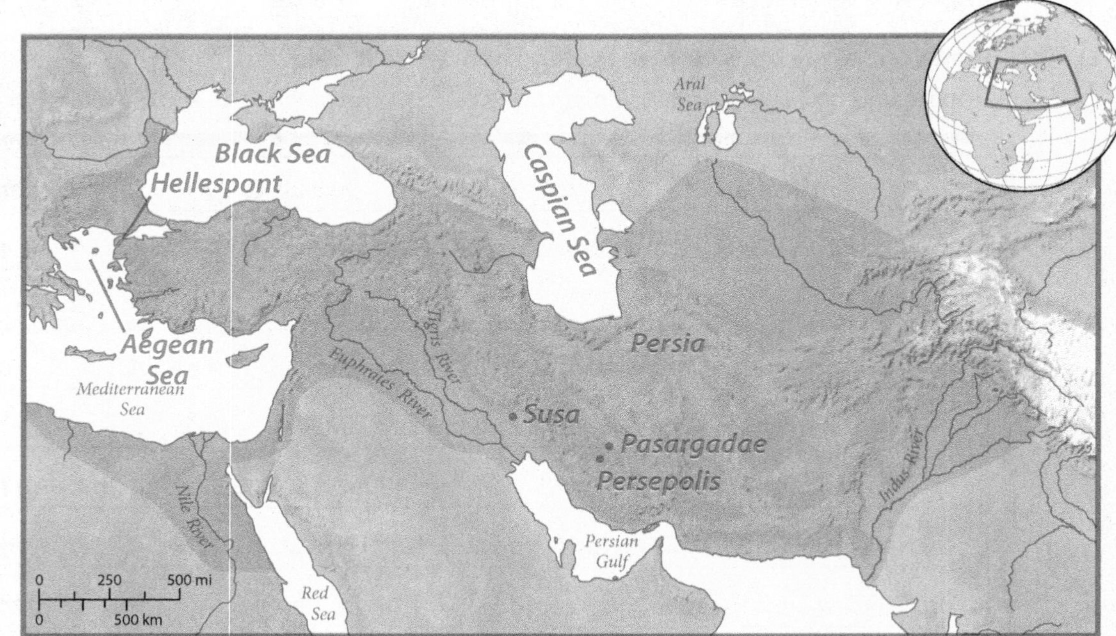

Persia and the Israelites

Name ______________________________

Use the Bible to complete the chart.

Reference	Israelite	Persian	Situation	Outcome
Esther 5:9–14 Esther 7:9–10	*Mordecai*	*Haman*	*Haman built gallows for Mordecai and was invited to the feast with Esther.*	*Haman was hanged on the gallows that he had built for Mordecai.*
Esther 7:1–6 Esther 8:9–11	*Esther*	• *Haman* • *Ahasuerus*	*Esther pleaded for the lives of the Israelites.*	*Ahasuerus signed a decree that allowed the Israelites to fight back when the Persians came to kill them.*
Nehemiah 2:1–8	*Nehemiah*	*Artaxerxes*	*Nehemiah wanted to go back to Jerusalem and rebuild the walls.*	*Artaxerxes allowed him to go and gave him letters for safe passage.*
Ezra 1	The Israelites	*Cyrus*	*Cyrus made a decree that the Israelites could go back to Jerusalem to rebuild the temple and take all the vessels that Nebuchadnezzar removed from the temple with them.*	*The Israelites returned to Jerusalem and began rebuilding the temple and brought with them the vessels that Nebuchadnezzar took from the temple.*
Ezra 5:9–17 Ezra 6:1–12	The Israelites	*Darius*	*There was a question as to whether the Israelites were supposed to rebuild the temple.*	*Darius found the decree that Cyrus had given and gave the Israelites provisions to help them finish.*

The study of Persian history repeatedly overlaps that of Israelite history. Many of the Persians were a part of God's plan for the Israelites. God is not limited to using believers to complete His work. He can use whomever He chooses to accomplish His plan.

Zoroastrianism

Name ______________________

Use your Bible and Student Text pages 181–82 to complete the chart.

Zoroastrian religious beliefs	Biblical truth
Zoroastrianism teaches that *Ahura Mazda* is the creator and the only god.	The Bible teaches that there is one God, Whose name is *Jehovah/Yahweh/Lord* (Ps. 83:18).
Zoroastrianism teaches that the good god, *Ahura Mazda*, struggles with an equally powerful evil being, *Ahriman*.	The Bible teaches that the true God rules over all. Satan is an evil spirit who is the *enemy/adversary* of God and all Christians (1 Pet. 5:8). God is *greater* than Satan (1 John 4:4).
Zoroastrianism teaches that what man does in this life determines what his *eternity* will be like.	The Bible teaches that where man spends eternity depends on his relationship with *Jesus Christ* (Titus 3:5–6). God requires that a person be born again to go to heaven (John 3:3).
Zoroastrianism teaches that a battle rages between *good* and *evil*. People must choose which side they are on.	The Bible teaches that all people have *sinned* (Rom. 3:23) and that those who call on Jesus shall be *saved* (Rom. 10:13). Salvation is only through Jesus Christ, Who *died* for sin, was *buried*, and "*was raised/rose again* the third day according to the scriptures" (1 Cor. 15:1–4).
The Zoroastrian holy writings are called the *Avesta*.	The Bible is the Word of God. It was written by holy men who were led by the *Holy Spirit/Holy Ghost* (2 Pet. 1:21).

Study Guide

Use with Student Text pages 188–94.

Name ______________________

Fill in the blanks.

1. An artist painted his interpretation of how the scene looked in his ___rendering___ of Noah and the ark.
2. The book of Esther uses the Hebrew name for the Persian king Xerxes, which is ___Ahasuerus___.
3. The Persian official who plotted to destroy all the Jews was ___Haman___.
4. The historian Josephus claimed no one approached Xerxes without a summons from him because he was guarded by ___men with axes___.
5. God gave the queen favor with Xerxes, and He brought about deliverance for His people through ___Esther___.
6. The expenses for Ezra's journey to Jerusalem were paid by ___Artaxerxes I___.
7. Artaxerxes I supplied the wood needed to build the city gates and sent letters to guarantee safety for ___Nehemiah___ as he traveled.
8. After Artaxerxes, the Persians became discontent with the high ___taxes___ and with their ___rulers___.
9. The city of Persepolis was burned by ___Alexander the Great___.
10. Alexander continued the Persian form of centralized ___government___, placed the Persian ___cavalry___ in his own army, and blended some Persian customs with ___Greek___ culture.
11. After Alexander's death, Persia came under the control of a family called the ___Seleucids___.
12. After Alexander's conquests, Greek culture that made its way into other lands was called ___Hellenistic___.
13. Art and coins that survived show that the Parthians had close contact with the ___Greeks___.
14. The Parthians lacked a strong central ___government___.
15. The Sassanid kings wanted to rid the culture of ___Greek___ influences and bring back all that was truly ___Persian___.
16. Persia achieved its greatest wealth during the ___Sassanid___ period.

A marble sculpture of Alexander the Great

Chapter 7 Summary

Name ____________________

Define these terms

Avesta	rendering
daric	rhyton
Hellenistic	satrap
magi	satrapy
marathon	

A Zoroastrian fire temple

Locate these places

Aegean Sea	Pasargadae
Black Sea	Persepolis
Caspian Sea	Persia
Hellespont	Susa

Tell about these people

Ahasuerus/Xerxes	Cyrus II
Alexander the Great	Darius the Great
Artaxerxes I	Herodotus
	Zoroaster

Explain what happened

at the three major battles of the Persian Wars

Be able to . . .

- Write an essay comparing and contrasting Zoroastrianism with biblical truth
- Identify the two nations that Cyrus II conquered
- Describe the writing that Daniel interpreted for Belshazzar
- Explain how the Cyrus Cylinder became an important testimony to the truth of God's Word
- Identify the Persian period that Cyrus II began
- Describe the three challenges that faced Darius with his large empire and how he solved them
- Identify the purpose of the Royal Road and the two cities it connected
- Identify the source of the popular quotation that the United States Postal Service uses
- Identify two things that encouraged trade during the rule of Darius
- Identify the special military force of Darius
- Describe the language, writing, and art of the Persians
- Explain the importance of the inscription on the Behistun cliff face
- Explain how God used two kings who did not worship Him to help rebuild the temple
- Describe the events that led to the Persian Wars
- Explain how through Esther God brought about deliverance for His people
- Describe the kindness that Artaxerxes I showed to the Israelites
- Explain why the Persians became discontented with the Achaemenid rulers after Artaxerxes I
- Describe the reigns of Alexander the Great, the Parthians, and the Sassanids

Places Organizer

Use with Student Text pages 196–209.

Name ____________________________

Describe the location of each place on the web as you study the chapter. Write an important fact about the *Peloponnesus*, *Crete*, *Athens*, *Sparta*, and the *Aegean Sea*. You may also use the gazetteer. *Possible answers are given.*

Peloponnesus

southern end of the Balkan Peninsula; location of the Peloponnesian War

Greece

a peninsula bordered by the Ionian Sea on the west, the Mediterranean Sea on the south, and the Aegean Sea on the east

Ionian Sea

on the west side of Greece

Aegean Sea

on the east side of Greece; mostly controlled by Athens

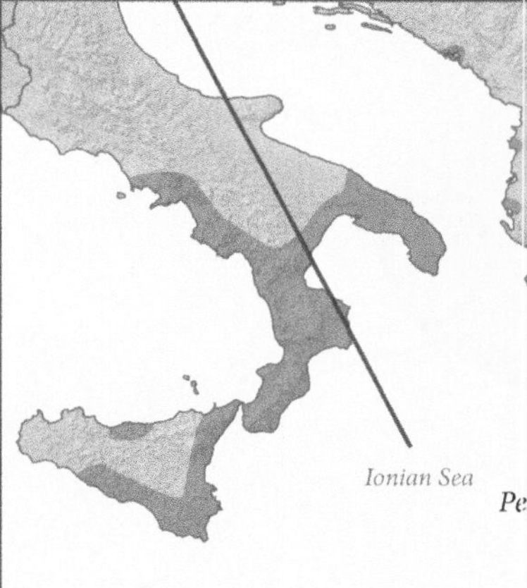

Aegean Sea

GREECE

Athens

Peloponnesus

Sparta

Mediterranean Sea

Crete

Mediterranean Sea

south of Greece

Athens

famous city-state located on the Balkan Peninsula; a successful democracy

Sparta

famous city-state located on the Peloponnesus; ruled by an oligarchy

Crete

largest island of Greece located in the Mediterranean Sea; location of the Minoan civilization

Terms Organizer

Name ______________________________

Use with Student Text pages 200–220.

Define each term on the web as you study the chapter. You may also use the glossary.

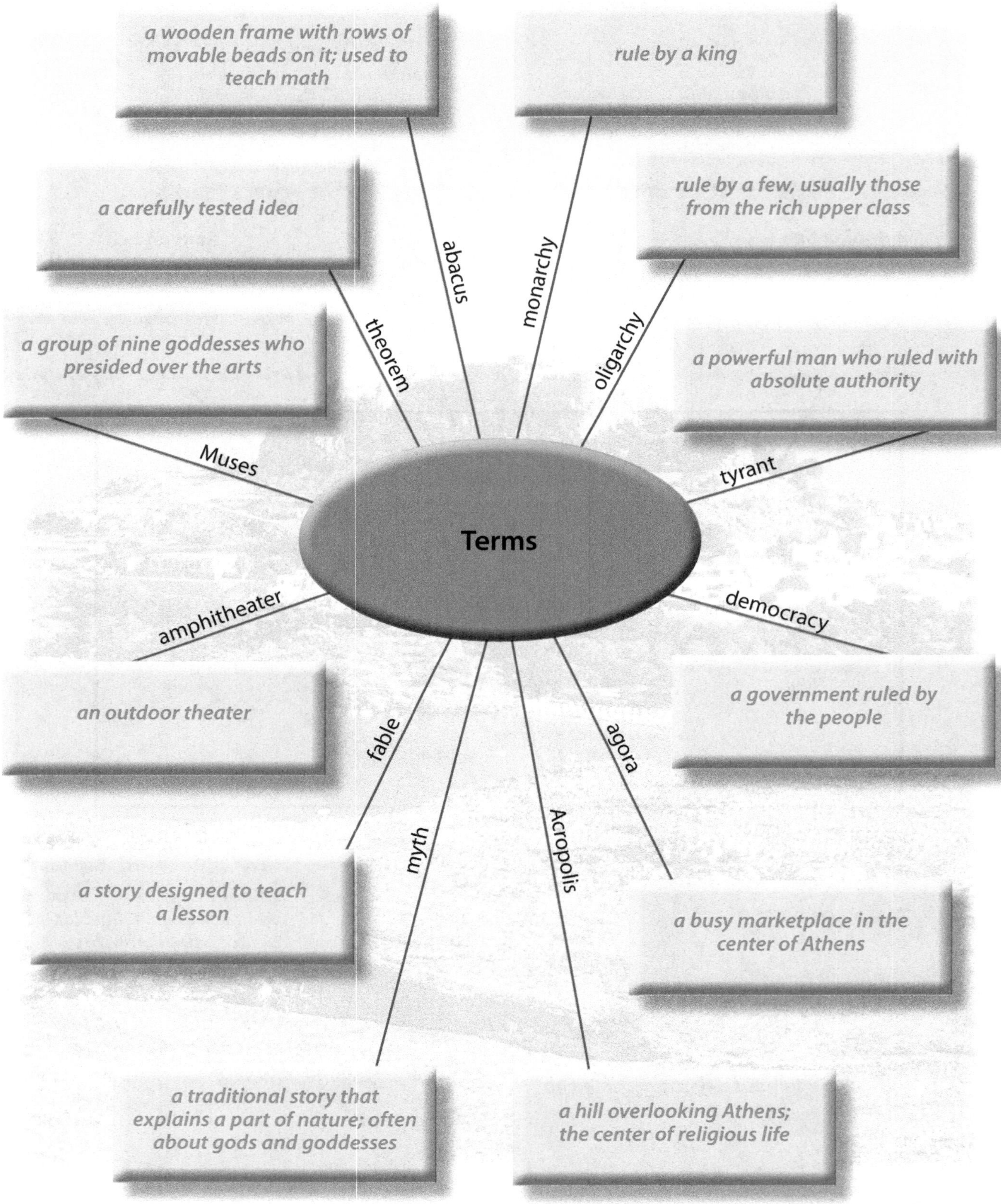

Terms

- abacus: *a wooden frame with rows of movable beads on it; used to teach math*
- monarchy: *rule by a king*
- theorem: *a carefully tested idea*
- oligarchy: *rule by a few, usually those from the rich upper class*
- Muses: *a group of nine goddesses who presided over the arts*
- tyrant: *a powerful man who ruled with absolute authority*
- amphitheater: *an outdoor theater*
- democracy: *a government ruled by the people*
- fable: *a story designed to teach a lesson*
- agora: *a busy marketplace in the center of Athens*
- myth: *a traditional story that explains a part of nature; often about gods and goddesses*
- Acropolis: *a hill overlooking Athens; the center of religious life*

Greece

Use with Student Text pages 196–99.

Name ______________________

A. Label the statements as describing the Minoans (Mi) or the Mycenaeans (My).

__Mi__ 1. Lived on the island of Crete

__My__ 2. Lived on the mainland of Greece

__Mi__ 3. Existed at the same time as the Shang dynasty in China and the New Kingdom in Egypt

__Mi__ 4. Built heavily adorned palaces with unusual luxuries

__My__ 5. Attacked cities and pirated ships instead of trading peacefully

__Mi__ 6. May have been the Philistines, the enemies of the Israelites

__My__ 7. May have started the legendary Trojan War

__My__ 8. Constructed a massive gate carved with two stone lions

__Mi__ 9. Focused on trade and relations with other countries

__My__ 10. Focused on their armies and building their cities through war

B. Number the map.

11. Knossos
12. Crete
13. Peloponnesus
14. Mycenae
15. Ionian Sea
16. Mediterranean Sea
17. Aegean Sea

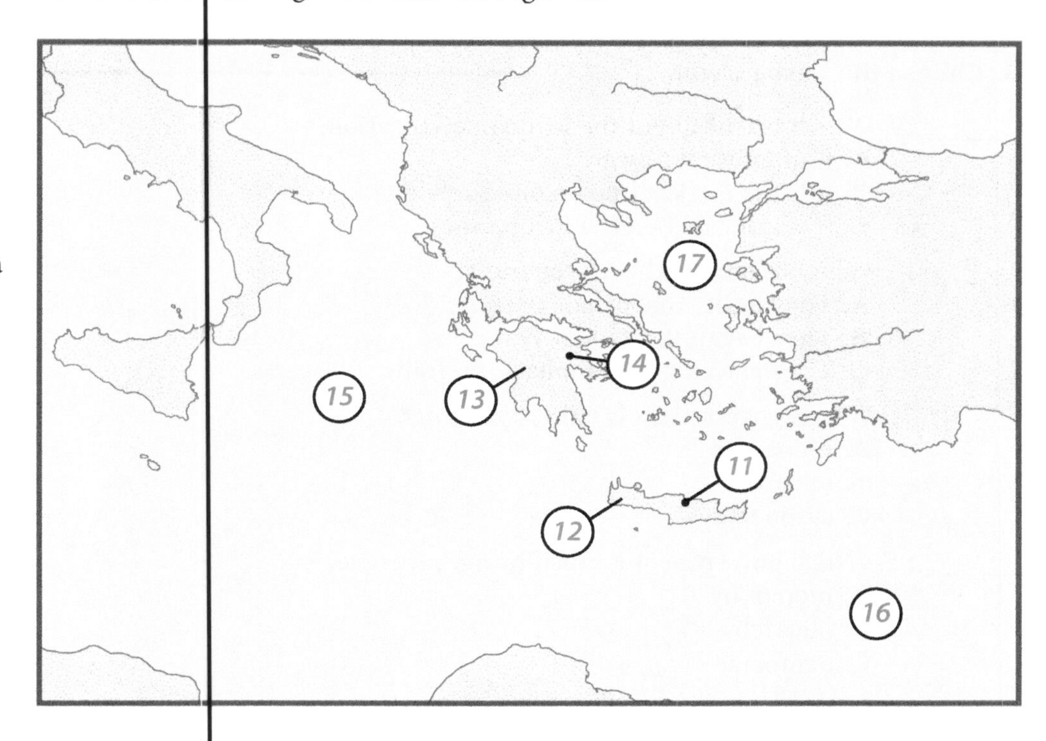

C. Complete the section.

18. Why was it difficult for the Greek farmers to grow crops? *The soil was rocky, making farming difficult.*

19. What were some of the unusual luxuries that the palace of Knossos could boast? *It had bathtubs and piped (running) water.*

20. The fall of the Mycenaean civilization marked the beginning of what kind of period in Greek history? *a dark age*

Study Guide

Name ____________________

Use with Student Text pages 196–203.

A. Write the correct location in the blank.

1. Peloponnesus
2. Greece
3. Aegean Sea
4. Mediterranean Sea
5. Ionian Sea
6. Crete
7. Athens
8. Sparta

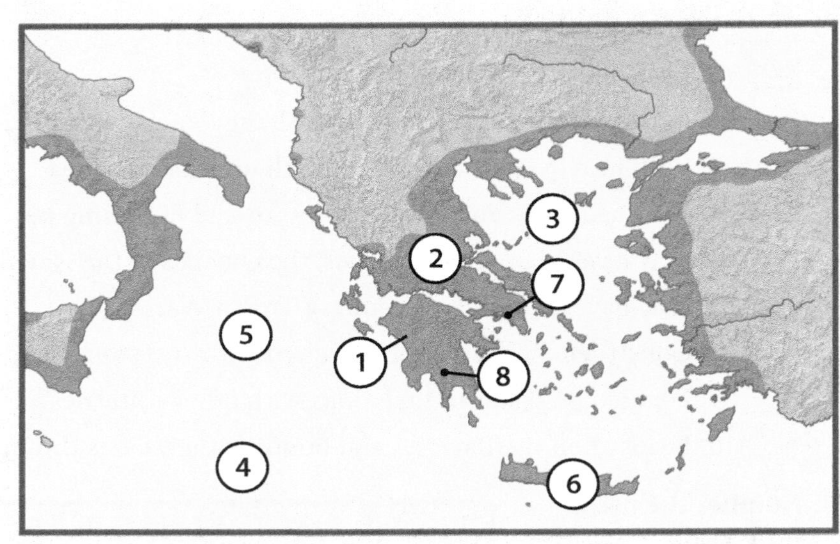

B. Choose the best answer.

B 9. Which is true about the Minoan civilization?
A. It often went to war.
B. It is the earliest known Greek civilization.
C. It was located on the Peloponnesus.

B 10. Which is true of the Mycenaeans?
A. They built large ornate palaces.
B. They began the Trojan War.
C. They placed great emphasis on trade.

A 11. Which government is ruled by a king?
A. monarchy
B. oligarchy
C. democracy

B 12. Which government is ruled by a few people?
A. monarchy
B. oligarchy
C. democracy

C 13. What was the name of the Greek marketplace?
A. Parthenon
B. Acropolis
C. agora

B 14. What were men who ruled Athens with absolute authority called?
A. monarchs
B. tyrants
C. rulers

C 15. Which government means rule by the people?
A. monarchy
B. oligarchy
C. democracy

Study Guide

Use with Student Text pages 196–203.

Name ____________________

C. Complete the section.

16. Describe the Assembly. *Possible answers should include that it was a group of citizens who met together to make laws. In these meetings, people could speak out and give their opinions and vote regardless of their standing in society. Women were not allowed to participate.*

17. When did the classical age of Greece begin? *ca. 500 BC*

18. Describe Sparta's army. *Possible answers should include that Sparta wanted a strong army. The society lived to build and maintain its army. Military training was harsh.*

D. Complete the chart.

19–24. Compare and contrast the city-states of Athens and Sparta. *Possible answers are given.*

	Athens	Sparta
Government	*Athens started with an oligarchy that turned to rule by tyrants. Then a democratic government was set up.*	*Sparta was ruled by an oligarchy.*
Male citizens	*The men were educated and allowed to participate in the Assembly.*	*The men were expected to participate in the army. They were taught from a very young age to fight, steal, and protect themselves.*
Women	*Women were rarely seen in public. They rarely shopped or worked outside the home. Women went out for festivals and plays. They were skilled at spinning and weaving. A few received an education at home.*	*Spartan women were trained to be strong mothers. They often did the work of the men. They were expected to bring up strong sons to fight for Sparta. They encouraged their men to be brave warriors.*

Athenian Democracy

Name ______________________

Use with Student Text page 204.

A. Record the votes for each method of voting. Complete a bar graph for each method.

1. Record the results for a vote by show of hands.

   yes votes ______ no votes ______

   Vote by show of hands

   Number of votes: 30, 25, 20, 15, 10, 5

   Yes No

2. Record the results for a vote by pebbles.

   yes votes ______ no votes ______

   Vote by pebbles

   Number of votes: 30, 25, 20, 15, 10, 5

   Yes No

3. Record the results for a vote by potsherds.

   yes votes ______ no votes ______

   Vote by potsherds

   Number of votes: 30, 25, 20, 15, 10, 5

   Yes No

B. Write a paragraph to answer the question.

4. Compare and contrast the methods of voting.

   Answers will vary but should include the idea that voting by a show of hands does not give a person the privacy of voting as does voting by pebbles or potsherds.

People Organizer

Use with Student Text pages 205–26.

Name ______________________________

Write a description on the web for each person as you study the chapter. You may also use the biographical dictionary.

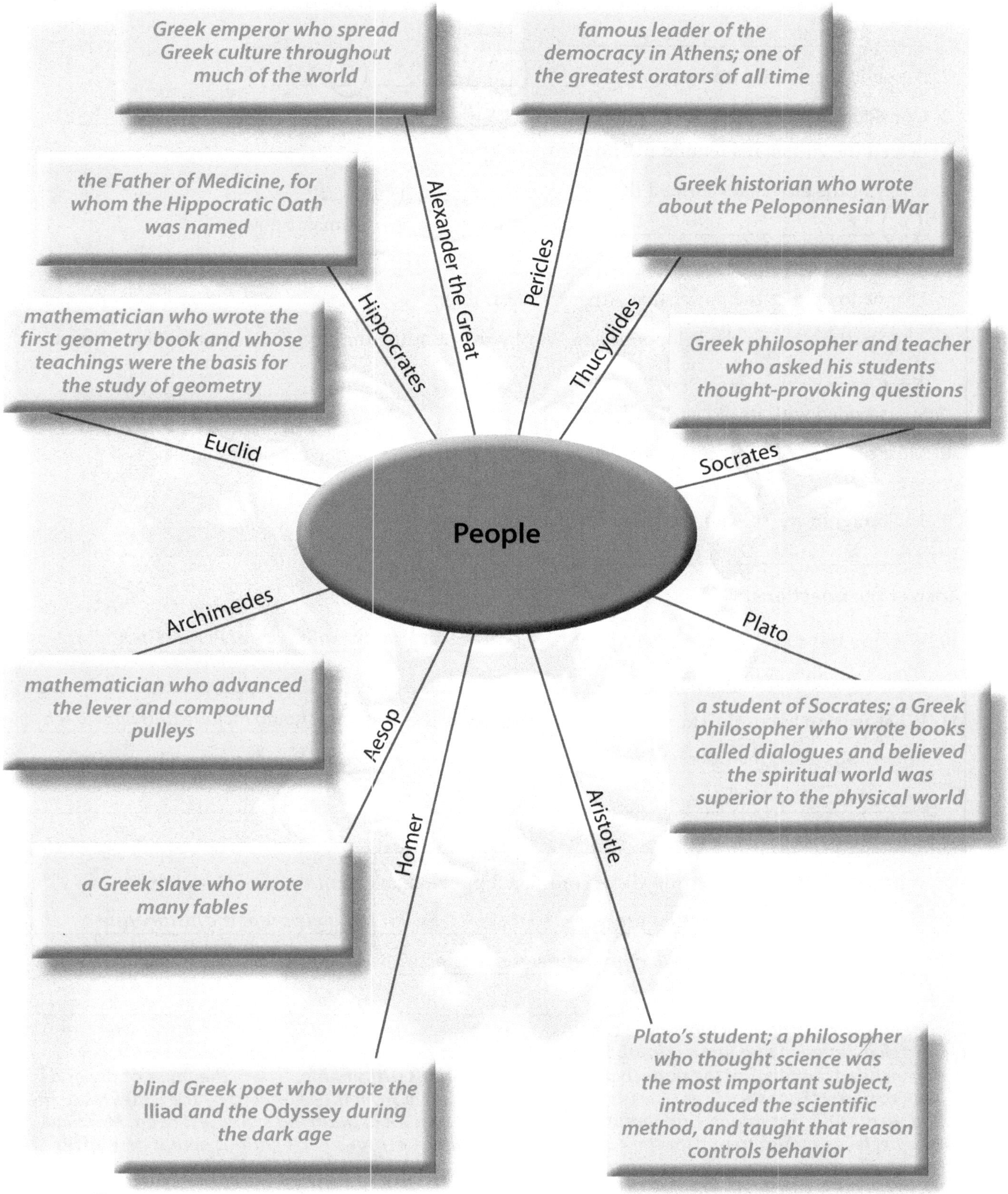

People

- **Alexander the Great**: *Greek emperor who spread Greek culture throughout much of the world*
- **Pericles**: *famous leader of the democracy in Athens; one of the greatest orators of all time*
- **Hippocrates**: *the Father of Medicine, for whom the Hippocratic Oath was named*
- **Thucydides**: *Greek historian who wrote about the Peloponnesian War*
- **Euclid**: *mathematician who wrote the first geometry book and whose teachings were the basis for the study of geometry*
- **Socrates**: *Greek philosopher and teacher who asked his students thought-provoking questions*
- **Archimedes**: *mathematician who advanced the lever and compound pulleys*
- **Plato**: *a student of Socrates; a Greek philosopher who wrote books called dialogues and believed the spiritual world was superior to the physical world*
- **Aesop**: *a Greek slave who wrote many fables*
- **Homer**: *blind Greek poet who wrote the* Iliad *and the* Odyssey *during the dark age*
- **Aristotle**: *Plato's student; a philosopher who thought science was the most important subject, introduced the scientific method, and taught that reason controls behavior*

War and Restoration

Name ______________________

Use with Student Text pages 205–9.

A. Complete the statements. Unscramble the circled letters to complete the last statement.

1. One of the most decisive battles of the Persian War was the Battle of S (A) L A M I S.
2. A public speaker is also known as an O (R) A T (O) R.
3. Considered one of the greatest public speakers, P E R I C L E S helped the Athenians rebuild their destroyed city.
4. Many of the city-states formed the D E L (I) A N (L) E A G U E to defend themselves against major powers.
5. Sparta formed the P E L O P (O) N N E S I A N League to oppose the power that Athens was gaining.
6. The Spartans began the Peloponnesian War by surrounding the city of Athens and beginning a (S) I E G E.
7. Sparta sided with its old enemy, (P) E R S I A, and defeated Athens.
8. Most of what we know about the Peloponnesian War comes from a historian named T H U (C) Y D I D E S.
9. The center of worship and religious life in Athens was the A C R O P O L I S.

B. Answer the questions.

10. Why are the 400s BC called the Age of Pericles? *because of the influence of Pericles in Athens (More specific answers from the text may be given.)*
11. What tension led to the start of the Peloponnesian War? *Answers should include that Sparta felt Athens was using the Delian League to gain power and so began the Peloponnesian League to prevent this growth in power.*
12. Why are the histories of Thucydides considered more reliable than those of Herodotus? *Thucydides was the more accurate recorder of events. He left out any part of the history that sounded biased or far-fetched. Herodotus was not as accurate.*

Answer for essay question on page 121

The student's essay should include these contrasts: The Greeks worshiped gods and goddesses who were very much like humans and just as sinful. The true God of the Bible is perfectly holy. The Greeks believed that they needed the favor of the gods to accomplish the various tasks of life. To win the favor of the gods, the Greeks offered them sacrifices. These sacrifices were different from those offered by the Israelites to the true God. In the Old Testament, God required sacrifices as a symbol of mankind's greatest need. Mankind needed a perfect sacrifice to pay for their sins. Since God cannot accept sin, He cannot accept man in his sinful condition. When Jesus died on the cross, He paid the sacrifice for all mankind. God provided the perfect sacrifice so that we can be acceptable in His sight.

Study Guide

Use with Student Text pages 205–13.

Name ______________________

A. Match the term to its description.

___D___ 1. Acropolis
___B___ 2. Aristotle
___E___ 3. Mount Olympus
___A___ 4. myth
___H___ 5. Plato
___G___ 6. Socrates
___C___ 7. Thucydides

A. a traditional story about gods and goddesses
B. a Greek philosopher who introduced the scientific method
C. a Greek historian who wrote about the Peloponnesian War
D. a hill overlooking Athens; the center of religious life
E. the highest mountain in Greece where the Greek gods lived
F. a great orator and famous leader of democracy
G. a Greek philosopher and teacher who asked his students thought-provoking questions
H. a Greek philosopher who believed the spiritual world was superior to the physical world
I. a busy marketplace in the center of Athens

B. Write *E* if the statement is an event leading up to the Peloponnesian War. If the statement is a consequence of the war, write *C*.

___E___ 8. Athens formed an alliance called the Delian League with many other city-states.
___C___ 9. Sparta took control of Greece for about thirty years.
___E___ 10. The Delian League city-states contributed money, troops, and ships.
___C___ 11. Athens lost its democracy.
___E___ 12. Athens grew wealthier from taxes and guarding the treasury.
___C___ 13. The Spartan oligarchy was unpopular with the other city-states.
___E___ 14. Athens grew more powerful by maintaining a navy and controlling most of the Aegean Sea.
___C___ 15. Buildings lay in ruins, and farmland was ravaged.
___E___ 16. Tension grew between Athens and Sparta.
___E___ 17. Sparta and other city-states formed the Peloponnesian League.
___C___ 18. Athens and Sparta were weakened by their losses.
___C___ 19. The "glory that was Greece" would never return.

C. Complete the chart.

20–23. Contrast Greek philosophy with biblical truth.

	Greek philosophy	Biblical truth
Wisdom	*Greek philosophers believed that they could use their own reason and clear thinking to arrive at true wisdom.*	*The Bible says that "the fear of the Lord is the beginning of wisdom" (Prov. 9:10).*
Virtues	*Greek philosophers emphasized many of the same virtues that the Bible does, such as truth, love, wisdom, and discipline.*	*The Bible teaches that these virtues are granted only through a true knowledge of Christ. It is impossible to live a godly life without the power of the Holy Spirit.*

D. First, plan the essay on your own paper. Then, write it on a new sheet of paper.

24. Contrast the Greek religious beliefs with biblical truth.

The answer to the essay question is located on page 120.

Education and Literature

Name ____________________

Use with Student Text pages 214–17.

A. Write the Greek letter of the correct term beside each description. The Greek letters may be used more than once.

__Ξ__ 1. a servant who accompanied boys to school

__Θ__ 2. twenty-four letters

__Κ__ 3. Greek poet who wrote the *Iliad* and the *Odyssey*

__Ε__ 4. a lengthy poem about the actions of a hero

__Η__ 5. a story designed to teach a lesson

__Α__ 6. a Greek slave who wrote many fables

__Η__ 7. main characters that were animals that talked and acted similarly to humans

__Β__ 8. a huge outdoor theater

__Η__ 9. a brief closing statement called the moral

__Δ__ 10. Greek drama that ended happily

__Ψ__ 11. Greek drama that had a sober ending

__Γ__ 12. playwright of comedies

__Λ__ 13. a tool that actors used to show whether the characters felt happy, sad, or angry

__Φ__ 14. playwright of tragedies

__Μ__ 15. a traditional story about gods and goddesses

B. Number the events of the myth of Midas in the order that they occurred.

__2__ 16. Midas wished that everything he touched would turn to gold.

__1__ 17. Midas was granted a wish by Dionysus, the god of wine.

__4__ 18. As the first sip touched Midas's lips, the liquid turned into a lump of gold.

__3__ 19. Midas leaped and danced around the palace grounds, touching trees, fountains, and benches and watching them turn to gold.

__9__ 20. The river Pactolus gleams with the last traces of King Midas's golden touch.

__6__ 21. Midas asked Dionysus to have pity on him and to take the gift back.

__5__ 22. The moment Midas touched the fingers of the princess, she froze into a solid gold statue.

__7__ 23. Dionysus told Midas to go and wash in the river Pactolus to lose his golden touch.

__8__ 24. Midas ran to the river and bathed in it.

The Olympic Games

Name ______________________

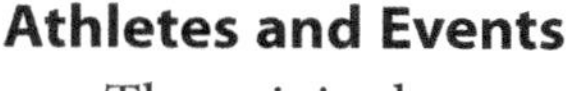

Every four years people from all over Greece gathered at Olympia to celebrate and compete in the Olympic Games. The festivities centered on the worship of Zeus. An enormous temple in the center of Olympia housed one of the wonders of the ancient world. This breathtaking statue of Zeus was six times as large as an average man and was crafted from gold and ivory. The competitors, judges, and observers all made sacrifices before the statue. Entire days of the festivities were dedicated to the worship of Zeus. According to tradition, the statue of Zeus was dismantled and moved to Constantinople when the capital of the Roman Empire moved there. It was then destroyed by a fire.

The Sacred Truce

Since many of the city-states constantly warred with each other, travel to Olympia was very dangerous. However, because this was a religious festival, messengers went out from Olympia a month before the beginning of the games. The messengers carried a "sacred truce" that prohibited attacking any travelers to the games. The truce allowed both competitors and spectators to travel safely to Olympia. Zeus's festival was to be observed in peace. However, it was not easy for the Spartans, Athenians, and other enemies to put their hatred aside. Each city-state used the competitions to try to show its superiority over the others. Skirmishes often broke out between those attending the games.

Athletes and Events

The original games included only a foot race. As the games grew in popularity, events were added. Men would train for months to compete in events such as throwing the javelin or discus, the long jump, boxing, wrestling, and horse and chariot races. There were several different lengths of foot races. Each race was a different number of "stades." A *stade* was the length of the arena and is where we get our word *stadium*. Some events were combined, and athletes were expected to perform well in the combinations. All events showcased the competitors' skill in battle. Because there were very few rules, the wrestling and boxing events were very fierce. Often a participant continued to beat his opponent after he was down.

All participants in the events competed naked, and only men could compete. Men and young, unmarried women were allowed to watch the events, but married women were barred from attending. They were, however, permitted to own the horses that competed in the horse and chariot races. Since the owners were the only ones that could afford to keep and train horses as well as pay for the riders, it was the owners that received the prize if their horse won. For all the events, the winners received olive wreaths as their reward. They also gained the fame and prestige that came with winning the major sporting event for their country. Athletes often married well and were taken care of for the rest of their lives.

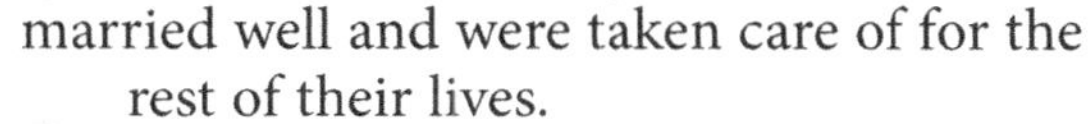

The Olympic participants walked through this archway on their way to their competitions.

The Olympic Games

Name ______________________________

Design a program for the Olympic Games at Olympia. In the largest rectangle, design the order of events for the five-day competition. In the smaller rectangles, design advertisements for some of the key sights in Olympia and for the vendors at the games.

Greek Culture

Name ______________________

Use with Student Text pages 219–22.

Choose the best answer.

__C__ 1. Advances in levers and other simple machines were made by ___.
- A. Pythagoras
- B. Euclid
- C. Archimedes

__A__ 2. A theorem is a ___.
- A. carefully tested idea
- B. distorted map projection
- C. mathematical book

__B__ 3. The first man to draw lines of latitude and longitude was ___.
- A. Pythagoras
- B. Eratosthenes
- C. Archimedes

__B__ 4. Most people in Aristarchus's day believed ___.
- A. the sun was the center of the universe
- B. the earth was the center of the universe
- C. Zeus lived at the center of the universe

__A__ 5. Hippocrates is called the Father of Medicine because ___.
- A. he did not rely on magic to treat patients
- B. he made great advances in medicine
- C. he healed the emperor of leprosy

__C__ 6. The Olympics were held to ___.
- A. cease war for a time
- B. help with city-state relations
- C. worship the gods

__A__ 7. One god associated with the arts was ___.
- A. Apollo
- B. Zeus
- C. Nike

__B__ 8. Important qualities of Greek art did *not* include ___.
- A. harmony
- B. asymmetry
- C. simplicity

__A__ 9. Much of what is known about Greek dress comes from ___.
- A. works of art
- B. historical records
- C. oral tradition

__C__ 10. One type of Greek column was the ___ column.
- A. Thessalonian
- B. Abstract
- C. Doric

__A__ 11. The Parthenon was dedicated to the goddess ___.
- A. Athena
- B. Aphrodite
- C. Hera

__B__ 12. An optical illusion occurs when ___.
- A. your eyes see spots in different patterns
- B. an object appears to take a shape it does not have
- C. different people see the same object as having a different color

Greek Cities

Name ______________________

The Lord can use even the unsaved to accomplish His purposes. Looking back at history, we can see how God directed events to prepare the way for Jesus to come. Alexander had conquered much of the known world. Even though the Greek empire had long since fallen when Christ came to earth, its influence still lived on. Greek was the language of business, and nearly everyone spoke some Greek. When it came time for the disciples to go out and spread the gospel, there was no need for them to go to language school or speak through a translator. They could preach in Greek, and people everywhere would understand. Even though Alexander the Great did not fear God, God used Alexander's thirst for power to prepare the way for the Messiah.

A. Read the passages listed. Write the Greek city in which the passage takes place and explain the events that occurred there.

	Greek city	What happened
Acts 16:11–40	*Philippi*	*Paul and Silas were preaching and were thrown into prison. They sang late into the night, and an earthquake opened the doors of the prison. The jailer came to know Christ as a result of their testimony.*
Acts 17:1–9	*Thessalonica*	*Paul and Silas began preaching in the synagogue and caused an uproar, but many accepted Christ as their Savior.*
Acts 17:16–34	*Athens*	*Paul was preaching at Mars' Hill concerning the altar to the unknown god.*
Acts 18:1–17	*Corinth*	*Paul met with Priscilla and Aquila who were tent-makers like he was. He preached for many months and the church grew.*
Acts 18:24–28	*Ephesus*	*Apollos began preaching boldly in Ephesus. Priscilla and Aquila took him under their wing and taught him more about God so that he might communicate the Word of God better.*

B. Label the cities from the chart on the map using a Bible atlas.

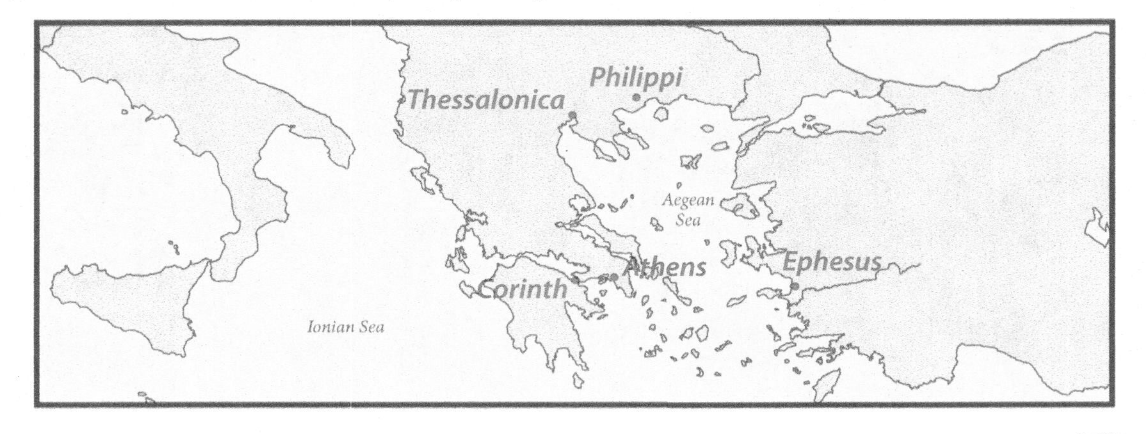

Study Guide

Name ______________________

Use with Student Text pages 214–26.

A. Match the descriptions to the terms.

A.	abacus
B.	Aesop
C.	Alexander the Great
D.	amphitheater
E.	Archimedes
F.	Euclid
G.	fable
H.	Hippocrates
I.	Homer
J.	Muses
K.	myth
L.	Peloponnesus
M.	theorem

__I__ 1. poet who wrote the *Iliad* and the *Odyssey*

__G__ 2. a story designed to teach a lesson

__B__ 3. Greek slave who wrote fables

__D__ 4. a huge outdoor theater

__E__ 5. mathematician who advanced the lever and compound pulleys

__F__ 6. author of the first geometry book

__H__ 7. Father of Medicine

__J__ 8. a group of nine goddesses who presided over the arts

__C__ 9. emperor who spread Greek culture throughout much of the world

__A__ 10. a special instrument used to teach math

__M__ 11. a carefully tested idea

B. Fill in the blanks.

12. The point of a fable is found in a brief closing __*statement*__ called the __*moral*__.

13. The emotions of characters in Greek plays were shown on the actors' __*masks*__.

14. Developing the body through athletics was as important to the Greeks as __*developing the mind*__.

15. The important qualities of Greek art were balance, __*harmony*__, __*simplicity*__, __*beauty*__, and __*completeness*__.

16. To hold up buildings, the Greeks perfected the construction of __*columns*__.

17. The Parthenon was a temple of white marble that included several optical __*illusions*__ in its design.

18. The spread of Greek culture brought a common __*language*__ to the Western world.

C. Complete the chart.

19–21. Fill in the details about the Olympic Games.

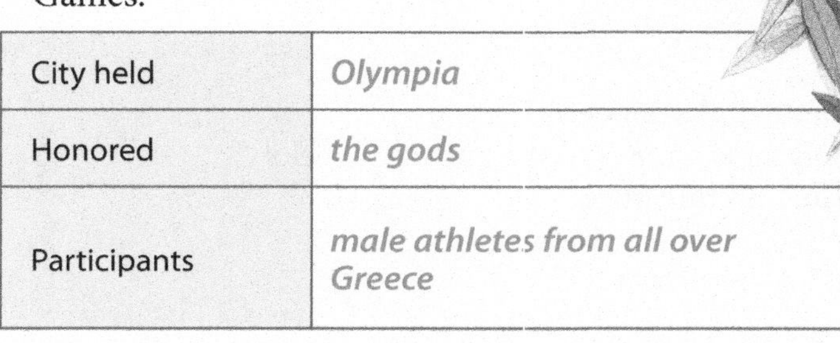

City held	*Olympia*
Honored	*the gods*
Participants	*male athletes from all over Greece*

Chapter 8 Summary

Name ____________________

Define these terms

abacus
Acropolis
agora
amphitheater
democracy
fable
monarchy
Muses
myth
oligarchy
theorem
tyrant

Locate these places

Aegean Sea
Athens
Crete
Greece
Ionian Sea
Mediterranean Sea
Peloponnesus
Sparta

Tell about these people

Aesop
Alexander the Great
Archimedes
Aristotle
Euclid
Hippocrates
Homer
Pericles
Plato
Socrates
Thucydides

Modern seacoast of Syme, Greece

Explain what happened

ca. 500 BC—beginning of Greece's classical age

Be able to . . .

Write an essay contrasting Greek religious beliefs with biblical truth
Identify the earliest known Greek civilization and where it was located
Relate the Mycenaean civilization to its military strength and the Trojan War
Identify which types of governments Athens and Sparta had: monarchy, oligarchy, or democracy
Describe the Assembly
Compare and contrast Athens and Sparta: government and men's and women's roles
Describe the events leading up to the Peloponnesian War and its consequences
Identify Mount Olympus
Contrast Greek philosophy with biblical truth
Describe the forms of Greek literature
Describe the achievements Greeks made in math and science
Explain the importance of athletics and the Olympic Games to the ancient Greeks
Identify the important qualities of Greek art and architecture
Describe the Parthenon
Explain why spreading the Greek culture was so important

Chapter 9 Organizer

Name ______________________

Use with Student Text pages 228–53.

Complete the PERSIA organizer for Rome as you read the chapter.

Rome

Political Influences
Economic Influences
Religious Influences
Social Influences
Intellectual Influences / Arts
Area/Geographic Influences

Political Influences

- government ruled by laws and representatives chosen by the people—*republic*
- three governing branches—*consuls*, *Senate*, and *Assembly*
- written Roman law—Law *of the Twelve Tables*
- three major wars between Rome and Carthage—the *Punic Wars*
- Caesar's death—the beginning of Rome as *an empire*

Economic Influences

- used a system of *roads* to transport goods to other lands for trade
- imported slaves, money, grain, and precious metals as *tribute*
- collected taxes through men called *publicans*

Religious Influences

- used Roman roads to carry the *gospel*
- two Greek philosophies—*Epicureanism* and *Stoicism*
- adopted *gods* from conquered peoples
- the Pax Romana—God's perfect time for *Jesus* to come

Social Influences

- two social classes—*patricians* and *plebeians*
- children's education during the Pax Romana—the *father's* responsibility

Intellectual Influences / Arts

- an influential master of Latin prose—*Cicero*
- the poet who wrote the epic *Aeneid*—*Virgil*
- architectural features of the Colosseum and Pantheon—concrete, *arches*, and *dome*

Area/Geographic Influences

- *fertile soil* and a *climate* for farming
- migration of the Latins to the *Italian Peninsula*
- early settlement—a village on Palatine Hill, one of *seven* hills near the *Tiber* River

Rome

Name ______________________

Use with Student Text pages 228–31.

A. Label and color the map according to the instructions given.

1. Label Rome.
2. Color the Italian Peninsula brown.
3. Label the sea to the west of Italy and color it blue.
4. Label the sea to the east of Italy and color it purple.
5. Label France, Switzerland, and Austria.
6. Color Sardinia and Sicily green.
7. What provided natural defenses for Rome? *the seven hills*

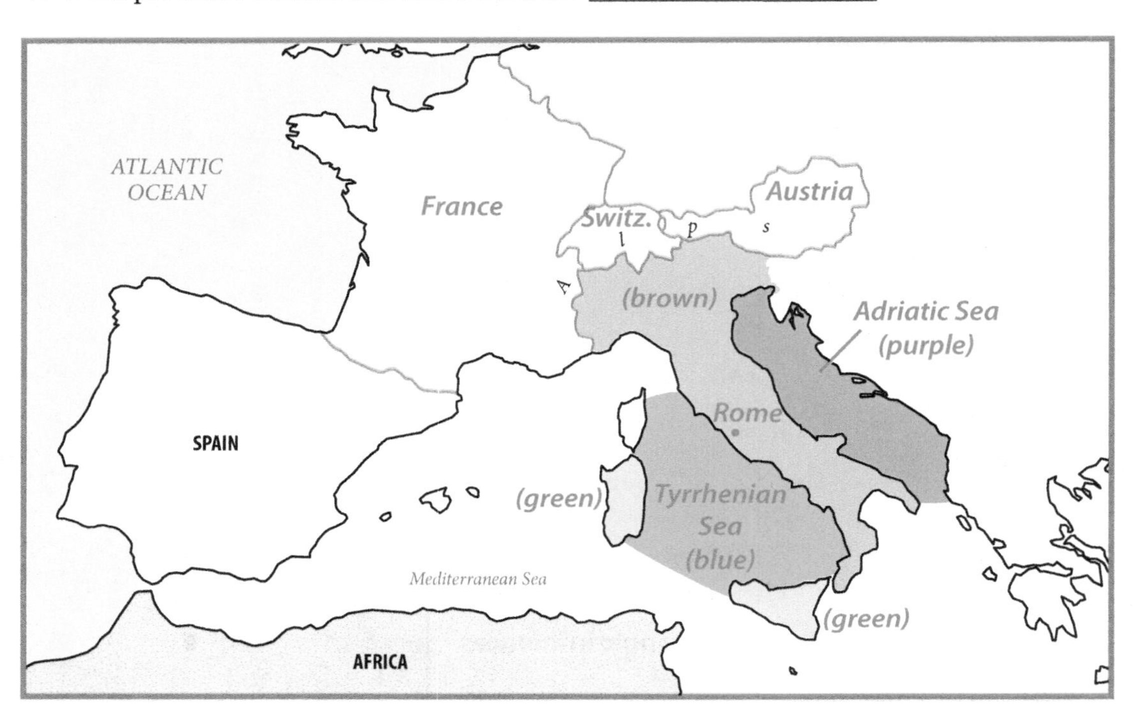

B. Write a sentence that shows how the pair of terms are related. *Possible answers are given.*

8. Italian Peninsula ◆ Italy

   Modern Italy is located on the Italian Peninsula.

9. Remus ◆ Romulus

   Romulus got angry with his twin brother, Remus, killed him, and built the city of Rome.

10. Rome ◆ Tiber River

    Rome was located on Palatine Hill, one of seven hills near the Tiber River.

11. Latins ◆ Etruscans

    The Latins were living in Rome when the Etruscans from the north conquered it.

12. patricians ◆ plebeians

    There were two Roman social classes, the patricians and the plebeians.

Government Organizer

Name ______________________

Use with Student Text pages 232–34.

A. Complete the diagram as you read about the Roman government.

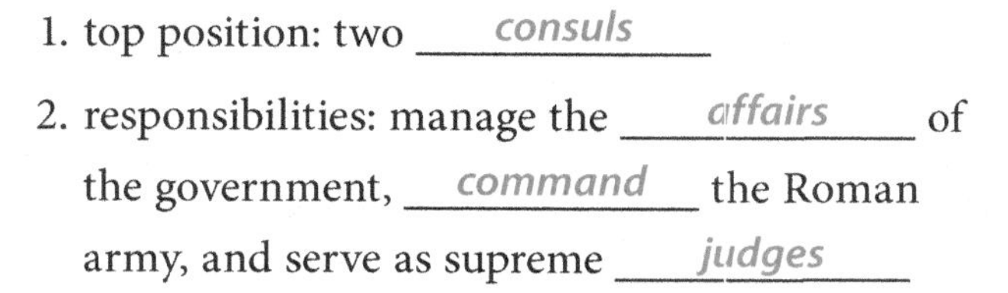

1. top position: two *consuls*
2. responsibilities: manage the *affairs* of the government, *command* the Roman army, and serve as supreme *judges*
3. terms lasting for *one year*

Both red.

All red.

All blue.

4. the most powerful branch: *Senate*
5. *300* members
6. responsibilities: controlled the *finances*, passed *laws*, and oversaw foreign *affairs*
7. served for *life*

8. *10* leaders called *tribunes*
9. responsibilities: protected the *rights* and the *interests* of the *common* people
10. could stop the Senate's actions by shouting, "*Veto*!"

Some red; some blue. The amount of each does not matter.

11. Assembly of *Centuries* and *Tribal* Assembly
12. responsibilities: voted on *new laws*, made declarations of *war*, and elected the *consuls*

B. Color the clothing of the Roman officials in the diagram according to the key.

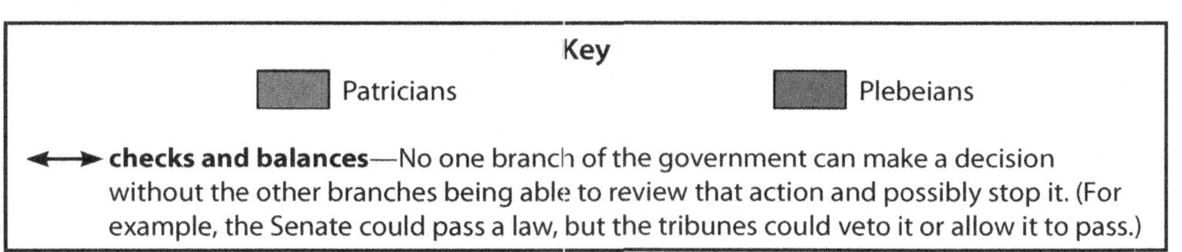

Key

Patricians

Plebeians

↔ **checks and balances**—No one branch of the government can make a decision without the other branches being able to review that action and possibly stop it. (For example, the Senate could pass a law, but the tribunes could veto it or allow it to pass.)

Fasces

Name ______________________

Historians believe the symbol of the fasces was first used by the Etruscans. Some think that the rods surrounding the axe represented justice. It was a leader's power to punish offenders. The axe was then a symbol of the power to execute those who rebelled. However, this was not the situation during the Roman Republic. Any Roman citizen had the right to appeal any ruling.

> The word *fasces* is plural; the singular form is *fascis*.

The fasces in Rome represented power. They were carried in parades and celebrations for victory. When a higher-ranking person entered a room, the fasces were lowered as a salute.

After the Romans the fasces were used as a symbol of power in other places. Benito Mussolini used the fasces as a symbol for his political movement and even named his movement Fascism. Unlike Hitler's use of the swastika, Mussolini's use of the fasces did not leave it with the same lasting evil association. The fasces appear on either side of the American flag in the House of Representatives. The official seal of the United States Senate also shows two crossed fasces.

A. Answer the question.

1. Why do you think governments choose to use the fasces as a symbol? *Possible answers include that it already held meaning that was important to them and they could capitalize on that meaning.*

> Many nations have chosen symbols to represent their heritage. Some are shown on the countries' flags. Some represent the history of the nation or the patriotism that their people display.

B. Match the symbols with the country.

D 2. bald eagle

A 3. swastika

C 4. Union Jack

B 5. eagle devouring a snake

> A. Hitler's Germany
> B. Mexico
> C. United Kingdom
> D. United States of America

C. Circle the fasces in the pictures.

United States Supreme Court Building

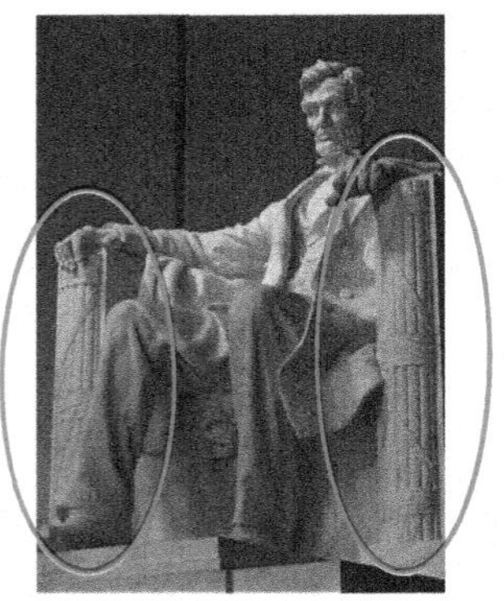

Lincoln Memorial

Study Guide

Use with Student Text pages 228–34.

Name ______________________

A. Write a second sentence that illustrates the first sentence and clearly shows your understanding of the bolded word. *Possible answers are given.*

1. His father told him a **legend** about the founding of Rome. *According to the story passed down for generations, Rome was founded by twin brothers.*

2. The Latins established a form of government called a **republic**. *Roman citizens could vote and control the power of government through officials they elected under law.*

3. The plebeians of the Tribal Assembly elected ten **tribunes**. *The ten leaders protected the rights and the interests of the common people.*

4. The Law of the Twelve Tables was displayed in the **Roman Forum**. *The law could now be read by everyone in the public meeting place.*

B. Write the correct answer.

B 5. Who were the earliest inhabitants of Italy?
A. Phoenicians
B. Latins
C. Etruscans

C 6. Which was *not* a way that the Etruscans improved the Roman way of life?
A. constructed a sewage system
B. paved roads
C. running water and indoor plumbing

A 7. Which branch of the Roman Republic managed the affairs of government and commanded the army?
A. consuls
B. Senate
C. Assembly of Centuries

C 8. Which governmental branch voted on new laws and made declarations of war?
A. consuls
B. Senate
C. Assembly of Centuries

B 9. Which governmental branch controlled the finances and passed laws?
A. consuls
B. Senate
C. Assembly of Centuries

B 10. Who struggled to gain social and political equality?
A. patricians
B. plebeians
C. consuls

C 11. What was the importance of the Law of the Twelve Tables?
A. The law was displayed in the Forum.
B. Most lawmakers wanted to help and protect the citizens of Rome.
C. The written law could be understood by all and equally applied to all.

A 12. What were the two Roman social classes?
A. patricians and plebeians
B. nobles and farmers
C. consuls and tribunes

B 13. Which was *not* a concession that was given to the plebeians by the patricians?
A. the Tribal Assembly
B. access to the Forum
C. the power to veto

C 14. Which statement was true after the Tribal Assembly was established?
A. A democracy was established.
B. Only patricians were elected as consuls.
C. Plebeians and patricians had equal say in the government.

Punic Wars

Name ______________________________

Use with Student Text pages 236–40.

A. Draw a circle around the part of the sentence that states the cause. Underline the part of the sentence that states the effect.

1. The Roman ships dropped planks with spiked tips on the Carthaginian ships, so the Romans could easily board the enemy ships.
2. As a result of Rome and Carthage's peace settlement, Rome gained control of Sicily and Carthage was forced to pay for Roman losses.
3. The Second Punic War began when Carthage violated its treaty with Rome.
4. Hannibal invaded the regions of the peninsula outside Rome to win the support of the people against the Romans.
5. To avoid having the Romans see him, Hannibal marched his soldiers across the Alps.
6. To be seen easily, centurions and other Roman officers wore tall crests on top of their helmets.
7. Hannibal's army was much smaller than Rome's because the cold weather and the fierce tribes in the Alps had killed many of his soldiers.
8. Hannibal's soldiers formed a U-shaped trap around the Romans and almost completely wiped out the Roman army.
9. Because the Romans had constructed over fifty thousand miles of roads, their armies could travel to all of Rome's provinces.
10. The Romans exchanged philosophies, religious ideas, inventions, and discoveries with other peoples along their many roads; as a result, cultures from the East and the West blended and changed.

B. Complete the chart.

11–16. Compare and contrast Rome with Carthage according to Polybius's historical account.

	Rome	Carthage
Type of soldiers	*citizens and people of the country*	*foreign mercenaries*
Able to renew (restart or continue) the war	*fighting for their country, so able to gather army to continue*	*rehired or hired armies with difficulty*
Superiority of naval knowledge and experience	*inferior but obtained success through bravery*	*superior naval forces*

Soldiers of Rome

Name ______________________________

Paul wrote his letter to the Ephesians while he was in prison. As he penned this letter, he was surrounded by Roman soldiers. Under the inspiration of God, Paul described the Christian life as a battle and used imagery that all those living in the Roman Empire would have been familiar with. He compared the Christian's need to be prepared to that of a soldier suiting up for battle.

A. Read Ephesians 6:10–20. Label each part of the Christian soldier's armor.

breastplate of righteousness

The breastplate varied based on the rank of the soldier. The lowest-ranking soldiers had leather breastplates, sometimes with metal pieces tied together. The highest-ranking soldiers had breastplates made of a solid piece of bronze. Bronze was used because it was one of the lightest metals known at that time. No matter what the material, the purpose was still the same. The breastplate's job was to protect the vital organs from harm.

helmet of salvation

The helmets used in the Roman army varied greatly by rank, location, and time period. Some were made exclusively of metal. All helmets were designed to protect the head.

sword of the Spirit

The Roman soldier went into battle with two swords. A short dagger was called a *pugio*. Longer than the *pugio* was the *gladius*. It was tapered at the end and sharp on both sides. Both were fearsome weapons in close contact.

belt of truth

The belt was worn around the waist to anchor all the armor and to hold the sword and other instruments.

feet shod with the gospel of peace

The Roman soldiers wore a bootlike sandal called a *caliga*. It had a thick leather piece on top of the foot and laced up the back. Fastened on the sole were small metal spikes, which served two purposes. The first purpose was to give the soldiers more traction during hand-to-hand combat. The second was to be used as a weapon.

shield of faith

The *scutum*, or Roman shield, was a curved rectangular piece that could be up to four feet tall. The front had a piece that stuck out called an *umbo*. It was used offensively as well as defensively. Because the shield was slightly curved, it helped reduce the impact of blows. Shields could be overlapped to make a wall that provided protection for a number of soldiers.

B. First, plan the essay on your own paper. Then, write it below.

Choose two of the pieces of armor. Explain why you think God used those pieces to illustrate that particular part of the Christian life.

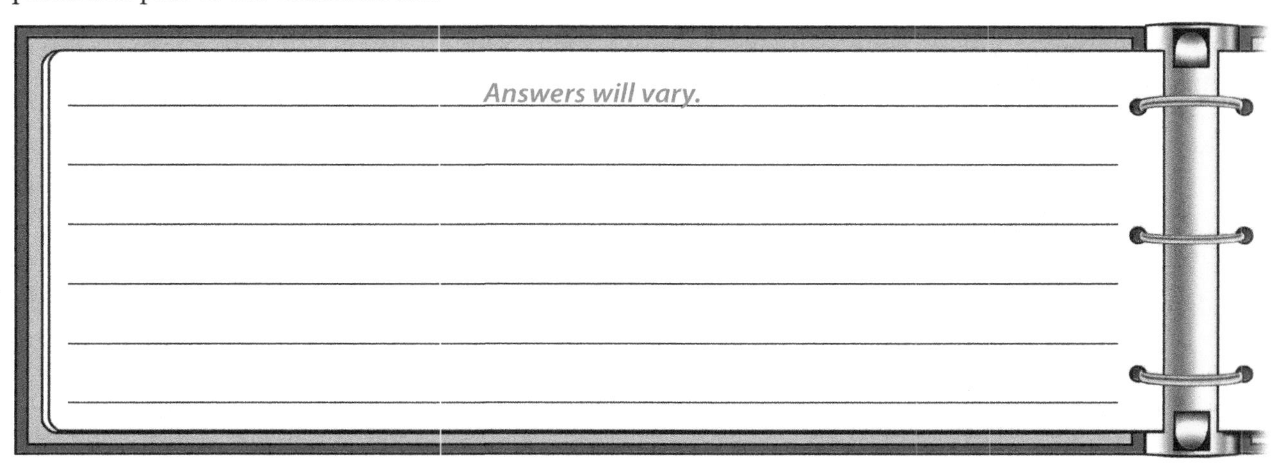

Study Guide

Name ____________________

Use with Student Text pages 236–45.

A. Who was I? Write the name of the person identified by each clue.

1. I was a general of the Carthaginian army and arranged my soldiers so they formed a bulge in the center of the front lines. *Hannibal*
2. I allowed poor citizens to become soldiers and receive a share of land, money, and the spoils of war. *Marius*
3. I declared myself the dictator and reorganized the Roman government. *Sulla*
4. I was popular with the Senate for turning Asia Minor, Syria, and Palestine into Roman provinces and ridding the Mediterranean Sea of pirates. *Pompey*
5. I became dictator of Rome, unified Rome, and strengthened its bonds with its conquered peoples. *Julius Caesar*
6. I was Caesar's nephew and won at the Battle of Actium to become the ruler of Rome. *Octavian*
7. I was one of Caesar's generals who later ruled the eastern part of the Roman Empire but was defeated at the Battle of Actium. *Mark Antony*

I was assassinated on the Ides of March.

B. Fill in the blanks.

8. A tribe is a group of people who share common *ancestors* and a common *culture*.
9. Most countries use a version of Caesar's calendar called the *Gregorian calendar*.
10. To rule Rome together against the Senate, three men formed an alliance called the *Triumvirate*.
11. The men who formed the alliance were Crassus, *Pompey*, and *Julius Caesar*.

C. Answer the questions.

12. What day in March is the Ides of March? *the fifteenth* What happened on this day? *Brutus and Cassius hid in the Senate chamber and assassinated Caesar when he entered the room.*

D. First, plan the essay on your own paper. Then, write it on a new sheet of paper.

13. Describe three of the problems that arose from Rome's expansion.
The answer to the essay question is located on page 137.

Name ______________________

E. Write the name of each place on the map.

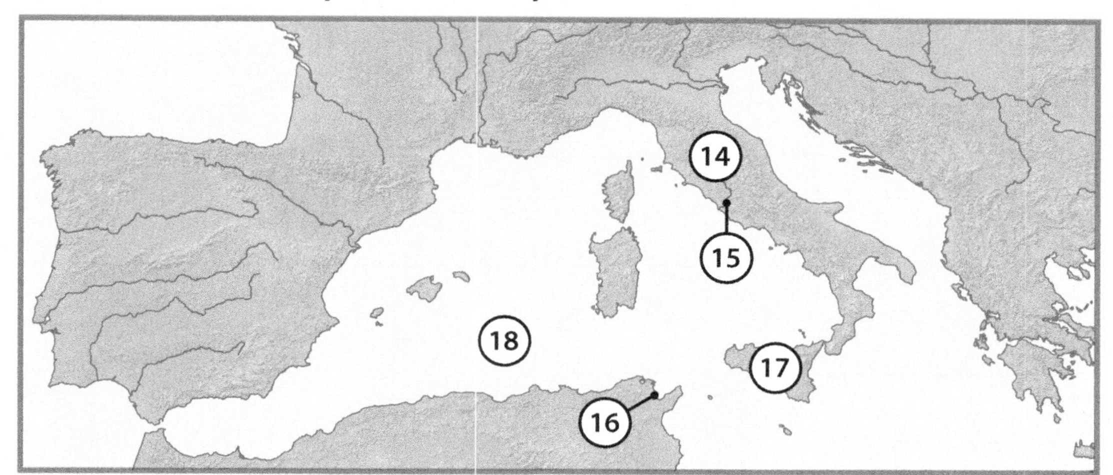

14. *Italian Peninsula*
15. *Rome*
16. *Carthage*
17. *Sicily*
18. *Mediterranean Sea*

Answer for essay question on page 136

The student's essay should include three of these problems: Farmers came back from fighting to find their property ruined from neglect. Those who sold their farms and moved to the city found most jobs were taken by slaves. Because the wealthy bought the farms and had slaves run them, not many farm jobs were available. The wealthy took advantage of the poorer plebeians by buying their votes in the Tribal Assembly. This filled the government with more rich men. The Senate increased in power and dominated the republic. The Senate was unwilling to address Rome's social and economic problems. Governmental corruption spread throughout the provinces. Many publicans collected higher taxes than needed and kept the extra money for themselves. Plebeians in Rome no longer studied the issues so that they could vote wisely. They cared only for what gain they could get by selling their votes.

F. Match the effect with its cause.

Effects

C 19. Rome could easily board Carthaginian ships

E 20. Rome gained control of Sicily and Carthage was forced to pay for Roman losses

A 21. The Second Punic War began

B 22. Hannibal's army marched across the Alps

D 23. Centurions and other Roman officers wore tall crests on top of their helmets

F 24. Hannibal's army was much smaller than the Roman army

J 25. The Roman army was almost completely wiped out

I 26. Rome's armies could travel to all its provinces

G 27. Cultures from the East and the West blended and changed

Causes

A. because Carthage violated its treaty with Rome.
B. because Hannibal wanted to avoid being seen by the Romans.
C. because Roman ships dropped planks with spiked tips on the enemy ships.
D. because they wanted to be seen easily.
E. because Rome and Carthage formed a peace settlement.
F. because it had traveled through cold weather and fierce tribes.
G. because philosophies, religious ideas, and inventions were exchanged.
H. because the Romans knew that as long as Caesar was dictator, Rome could no longer be a true republic.
I. because the Romans constructed over fifty thousand miles of roads.
J. because Hannibal's soldiers formed a U-shaped trap around them.

The Roman Empire

Name ____________________

Use with Student Text pages 247–50.

Fill in the blanks with the answers to the clues given. Use the shaded letters to form two words to complete the paragraph.

1. A B A C U S
2. O C T A V I A N
3. P R I N C E P S
4. M A R C U S A U R E L I U S
5. V I R G I L
6. C O L O S S E U M
7. T O G A
8. S I X T E E N
9. P A X R O M A N A
10. C H A R I O T
11. C I C E R O
12. F A T H E R
13. A Q U E D U C T
14. A U G U S T U S

1. a tool used in studying math
2. the same person as Caesar Augustus
3. a title meaning "first citizen"
4. the last good emperor of Rome
5. the greatest Roman poet
6. the massive Roman arena
7. an official citizen's garment
8. the age a boy became a Roman citizen
9. the period of peace and prosperity in Rome
10. a kind of race held in the Colosseum
11. a master of Latin prose
12. the person responsible for children's education
13. a raised trough that carried water
14. a name meaning "revered one"

The Pantheon was constructed from bricks and ___concrete___ with a dome that has a diameter of 142 feet. A dome is a collection of ___arches___ with a common center. To lighten the heavy concrete dome, 140 coffers, or sunken panels, were carved. An opening, called an *oculus*, was carved at the top. The oculus helps lighten the dome and creates a daily light show.

Philosophies and Christianity

Name ____________________

Use with Student Text pages 251–53.

A. Write the best answer.

__A__ 1. The Romans had a polytheistic religion since
A. they adopted the gods of many of the people they conquered.
B. they honored their gods with temples and by naming planets after them.
C. they thought happiness was gained through pleasures and peace of mind.

__B__ 2. Epicureanism and Stoicism were two ___ philosophies.
A. Roman
B. Greek
C. Christian

__B__ 3. Jesus began His earthly ministry at age
A. twenty.
B. thirty.
C. forty.

__C__ 4. After Christ's death and resurrection, His followers came to be called
A. Romans.
B. disciples.
C. Christians.

__A__ 5. The Roman emperor who blamed the Christians for the fire that destroyed most of the city of Rome was
A. Nero.
B. Caesar Augustus.
C. Marcus Aurelius.

__B__ 6. Roman Christians buried their dead in underground tombs called
A. caves.
B. catacombs.
C. sepulchers.

__C__ 7. God used the decree of Caesar Augustus to fulfill the prophecy in Micah 5:2 that the Messiah
A. would submit to the government by paying the tax to Caesar.
B. would die for the sins of everyone and rise again.
C. would be born in Bethlehem.

__B__ 8. For many surviving Christians the persecutions by Nero and other emperors
A. caused them to hide in fear.
B. strengthened their faith in Christ.
C. made them turn to Stoicism.

B. Complete each statement.

9. Epicureans believed that there is no life after death, but the Bible teaches that *there is everlasting life for those who put their trust in Christ*.

10. Epicureans believed that happiness is achieved through simple pleasures and peace of mind, but the Bible teaches that all who trust God *will find joy in this life and in the life to come*.

11. Stoics believed that there is no beginning or end to the universe, but the Bible teaches that *God has eternally existed and that He created the world*.

12. Stoics believed that their good behavior would make them good people, but the Bible teaches that *a person must first be changed by God to do works that are pleasing to Him*.

Name ____________________

A. Write the term identified by each clue.

1. My birth name was Octavian, but I used several different titles, such as *princeps*. Who am I? ___Caesar Augustus___
2. I was an orator and master of Latin prose who influenced other writers and students. Who am I? ___Cicero___
3. I was considered the greatest Roman poet, and I wrote the *Aeneid,* an epic about Rome's glory. Who am I? ___Virgil___
4. I was a Roman emperor who blamed Christians for a fire that destroyed nearly two-thirds of Rome and ordered them to be put to death by crucifixion or burning. Who am I? ___Nero___
5. I was born during the reign of Caesar Augustus and condemned to die by crucifixion. Who am I? ___Jesus Christ___
6. We followed Jesus Christ and were hated by both the Romans and the Jews. Who are we? ___Christians___
7. I am a loose, one-piece robe, the official garment of a Roman citizen. What am I? ___toga___
8. I was a man who fought animals and other men to the death in large arenas. What am I? ___gladiator___
9. I am the date historians give for the fall of the Roman Empire due to barbarian invasions and the decline of the government, economy, and society. What year am I? ___AD 476___

I am the official garment of a Roman citizen.

B. Fill in the blanks.

10. During the Pax Romana the empire experienced a period of ___prosperity___ and ___peace___.
11. Students today write on paper. During the Pax Romana students wrote on ___wax tablets___.
12. Today a student studies math using manipulatives. A Roman student used an ___abacus___.
13. God used the decree of Caesar Augustus to fulfill the prophecy in Micah 5:2 that the Messiah would ___be born in Bethlehem___.
14. For many surviving Christians, persecution strengthened their ___faith___ in Christ.
15. Christ told Christians to teach all nations how to be forgiven of ___sin___ and to live ___God's way___.
16. The Roman roads enabled Christians to carry the ___gospel___ to many parts of the world.

Study Guide

Use with Student Text pages 247–56.

Name ______________________

C. Label the architectural features: *C* for Colosseum, *P* for Pantheon, or *B* for both the Colosseum and Pantheon.

__C/B__ 17. arches

__P__ 18. dome

__P__ 19. columns

__B__ 20. concrete

D. Write *F* if the statement was a factor that led to the collapse of the Roman Empire. If the statement was not a factor, write *N*.

__F__ 21. The government raised taxes to pay for the army and governmental officials.

__N__ 22. The Triumvirate competed for fame and power.

__F__ 23. Constantine built a new capital called Constantinople.

__N__ 24. The Senate was unwilling to address Rome's social and economic problems.

__F__ 25. Many Romans looked to the government to supply free food.

__F__ 26. Barbarian tribes assaulted the western part of Rome.

E. Complete the chart.

27–30. Compare Epicureanism with biblical truth.

Epicureanism	Biblical truth
Epicureans used knowledge to help rid them of their fear of __death__ and the __gods__. They believed that there is no __life__ after death.	The Bible teaches that there is __everlasting (eternal)__ life for those who put their trust in Christ (John 3:16). Those who love God have nothing to __fear__ (1 John 4:16–19).
Epicureans believed that happiness is achieved through simple __pleasures__ and peace of __mind__.	The Bible teaches that anyone who hopes to find happiness in this life will be disappointed. All who trust God will find __joy__ in this life and in the life to come (Ps. 16:11).

F. First, plan the essay on your own paper. Then, write it on a new sheet of paper.

31. Compare Stoicism with biblical truth.

The student's essay should include the following two comparisons: Stoics believed that there is no beginning or end to the universe. The Bible teaches that God has eternally existed and that He created the world. Stoics believed that their good behavior would make them good people. The Bible teaches that a person must first be changed by God to do works that are pleasing to Him.

Chapter 9 Summary

Name ______________________________

Define these terms

gladiator
legend
republic
Roman Forum
toga
tribe
tribune

Inside the Roman Colosseum

Locate these places

Carthage
Italian Peninsula
Mediterranean Sea
Rome
Sicily

Tell about these people

Christians
Cicero
Hannibal
Jesus Christ
Julius Caesar
Marius
Mark Antony
Nero
Octavian / Caesar Augustus
Pompey
Sulla
Virgil

Explain what happened

the Punic Wars
the Ides of March
AD 476—fall of the Roman Empire

Be able to . . .

Write an essay comparing Stoicism with biblical truth
Identify the Latins as the earliest inhabitants of Italy
Explain how the Etruscans improved the Roman way of life
Describe the two Roman social classes
Describe the purpose of each of the three governing branches in the Roman Republic
Describe the concessions that the patricians gave to the plebeians
Explain the importance of the Law of the Twelve Tables
Identify the Roman Forum as the location where the Law of the Twelve Tables was displayed
Explain the purpose and importance of the Roman roads
Describe the problems that arose from Rome's expansion
Explain the alliance called the Triumvirate
Explain the significance of the Gregorian calendar
Tell why the Pax Romana was significant to Rome's history
Compare the education during the Pax Romana to education today
Identify the architectural features in the Colosseum and the Pantheon
Compare Epicureanism with biblical truth
Tell about the fulfillment of the prophecy of Micah 5:2
Tell about the spread of Christianity and the persecution of Christians
Explain the factors that led to the collapse of the Roman Empire

Chapter 10 Organizer

Name ______________________________

Use with Student Text pages 258–88.

Complete the two-column organizer as you study the chapter.

Paving the way (pp. 260–63)	Constantine decided to move the empire's capital to . . .	the city of *Byzantium* and renamed it *Constantinople*.
	In early church history, believers faced persecution until Constantine . . .	issued the *Edict of Milan*, which legalized Christianity.
	Some false teachers in the early church denied . . .	Christ's *deity*, that He was God.
	True believers in the church who defended the truth were called . . .	*orthodox*, a term that means "*right belief*."
	The bishops tried to define what true Christians should believe about each person of the Trinity at . . .	the *Council of Nicaea*.
	What a certain group or church believes and teaches is . . .	known as *doctrine*.
	Theodosius I permanently divided the empire into . . .	the *Western* Roman Empire and the *Eastern* Roman Empire.
	The nomadic peoples who had not adopted Roman culture and who did not speak Latin or Greek . . .	were given the name *barbarian* by the Romans.
	The Eastern Roman Empire became . . .	known as the *Byzantine* Empire.
The rule of Justinian I (pp. 264–71)	Although Justinian's army did not conquer all the former Roman Empire, it did conquer . . .	every part it fought for under the leadership of his general *Belisarius*.
	Sporting and social events took place in . . .	open-air stadiums called *hippodromes*.
	Because of Justinian's high taxes and lack of respect for the privileges of others, the people started . . .	a riot called the *Nika Revolt*.
	Justinian's wise advisor who had a strong influence on him was . . .	his wife, named *Theodora*.
	The most famous structure built under Justinian was . . .	the church called the *Hagia Sophia*.
	After Justinian's rule there was no more money for lavish buildings because . . .	he had left the government *bankrupt*.
	The Byzantine army was made up of . . .	mercenaries, foreigners *hired* by the government to fight.
	The Persians attacked and took . . .	the province of *Syria*.

Invasion and decline (pp. 271–73)	The Avars and the Bulgars, barbarian tribes, conquered . . .	the ___Balkan___ Peninsula.
	The Lombards, another barbarian tribe, conquered . . .	the ___Italian___ Peninsula.
	The emperor Heraclius reformed the army by firing . . .	the ___mercenary___ soldiers and training peasant soldiers, whom he paid with ___land___ to support their families.
	Heraclius organized the land by dividing it . . .	into provinces called ___themes___.
	Trade flourished and the people formed . . .	groups with the same skills or occupations called ___guilds___.
	Byzantine spies discovered the secret of . . .	making ___silk___ and smuggled ___silkworms___ back from China.
	The Byzantine Empire fell . . .	in the year ___1453___.
A new idea (pp. 273–77)	A new belief formed on . . .	the ___Arabian___ Peninsula.
	The new belief was formed by . . .	a man who lived in Mecca named ___Muhammad___.
	Muhammad's revelations were put in a book . . .	called the ___Qur'an___.
	Muhammad taught that there was only . . .	one god, called ___Allah___.
	Muhammad's beliefs became the religion . . .	of ___Islam___, and its followers are called ___Muslims___.
	To conquer the entire Arabian Peninsula, the Muslim caliph Abu-Bakr led . . .	a ___jihad___, a holy war fought for the cause of Islam.
	The three cities Muslims consider sacred are . . .	___Jerusalem___, ___Medina___, and ___Mecca___.
Leo III (pp. 278–79)	Leo III had an advantage in fighting his enemies because . . .	he had lived among the ___Arabs___ and knew their language and customs.
	The Muslims closed off Constantinople by sea hoping to . . .	___starve___ the citizens into surrendering.
	Leo fought off the Muslim invasion with a new weapon . . .	called ___Greek fire___, a mixture that burst into flames when it touched water.
	Two other factors that allowed the Byzantine Empire to have victory were . . .	a harsh ___winter___ and a ___plague___ that killed many people the next summer.
	Sacred images of Christ, Mary, the saints, and other sacred subjects are . . .	called ___icons___.
	Leo III thought that icons were . . .	a type of ___idol___, and he ordered their destruction.

Chapter 10 Organizer

Name ______________________________

Use with Student Text pages 258–88.

Golden age (pp. 280–81)	During the golden age the emperors successfully fought . . .	their enemies on the *Balkan* Peninsula and in the *Middle East*.
	The empire became wealthier from . . .	its *trade* throughout Asia, Europe, and Africa.
	Basil II was one of the best emperors and became known as . . .	the *Bulgar Slayer* because of his defeat of the Bulgarian army.
The Crusades (pp. 282–83)	The pope of the Roman Church wanted to free the city of Jerusalem, so . . .	he started religious campaigns called the *Crusades*.
	In the first Crusade the crusaders were . . .	able to capture *Jerusalem*.
	The second and third Crusades ended with . . .	the Muslims regaining *Jerusalem* for Islam.
	In the fourth Crusade the crusaders began . . .	attacking cities that the *pope* did not intend.
	The crusaders had made an agreement with . . .	the navy of *Venice*.
	The fourth Crusade ended with the Venetians and the crusaders plundering . . .	the city of *Constantinople*.
Recovery and fall of the Byzantine Empire (pp. 284–88)	Some Byzantines fled . . .	to *Asia Minor* and organized a new empire with the capital at *Nicaea*.
	The emperors worked hard to strengthen the empire, and by the time of Michael VIII, . . .	the army was strong enough to recapture *Constantinople*.
	A group of Turks that invaded the Middle East and adopted Islam were . . .	called the *Ottomans*.
	Michael VIII did not have enough money for war, so he . . .	divided the empire among his *family*, hoping that they would each *defend* their part.
	By 1371 the Ottomans had conquered . . .	all the *Byzantine Empire* except the city of Constantinople.
	Different emperors tried to get help . . .	from *Europe*.
	In the 1300s all Europe was weakened . . .	from a fatal disease known as the bubonic plague or the *Black Death*.
	By March of 1453, the Ottomans conquered Constantinople by . . .	using *cannons* to fire on the walls.
	The ruler of the Ottomans was . . .	known as the *sultan*.

Eastern Roman Empire

Name ______________________

Use with Student Text pages 258–62.

A. Fill in the blanks.

1. The Byzantine Empire gets its name from the village named *Byzantium*.
2. This village grew prosperous because its location was ideal for *trade*.
3. The Roman emperor Constantine made Byzantium the new capital, which became known as Constantine's city or *Constantinople*.
4. The city is now located in modern-day Turkey and known as *Istanbul*.

B. Answer the questions.

5. How many continents is Turkey located on? *two* What are the continents? *Europe and Asia*
6. What two seas border Turkey? *the Black Sea and the Mediterranean Sea*
7. What causes the climate of Turkey to vary? *the topography*
8. What famous mountain is located in Turkey? *Mount Ararat*
9. What are four of Turkey's natural resources? *possible answers: oil, coal, chromium, mercury, copper, boron, and gold*
   - ______
   - ______
   - ______
   - ______

C. Complete the Venn diagram.

10–17. Compare and contrast Eastern Orthodox beliefs with Protestant Christian beliefs.

Possible answers are given.

Eastern Orthodox beliefs

equal authority of Scripture and church tradition

salvation obtained through sacraments

Both

belief in the Trinity

Christ as fully God and fully man

Jesus' death a victory over Satan

Protestant Christian beliefs

Scripture the only authority

Jesus' death in the place of sinners so they could be saved

salvation by faith alone in what Christ has done

Study Guide

Use with Student Text pages 258–67.

Name ____________________

A. Match the term with its description.

D 1. barbarian
A 2. deity
C 3. doctrine
E 4. hippodrome
B 5. orthodox

A. the nature of God
B. "right belief"; term referring to true believers in the church who defend the truth
C. what a certain group believes and teaches
D. a nomadic person who did not speak Greek or Latin and who did not adopt Roman culture
E. an open-air stadium for sporting and social events

B. Write *T* if the statement is true. If the statement is false, draw a line through the incorrect word and write the correction in the blank.

T 6. Two challenges early Christians faced were persecution and false teachers.

Nicaea 7. At the Council of ~~Constantine~~, the bishops tried to define what true Christians should believe about each person of the Trinity.

legal 8. The Edict of Milan made Christianity ~~illegal~~.

T 9. Moving the capital from Rome to Constantinople weakened the western part of the Roman Empire.

easy 10. The division of the Roman Empire into separate parts made it ~~difficult~~ for barbarians to invade the Western Roman Empire.

C. Complete the section.

11. What geographic features made Byzantium a strategic location for trade? *The Bosporus Strait was a popular trading route. There was a harbor to the north.*

12. What features protected Constantinople and made it a stronghold? *It had water and high cliffs on three sides and strong, high walls with towers around the city.*

13. Who were the earliest leaders of the church, and where did they meet for worship? *apostles; private homes*

Modern Istanbul's Galata Bridge spanning the Golden Horn inlet of the Bosporus. The Yeni Mosque is nearest the end of the bridge, and the Sultanahmet Mosque (the Blue Mosque) is in the background.

D. Write the correct name for each clue. Names will be used more than once.

Belisarius 14. I conquered all the regions of the former Roman Empire that the emperor sent me to reclaim.

Constantine 15. I moved the capital of the empire to Byzantium.

Theodora 16. I kept the emperor from fleeing during the Nika Revolt.

Justinian I 17. As emperor I had the code of Roman laws simplified.

Constantine 18. I issued the Edict of Milan.

Justinian I 19. I followed my wife's advice and did not run from the rioters.

Belisarius 20. With my men I defended the emperor in the Hippodrome.

Theodora 21. I gave good advice to the emperor in building projects and in running the government.

E. Answer the questions.

22. What was one reason the Nika Revolt began? *possible answers: The people were tired of the heavy taxes to finance building projects. Justinian ignored the positions people held in society and the privileges many had.*

23. Why did the nobles not rally to help defend Justinian I? *They saw the uprising as an opportunity to take over the throne.*

24. What does the word *nika* mean? *conquer*

F. First, plan your essay on your own paper. Then, write it below.

25. Compare and contrast Protestant Christian beliefs with Eastern Orthodox beliefs. Include at least two beliefs on which they agree and at least two beliefs on which they disagree.

The student's essay should include at least two of these beliefs on which there is agreement: God is a Trinity. The Son is both fully God and fully man. Jesus' death was a victory over Satan. The essay should include at least two of these beliefs on which there is not agreement: Protestants believe that Scripture is the only authority, while the Eastern Orthodox Church believes that its tradition is an equal authority to Scripture. Although the Protestants agree with the Eastern Orthodox Church that Jesus' death was a victory over Satan, they point out that the emphasis in Scripture is on Jesus' dying in place of sinners so they can be saved. The Eastern Orthodox Church teaches that salvation is obtained through the sacraments. Protestants believe that salvation can only be received by faith alone in what Christ has done.

A New Idea

Name ______________________

Use with Student Text pages 270–75.

Complete the section.

1. Name a success from the time of Justinian's reign. *possible answers: Improvements were made in the government. He had the law simplified. Improvements were made in the economy. He built many beautiful buildings. Every country his armies fought for was conquered.*
2. Name a failure from the time of Justinian's reign. *possible answers: He neglected the defense of the empire's eastern and northern borders. He left the empire financially drained.*
3. Why would hiring mercenary soldiers make the Byzantine army weak? *Soldiers from other countries will be motivated by the amount they are paid and not a love of their empire.*
4. How did Heraclius strengthen the Byzantine army? *He fired the mercenaries and trained Byzantine peasants.*
5. How did Heraclius organize the empire's land and its defense? *The land was divided into themes. Each theme was a military zone defended by peasant soldiers that lived in it.*
6. How did silk become a trade item for the Byzantine Empire? *Spies discovered how the Chinese made silk and smuggled some silkworms out of China.*
7. How did Muhammad's background influence his religious beliefs? *He came into contact with many different religions on his commercial trips along the trade routes.*
8. How were the teachings of Muhammad preserved? *His followers wrote down his revelations and compiled them in the Qur'an.*
9. What is a follower of Islam called? *Muslim*
10. Every follower of Islam is called to make a pilgrimage to what city? *Mecca*
11. What is the difference between the one God of Christianity and the one god of Islam? *The god of Islam is not a triune god like the God of Christianity. Each member of the Trinity has an important role in salvation.*
12. How do Christianity and Islam differ in their beliefs about eternity? *In Islam eternity depends on whether Allah will be merciful to the person. In Christianity the Bible teaches that a person can have assurance of eternity in heaven by trusting in the sacrifice Christ made on the cross to satisfy God's wrath against sin.*

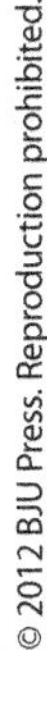

Bible Research

Name ____________________

Use with Student Text page 276.

Jesus is more than just a good man or a prophet. Jesus is the Son of God.

Answers will vary according to which Bible version is used. The answers shown are from the King James Version.

Complete the chart.

Bible verses	What phrase gives evidence that Jesus is more than just a good man?	What other phrase identifies Jesus as God's Son?
Matthew 17:2, 5	*"His face did shine as the sun, and his raiment was white as the light."*	*"This is my beloved Son, in whom I am well pleased."*
John 1:14	*"We beheld his glory."*	*"The Word was made flesh, and dwelt among us." or "the glory as of the only begotten of the Father"*
John 1:29, 34	*"which taketh away the sin of the world"*	*"Behold the Lamb of God." or "This is the Son of God."*
John 1:48–49	*"Before that Philip called thee, when thou wast under the fig tree, I saw thee."*	*"Rabbi, thou art the Son of God; thou art the King of Israel."*
John 10:28, 30	*"I give unto them eternal life."*	*"I and my Father are one."*

Study Guide

Use with Student Text pages 268–80.

Name ______________________

A. Write the correct answer.

Hagia Sophia 1. This church was built in the shape of a cross with a dome over its center and decorated with beautiful mosaics.

Muhammad 2. This man's revelations and beliefs developed into the religion of Islam.

Arabian Peninsula 3. This region between the Red Sea and the Persian Gulf was where Islam began.

Muslim 4. A person who follows Islam is called this.

jihad 5. This is a holy war fought for the cause of Islam.

mercenary 6. This type of soldier is a foreigner paid by the government.

pilgrimage 7. This is a sacred journey.

Qu'ran 8. The revelations of Muhammad were compiled by his followers into this book.

Jerusalem 9–11. Muslims consider these three cities to be sacred.

Mecca

Medina

Heraclius 12. This Byzantine emperor organized the land into themes.

1453 13. The fall of the Byzantine Empire happened in this year.

B. Complete the statement.

14. Even though Justinian was successful in conquering land and improving the government, law, and economy, he also failed because *he left the empire financially ruined (or he neglected the defense of the empire).*
15. The emperor Heraclius was able to strengthen the Byzantine army because *he fired the mercenary soldiers and trained peasants as soldiers.*
16. When attacking the Persian and the Byzantine empires, the Muslims had an advantage because *the Byzantines and Persians were weak from fighting each other for so long.*
17. Leo III had experience that benefited his rule because *as a boy he lived among the Arabs and among the barbarians on the Balkan Peninsula.*

C. Answer the questions.

18. What were the three main factors that helped Leo III defeat the Muslim attack on Constantinople?
    - *Greek fire*
    - *a cold winter*
    - *a plague*
19. What are sacred images called that represent Christ, saints, and other sacred subjects? *icons*
20. What area of land did Leo III take back from Muslim rule? *Asia Minor*

D. Write two supporting details for each statement. *Possible answers are given.*

21. Leo III considered icons a type of idol.
    - *He ordered the destruction of religious icons.*
    - *When an earthquake shook Constantinople, he believed it was God's judgment against the use of icons.*

22. Heraclius was a successful leader of the Byzantine Empire.
    - *He reformed the army, reconquered the land taken by Persia and the barbarians, and made the roads safe for commerce. He organized the land into themes protected by peasant soldiers that*
    - *lived there. Trade flourished during his reign. The process of making silk was brought back to his land. He changed the language of the empire to Greek, which was more widely spoken than Latin.*

23. The best and most powerful years of the Byzantine Empire were during the golden age.
    - *The emperors successfully fought off their enemies. Some rulers developed the government and culture. Michael III reorganized the University of Constantinople. Basil I oversaw the revision*
    - *of the law. The empire became wealthier from trade.*

24. Christian missionaries from Constantinople made important contributions during the golden age.
    - *They standardized the language, ethics, laws, and political patterns of the people.*
    - *Two missionaries developed an alphabet for the Slavic people and translated the Bible into Slavic.*

E. First, plan the essay on your own paper. Then, write it below.

25. Compare and contrast the beliefs of Islam with biblical truth.

The student's essay should include the following points: Both Christianity and Islam teach that there is only one god. But the god of Islam is not a triune god like the God of Christianity. Each member of the Trinity has an important role to play in providing salvation. Islam teaches that a person is not guaranteed an eternity in heaven by being a Muslim. Muslims' eternity depends on whether Allah will be merciful to them or not. The Bible teaches that people can have assurance of eternity in heaven because Christ fully paid the price for their sins by His death and resurrection.

The Crusades

Use with Student Text pages 281–84.

Name ____________________

A. Fill in the blanks.

1. Because of his harsh treatment of the Bulgarian captives, Basil II was often called the *Bulgar Slayer*.
2. The purpose of the Crusades was to free *Jerusalem* from Islamic rule.
3. The knights of France were called for the Crusades by the Roman Church leader *Pope Urban II*.

B. Answer the questions.

4. What made Basil II a fair ruler? *He made the nobles pay their taxes and kept the church from taking land from the peasants.*
5. What caused lasting problems between the Roman Church and the Eastern Orthodox Church? *the attack and destruction of Constantinople by the crusaders*
6. How did John III protect his people? *He built a system of fortifications and frontier defenses.*
7. What important city did Emperor Michael VIII recapture? *Constantinople*

C. Answer the questions about the time of the Crusades by using the map on Student Text page 282.

8. Who was in control of Spain? *Christians and Muslims*
9. Who was in control of Great Britain? *Christians*
10. Who was in control of Africa? *Muslims*
11. Which Crusade went to Jerusalem? *first*
12. On which Crusade did crusaders cross the Danube River? *first*
13. On which Crusade did some of the crusaders travel on the Atlantic Ocean? *third*
14. Which Crusades lasted the same number of years? *first and third*
15. Which Crusades left from the city of Lyon? *first and third*
16. Which Crusade went around the Peloponnesus by water? *fourth*
17. Which city did all the Crusades travel to? *Constantinople*
18. Which Crusades went across Asia Minor? *first and third*

Armed European crusaders

Political Cartoon Analysis

Name ______________________________

Use with Student Text page 285.

Complete the cartoon analysis for one of the cartoons.

First glance	
Visuals	**Words (Not all cartoons include words.)**
Objects or people	Caption or title
	Dialogue or labels
	Dates or numbers
A closer look	
Which objects are used as symbols?	Is the cartoon realistic or unrealistic?
What do the symbols represent, and why were they chosen?	Which words or numbers appear to be important? Why?
Is anything exaggerated? How?	List adjectives that describe emotions visible in the cartoon.
The big picture	
Describe the action taking place in the cartoon.	
Tell how the words in the cartoon explain the symbols.	
Identify the message of the cartoon.	
Identify groups of people who might agree and disagree with the cartoon.	

Political Cartoon Analysis

Name ______________________________

Use with Student Text page 285.

Spread of the Black Death

Name ______________________

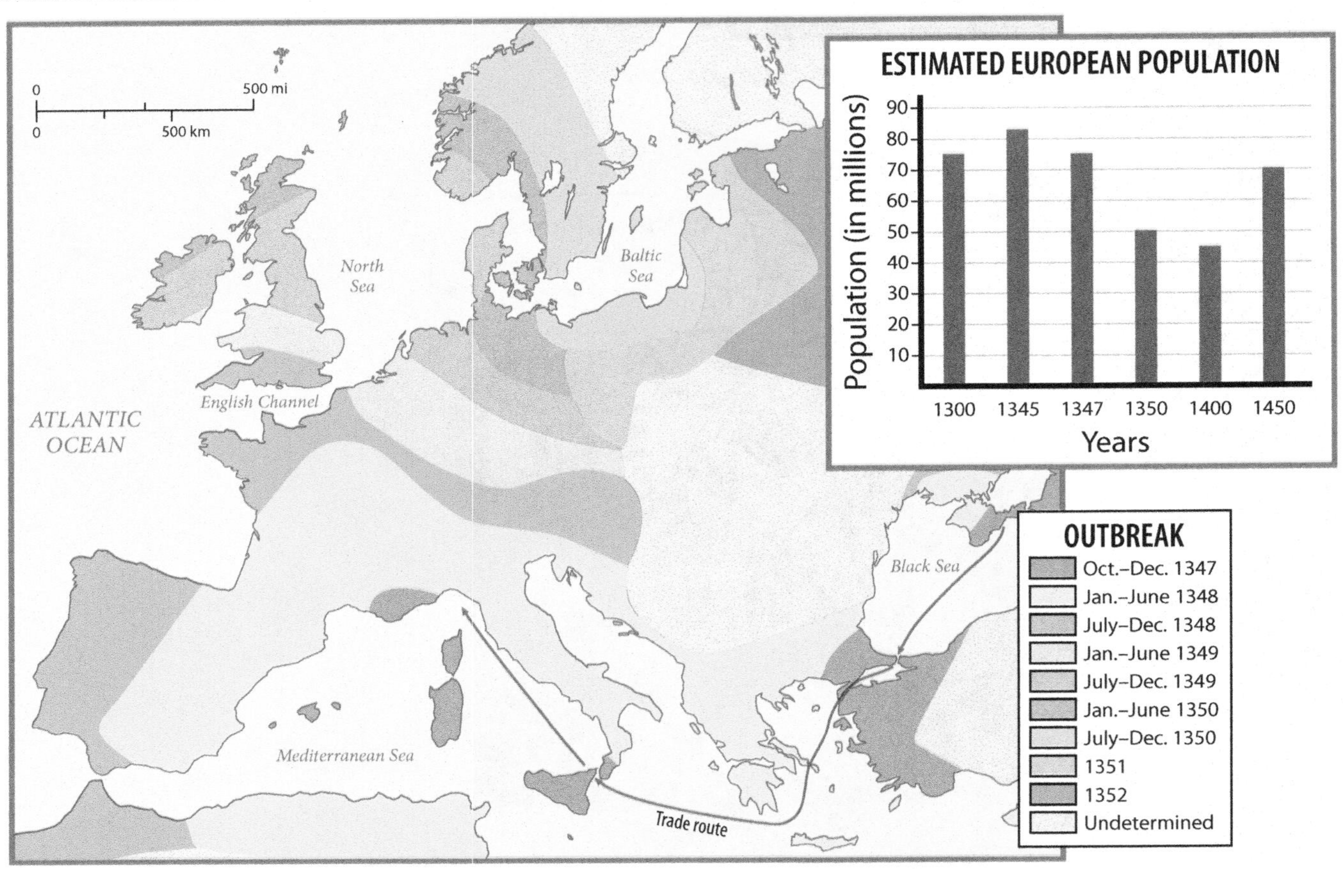

Complete the section.

The Black Death broke out several times in Europe during the Middle Ages. This map traces the first outbreak and does not show how long the plague lasted in these regions.

1. By what month and year had the Black Death arrived on the Italian Peninsula? *Oct. 1347*
2. By what year had the Black Death reached areas on the Baltic Sea? *1350*
3. What was the time span (month and year) over which the Black Death spread through the islands of the United Kingdom? *July 1348* to *June 1350* How many years and months was this? *2 years*
4. Did the Black Death reach Spain or Sicily first? *Sicily*
5. In what year was the population of Europe 70 million? *1450*
6. What was the difference in population between 1300 and 1450? *5 million*
7. Which year had the greater population—1300 or 1450? *1300* Why? *The Black Death had not yet occurred.*
8. In which year shown was Europe's population the smallest? *1400*
9. By 1450 was the population of Europe back to what it had been before the Black Death? *no*
10. What was the time span (month and year) over which the Black Death spread through Spain? *Jan. 1348* to *Dec. 1348* How many years and months was this? *1 year*

Study Guide

Use with Student Text pages 281–88.

Name ______________________

A. Write *T* if the statement is true. If the statement is false, draw a line through the incorrect word and write the correction in the blank.

Islamic/Muslim 1. The purpose of the Crusades was to free Jerusalem from ~~barbarian~~ rule.

first 2. The ~~second~~ Crusade was successful in capturing Jerusalem.

_T_ 3. During the fourth Crusade the crusaders made their own alliances.

money 4. The crusaders made a plan to invade other cities because they were short of ~~time~~.

Constantinople 5. During the fourth Crusade the crusaders and Venetians plundered the city of ~~Carthage~~.

_T_ 6. The ruler of the Ottomans was called the sultan.

_T_ 7. The Turks who conquered all the Byzantine Empire were the Ottomans.

fleas 8. A fatal disease spread by ~~mosquitoes~~ was known as the Black Death.

B. Complete the sentence.

9. The lasting contributions of the Byzantine Empire were that the Roman _law_ was kept from disappearing and that scholars preserved Greek learning, philosophy, and _literature_ and much of what is known about the _ancient_ world.

C. Identify the numbered places on the map.

10. _Balkan Peninsula_
11. _Black Sea_
12. _Asia Minor_
13. _Constantinople_ (city)
14. _Bosporus Strait_ (water)
15. _Mediterranean Sea_
16. _Jerusalem_
17. _Arabian Peninsula_
18. _Medina_
19. _Mecca_

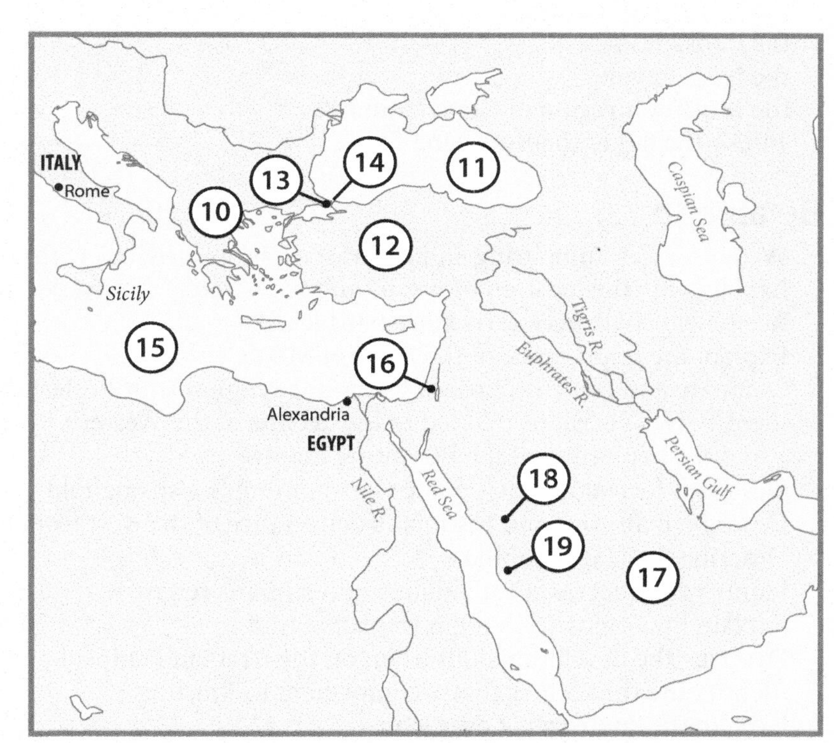

D. First, plan your essay on your own paper. Then, write it on a new sheet of paper.

20. Describe the recovery of the Byzantine Empire after the devastation of the Crusades.

The student's essay should include three of the following points: One emperor banned evil practices in government and the courts. The government built churches, hospitals, and charitable institutions. It gave land to its citizen-soldiers. The government also encouraged the improvement of agricultural methods and raising livestock. To protect the people, a system of fortifications and frontier defenses was built. The army was strengthened and used to recapture Constantinople.

Chapter 10 Summary

Name ______________________

Define these terms

Icon of Mary and Jesus

- apostle
- barbarian
- Black Death
- deity
- doctrine
- hippodrome
- icon
- jihad
- mercenary
- Muslim
- orthodox
- pilgrimage
- Qur'an
- sultan

Locate these places

- Arabian Peninsula
- Asia Minor
- Balkan Peninsula
- Black Sea
- Bosporus Strait
- Constantinople
- Jerusalem
- Mecca
- Medina
- Mediterranean Sea

Tell about these people

- Belisarius
- Constantine
- Heraclius
- Justinian I
- Leo III
- Muhammad
- Ottomans
- Theodora

Explain what happened

- the Council of Nicaea
- the Crusades
- the Nika Revolt
- the Muslim invasion of Constantinople
- 1453—the fall of the Byzantine Empire

Be able to . . .

- Write an essay comparing and contrasting Islamic beliefs with biblical truth
- Explain why the location of Byzantium was strategic for trade
- Relate two challenges early Christians faced
- Explain the importance of the Edict of Milan
- Compare and contrast Eastern Orthodox religion with Protestant Christianity
- Identify two decisions that led to the decline of the Western Roman Empire and the beginning of the Byzantine Empire
- Describe the features that made Constantinople a stronghold
- Describe Belisarius and Justinian's deliverance of the west from barbarians
- Describe the Hagia Sophia
- Identify the successes and failures of Justinian's reign
- Explain how Heraclius's reign was successful
- Describe the development of Islam on the Arabian Peninsula
- Identify the three cities that are important to Muslims
- Explain the controversy over icons
- Identify accomplishments of the Byzantine Empire during its golden age
- Describe the recovery of the empire after the devastation of the Crusades
- Identify the people who conquered the Byzantine Empire
- Identify the lasting contributions of the Byzantine Empire

Chapter 11 Organizer

Name ____________________

Use with Student Text pages 290–316.

Complete the codex organizer as you study the chapter. Follow the page numbers on the codex pages throughout the activity (pp. 159–62).

1

Mesoamerica (pp. 290–91)

- Scientists who study the origins of man are called *anthropologists*.
- The Yucatán Peninsula is a landmass that extends into the *Gulf of Mexico*.

Olmecs (293–94)

- One of the largest, most famous Olmec cities was *La Venta*.
- The most famous Olmec findings are the *stone heads*.
- The Olmecs used a type of volcanic rock called *basalt* for carving.

2

- The Olmecs were known as the "*rubber* *people*."

Mayan Land and Achievements (pp. 296–98)

- The Mayas got fresh water from deep sinkholes called *cenotes*.
- One of the largest Mayan city-states was *Tikal*.
- The Mayas developed the mathematical concept of *zero*.
- A Mayan book with accordion pages is called a *codex*.

Glue to A.

3

Mayan Appearance and Social Classes (pp. 299–303)

- The sloping forehead was considered a *true* *sign* of beauty.
- To achieve crossed eyes, parents hung a *bead* between the baby's eyes.
- The Mayas would often file their teeth into points and inlay them with *jade*.
- The top social class thought to have descended from the gods was the *kings*.
- The second social class included at least four classes of *priests* and the nobles.

4

- In the third level of the social classes were the hard-working *peasants*, soldiers, and laborers.

Clay figure of a Mayan official

Glue to B.

Cut on solid lines.

15

- Aztecs did not use animals for transporting goods but instead used ___dugout canoes___.

Spanish Invasion (pp. 315–16)

- When the Spanish conquistadors came, the Aztec emperor was ___Montezuma___.
- Cortés and the conquistadors gained control of all Tenochtitlán and many surrounding ___territories___.
- Not only were the Mesoamerican peoples defeated in battle with Europeans, but they also lost their ___culture___.

16

Glue this page to the front cover.

13

Mesoamerican Beliefs and the Bible (p. 312)

- The gospel message is the power of God to bring people ___salvation___ (Rom. 1:19–23).
- Mesoamericans believed in many ___gods___, but the Bible teaches that there is only one true ___God___.
- Mesoamericans worshiped ___nature___ rather than the Creator of nature.
- The Old Testament taught ___animal sacrifice___, and the New Testament teaches the only sacrifice necessary is the ___Son of God___.

14

Aztec Social Classes and Economy (pp. 313–14)

- Aztec warriors were brave and ___noble___.
- The social classes of the Aztecs were similar to those of other ___Mesoamerican___ civilizations.

Aztec Language and Technology (314–15)

- Like the Mayas, the Aztecs used ___hieroglyphs___ to represent their spoken language.
- The Aztecs developed technology based on the knowledge they gained from the ___Mayas___.

A

Cut on solid lines.

Chapter 11 Organizer

Use with Student Text pages 290–316.

Name ____________________

Complete the codex organizer as you study the chapter. Follow the page numbers on the codex pages throughout the activity (pp. 159–62).

Glue to C.

5

- At the bottom of society were the _*slaves*_ and prisoners of war.
- Important prisoners were _*sacrificed*_ to the gods.

Mayan Dress (p. 302)

- The men wore tunics, _*loincloths*_, and short capes.
- Women wore long blouses and wraparound skirts or _*straight, plain dresses*_.
- The Mayas considered the cacao bean very valuable and used it as their _*money*_.

6

Mayan Homes and Daily Life (pp. 304–5)

- Large houses near the city centers belonged to the _*nobles*_.
- The walls of the houses were covered with a decorative plaster called _*stucco*_.
- Another term for corn is _*maize*_.
- In the dry season, farmers would travel into the _*rainforest*_ and cut down trees.
- The farmers planted corn in the ashes of the burned stumps and the _*underbrush*_.

7

- A favorite Mayan drink made from corn paste and water was _*pozole*_.
- The blades of weapons and tools were made of a sharp glasslike volcanic rock called _*obsidian*_.

Mayan Religion (pp. 306–8)

- Religion dominated the whole Mayan _*society*_.
- The Mayas thought the world was a flat square atop a giant _*crocodile*_ god.
- The Mayas believed that almost everything had its own _*god*_.

8

- Mayas thought that the gods must be satisfied with _*human blood*_.
- Mayas were very fearful of _*death*_.
- So that they would have money for the next life, _*jade*_ was placed in the mouths of people who died.

Mayan Ball Game (p. 307)

- Every city had at least one ball _*court*_.
- The goal of the Mayan ball game was to hit a small _*rubber ball*_ through a vertical hoop.

Cut on solid lines.

11

- Lake Texcoco was where the Aztecs built one of the *largest cities* of their time.
- The Aztecs bunched twigs, limbs, and sticks together and piled silt on top to make garden islands called *chinampas*.

Aztec Religion (pp. 311–12)

- Most religious ceremonies and rituals took place at the *Templo Mayor*.
- The Aztecs believed their sun god had a tremendous appetite for blood and *human hearts*.
- The Spanish conquistador *Hernando Cortés* was horrified by the Aztecs' ritual sacrifices.

12

Aztec sun stone

B

9

Glue this page to the back cover.

10

- The only social class allowed to play the game was the *nobles*.
- Scholars believe that at the end of the game, some of the *losers* were sacrificed to the gods.

Aztecs (pp. 310–11)

- The Aztec civilization developed a complete *language* and amazing *technology*.
- Tenochtitlán, built on two small islands, is the site where *Mexico City* stands today.

C

Cut on solid lines.

Rubber People

Name ________________________________

Use with Student Text pages 290–94.

A. Fill in the blanks.

1. Scientists who study the origins of man are called (A) N T H R O P O L O G I S T S.
2. As people migrated to what is now Alaska, they may have passed over the B E R I N G (S) T R A I T.
3. The Yucatán Peninsula extends into the G U L F O F (M) E X I C O.
4. Rich sources of lumber and good places to grow coffee, cotton, and rubber trees can be found in the (R) A I N F O R E S T and H (I) G H L A N D S.
5. One of the earliest civilizations in Mesoamerica was the O L (M) E C S.
6. The major center of the Olmec civilization included the cities of Potrero Nuevo, S A N L O R (E) N Z O, and T E N O (C) H T I T L Á N.
7. The largest and most famous Olmec city was L A V (E) N T A.
8. A type of volcanic rock used by the Olmecs for carving was B A S (A) L T.
9. The name Olmec means "R U B B E R P E (O) P L E."

B. Unscramble the circled letters to complete the statement.

10. The lands from central Mexico to Costa Rica in Central America are known as M E S O A M E R I C A.

C. Color the map according to the key.

Key
Pacific Ocean
Gulf of Mexico
Yucatán Peninsula
Mexico

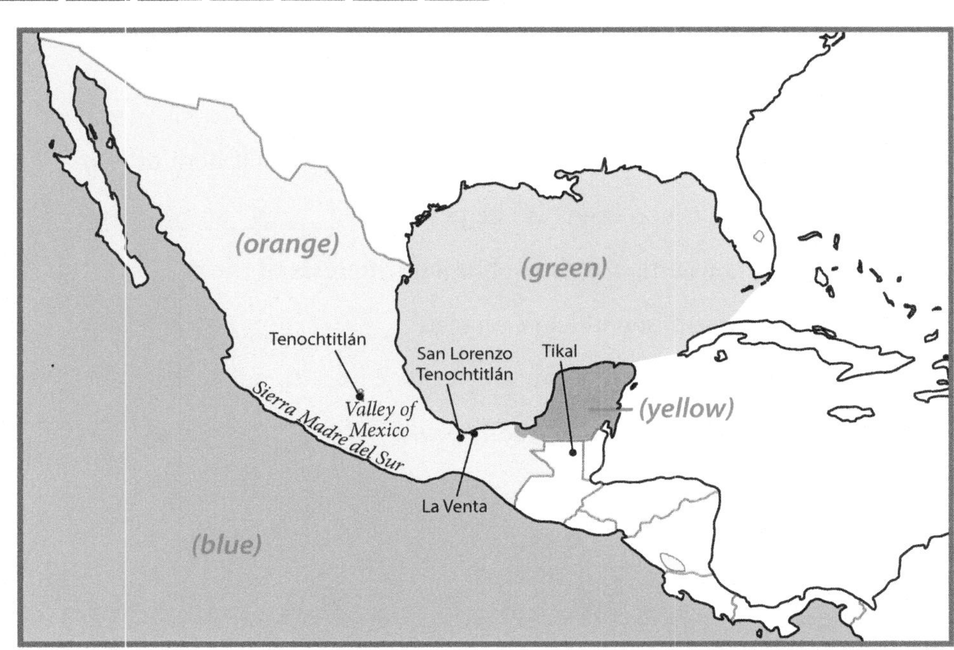

Drawing Conclusions

Name ____________________

Use with Student Text page 295.

A. Examine each item in the paper bag and record your observations. Use the topics below to help guide your observations.

buildings	languages	numbers	religion
dress	material made of	people	words

	Item	Observations
1.	*Answers will vary.*	*Answers will vary.*
2.		
3.		
4.		
5.		
6.		
7.		
8.		
9.		
10.		

B. Answer the questions.

11. Is the person male or female? __________ What item or items tell this? __________
12. What item tells you how old the person is? __________ Why? __________
13. What item or items tell the hobbies or interests of the person? __________
14. Does the person like to learn or read? __________ How do you know? __________
15. Can you determine the person's heritage or nationality? __________ How? __________
16. What language does the person speak? __________ How did you determine it? __________

____

C. Write the identity of the owner of the bag.

17. __________

Study Guide

Name ______________________

Use with Student Text pages 290–99.

A. Complete each sentence.

1. Someone who studies the origins of man is called an _anthropologist_.
2. The most famous archaeological find from the Olmec civilization is the _stone heads_.
3. Two of the earliest civilizations found in Mesoamerica are the _Olmecs_ and the _Mayas_.
4. A true sign of beauty to the Mayas was a _sloping forehead_.

B. Write *T* if the statement is true. If the statement is false, draw a line through the incorrect part and write the correction in the blank.

cenote 5. A ~~codex~~ is a deep sinkhole filled with fresh water.

Yucatán Peninsula 6. The ~~Valley of Mexico~~ is a landmass that extends into the Gulf of Mexico.

_T_ 7. The priest who tried to convert the Mayas to Roman Catholicism was Diego de Landa.

C. Match the description to the correct term.

_F_ 8. major urban center of Olmec civilization

_A_ 9. volcanic rock used for carving

_C_ 10. one of the largest and most famous Olmec cities

_E_ 11. first people to use rubber

_G_ 12. largest Mayan city-state

_B_ 13. Mayan accordion-style book

_D_ 14. one of the first peoples to develop the concept of zero

A. basalt
B. codex
C. La Venta
D. Mayas
E. Olmecs
F. San Lorenzo Tenochtitlán
G. Tikal

D. Complete the section.

15. The three geographic areas where the Mayas built their homes were _rainforests_, _high plateaus_, and _lowlands_.
16. Name six Mayan advances in art, architecture, literature, math, and astronomy.

possible answers: books, sculptures, construction of palaces and temples, irrigation systems, music and songs, games, idea of zero, calendar based on the cycles of the moon and sun, discovery of the orbits of the planets, and prediction of an eclipse of the sun

- ______________________ • ______________________
- ______________________ • ______________________
- ______________________ • ______________________

E. First, plan the essays on your own paper. Then, write them on a new sheet of paper. *Possible answers appear on page 165a.*

17. Describe the Mayan writing and the making of a codex.
18. Describe the Mayan physical appearance and how it was achieved.

Mayan Culture

Name ______________________

Use with Student Text pages 301–4.

A. Match the description to the correct social class.

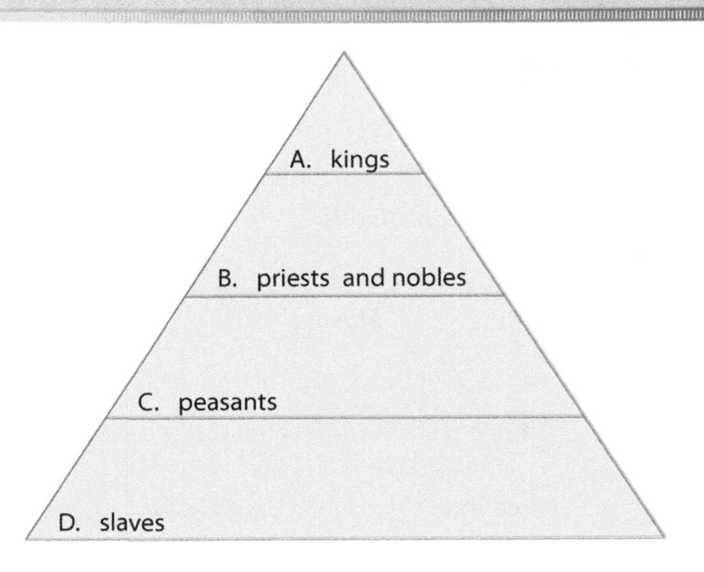

__B__ 1. teachers
__C__ 2. wooden houses with grass-thatched roofs
__B__ 3. large houses near the city center
__A__ 4. descendants of the gods
__D__ 5. prisoners of war
__B__ 6. doctors and fortunetellers
__D__ 7. debtors and criminals
__C__ 8. soldiers
__A__ 9. palaces that covered many acres
__B__ 10. governmental officials

B. Complete each sentence.

__money__ 11. Cacao beans were used for _____.
__stucco__ 12. Decorative plaster used in homes is called _____.
__maize__ 13. Mayas raised corn, which is also called _____.
__hot chocolate__ 14. Mayas invented a drink from powdered cacao beans called _____.
__sacrifices__ 15. Important prisoners were sometimes used for _____.

C. Number the steps in the order that the Mayas used when farming during the dry seasons.

__2__ 16. cut down the trees
__3__ 17. burned stumps and underbrush
__4__ 18. planted corn in the ashes
__1__ 19. went into the rainforest

D. Complete the Venn diagram to compare and contrast Mayan dress for men and women. *Possible answers are given.*

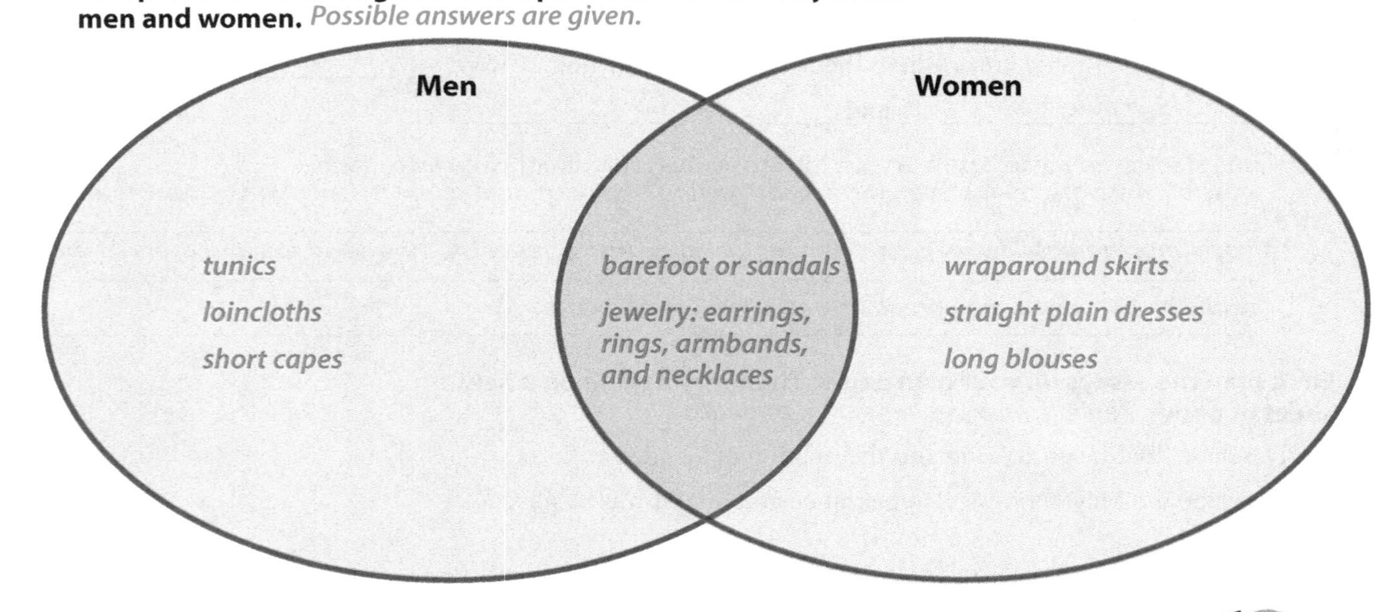

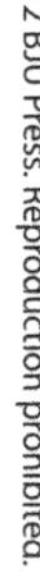

Study Guide

Name ______________________________

Use with Student Text pages 301–8.

A. Write the characteristics under the correct social class.

criminals	lived in palaces	wooden houses with thatched roofs
descended from the gods	offered sacrifices	wore jaguar skins
educated men and women	prisoners of war	wore plain tunics and dresses
feathers woven in clothes	scribes	
large houses near city center	soldiers	

Kings	Priests and nobles	Peasants	Slaves
descended from the gods *lived in palaces* *wore jaguar skins*	*educated men and women* *feathers woven in clothes* *large houses near city center* *offered sacrifices* *scribes*	*soldiers* *wooden houses with thatched roofs* *wore plain tunics and dresses*	*criminals* *prisoners of war*

B. Write *T* if the statement is true. If the statement is false, draw a line through the incorrect part and write the correction in the blank.

Obsidian 1. ~~Jade~~ is a glasslike volcanic rock that Mayas used to make the blades of tools and weapons.

T 2. The Mayas traded between the highlands and the lowlands to get what they needed.

T 3. The Mayas used cacao beans as money.

corn 4. Maize was a kind of ~~wheat~~ grown by the Mayas.

C. Answer the questions.

5. What is stucco and where was it used by the Mayas? *Stucco is a decorative plaster that was used on the walls of Mayan homes.*

6. What does the word *appease* mean? *to satisfy*

7. Why did the Mayas fear death? *Because the only people sure of entering paradise were the priests, the warriors who had died in battle, and the people who had been sacrificed by the priests. All others had to hope that some god did not condemn them to the underworld.*

D. First, plan the essays on your own paper. Then, write them on a new sheet of paper. *Possible answers appear on page 165a.*

8. Describe how the Mayas farmed during the dry season.
9. Describe the Mayan ball game.

Pyramids

Name ____________________

What is the first thing you think of when you hear the word *pyramid*? Egypt? Pharaohs? Pyramids have been built in many types and sizes and can be found not only in Egypt but all over the world, including Mesoamerica.

The Great Pyramid is the largest of the three Egyptian pyramids at Giza (top). This Mesoamerican pyramid is known as Chichén-Itzá (bottom).

Purpose

Egyptian pyramids were built as tombs for pharaohs. They were designed to protect the pharaoh as he waited to pass into the afterlife. The Mesoamerican pyramids on occasion were used as tombs. Their main purpose, however, was for religious rituals and ceremonies, such as human sacrifice.

Construction

The construction of the Egyptian pyramids occurred primarily during the Old Kingdom, which dates them around 2700–2100 BC. The Egyptians used only cut stone when building and decorating a pyramid. This enabled them to build a sturdy central core that lasted for centuries. This permanence was very important, since they believed that the pharaoh was a god.

Because the purpose of the Mesoamerican pyramid was different, its construction was also different. The core of the pyramid was assembled by piling up large stones of different sizes and was supported by an outer wall. These pyramids were probably not constructed until sometime between 100 BC and AD 300.

Appearance

The pyramid's appearance in both civilizations is immediately recognizable. Most Egyptian pyramids had a square base with four triangular sides with a common point at the top. The stones were very polished and not decorated or covered with any other material. Mesoamerican pyramids were wider and smaller in size. They rose in a series of steps. Stucco that was sometimes painted red covered each pyramid. They had a flat top where the temple was built.

Location

Since Mesoamerican pyramids were used for religious ceremonies and rituals, they were built in the center of the cities. Visible doors and staircases lead archaeologists to assume that the pyramids were built to be entered and ascended by people. The Egyptian pyramids were tombs, and no one entered once the dead pharaoh was buried. These pyramids were never built in the city but were built far away to symbolize the importance of the pharaoh as an Egyptian god.

Contrasting Pyramids

Name ______________________________

Fill in the pyramid charts.

Egyptian Pyramids

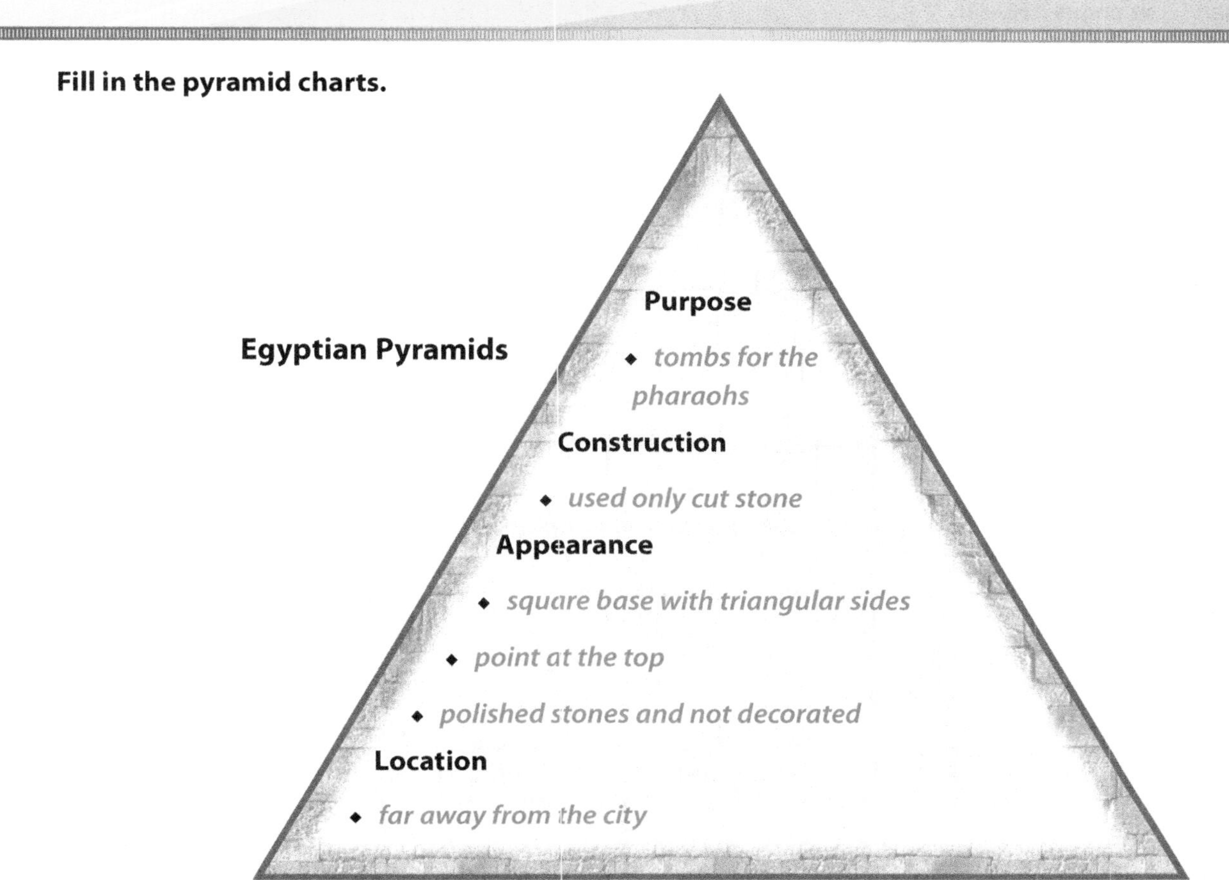

Mesoamerican Pyramids

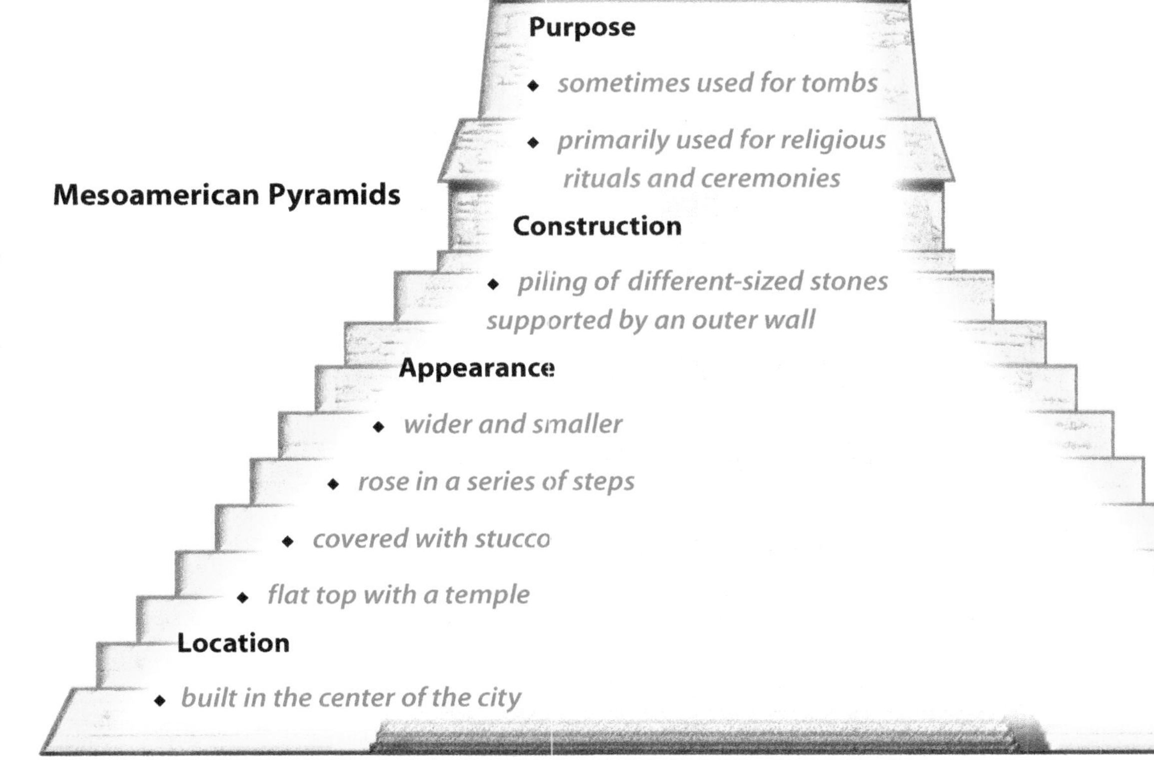

Comparison Organizer

Name ____________________

Use with Student Text pages 296–316.

Complete the Venn diagram as you read about the Aztecs. Compare and contrast the Aztecs with the Mayas by writing the phrases in the correct section.

- advances in art, architecture, and literature
- brick/stone houses
- calendar
- causeways
- city on a lake
- codex
- concept of zero
- defeated by Cortés
- developed medicines
- dominated by religion
- everything had a god
- farming
- feared death
- hieroglyphs
- highly structured economy
- human sacrifice
- mud/twig homes
- no one knows what happened to them
- pyramid temples
- rulers descended from the gods
- sloped foreheads
- social classes
- sun god showed them where to settle
- sun god with an appetite for blood
- traded to support economy
- traveled by canoes
- warriors trained at early age

Mayas

advances in art, architecture, and literature
calendar
codex
concept of zero
everything had a god
feared death
no one knows what happened to them
sloped foreheads

(Both)

brick/stone houses
dominated by religion
farming
hieroglyphs
human sacrifice
mud/twig homes
pyramid temples
rulers descended from the gods
social classes
traded to support economy

Aztecs

causeways
city on a lake
defeated by Cortés
developed medicines
highly structured economy
sun god showed them where to settle
sun god with an appetite for blood
traveled by canoes
warriors trained at early age

Idols of the Heart

Name ______________________

Ezekiel 14:3 tells about the Israelites worshiping idols of the heart. "These men have set up their idols in their heart, and put the stumblingblock of their iniquity before their face." The Israelites not only had material idols but also were so in love with their idols that they could not think of anything else. Their whole life was devoted to their idols.

The Mesoamerican culture had many idols or gods. Nearly everything had a god who had to be appeased by the shedding of human blood through sacrifices. One definition for the word *idol* is a statue, a picture, or another object that is worshiped as a god. Another definition is a person or a thing that is admired or loved very much. Christians do not worship a carved image. A Christian worships the one true God, Who sent His Son, Jesus, as the one-time sacrifice for sin. However, Christians may be guilty of worshiping idols of the heart, such as entertainment, money, sports, and people.

Is there something other than the Lord Jesus Christ that is consuming your time and affections? What is taking first place in your heart and life?

A. Complete the section.

Name something that may be an idol in your life, something that is taking the time and affections that should belong to Christ. *Answers will vary.*

B. Read the Bible verse. Write the part of the verse that answers the question. *Answers may vary depending on which Bible translation the student uses.*

Bible verse	Question	Answer in the Bible verse
Exodus 20:3	Are Christians to worship any other gods?	*"no other gods before me"*
Exodus 20:5	What does God command Christians not to do?	*"Thou shalt not bow down thyself to them, nor serve them."*
Deuteronomy 4:28	How does God describe idols?	*"the work of men's hands, wood and stone, which neither see, nor hear, nor eat, nor smell"*
Judges 3:7	What is worshiping other gods and idols described as?	*"evil in the sight of the Lord"*
2 Kings 17:12	What was God's command concerning idols?	*"Ye shall not do this thing."*
Psalm 37:4	Whom are Christians to take pleasure in?	*"Delight thyself also in the Lord."*
Luke 4:8	Whom does God's Word say that Christians should worship?	*"Thou shalt worship the Lord thy God, and him only shalt thou serve."*

Study Guide

Name ______________________

Use with Student Text pages 310–16.

A. Complete the section.

1. What is a chinampa? *a garden island made by bunching twigs, limbs, and sticks together and piling silt on top*
2. What was the primary location in Tenochtitlán for religious ceremonies? *Templo Mayor*
3. Why were the Aztecs feared by surrounding neighbors? *They fought to capture prisoners to sacrifice to their gods.*
4. Name two possible reasons for the downfall of the Aztecs. *possible answers:*
   - *Some of their superstitions led the Aztecs to believe that the enemy was a tool of the gods. The Aztecs had been weakened by an unknown epidemic. The attack during harvest time put the*
   - *Aztecs at a disadvantage. The Aztecs lost their will to survive since they had lost their culture and were unable to practice their religious beliefs.*

B. Match the description to the correct term. Not all answers are used.

I 5. emperor of the Aztecs
E 6. defeated the Aztec empire
D 7. wall to prevent flooding
C 8. conquistador
B 9. land bridge
A 10. developed a complete language and amazing technology
F 11. site of one of the largest cities of the then-known world
H 12. modern-day city on site of Tenochtitlán

A. Aztecs
B. causeway
C. conqueror
D. dike
E. Hernando Cortés
F. Lake Texcoco
G. La Venta
H. Mexico City
I. Montezuma

C. Fill in the blanks.

13–18. Contrast the Mesoamerican beliefs with biblical truth.

Mesoamerican beliefs	Biblical truth
Mesoamericans believed in many gods. They believed that the *sun god* was superior.	The Bible teaches that there is only one *true* *God* and no other gods.
Mesoamericans chose to worship *nature* rather than the Creator of *nature*.	God commands man to have dominion over *nature* and to be a good steward of it.
Mesoamericans believed a blood sacrifice was necessary and sacrificed *humans*.	The Old Testament taught animal *sacrifice*, and the New Testament teaches the only sacrifice necessary is the *Son of God*.

Study Guide

Use with Student Text pages 292, 310–16.

Name ______________________

D. Identify the places on the map.

19. *Valley of Mexico*
20. *Yucatán Peninsula*
21. *Gulf of Mexico*
22. *Pacific Ocean*
23. *Sierra Madre del Sur*
24. *San Lorenzo Tenochtitlán*
25. *La Venta*
26. *Lake Texcoco* (water)
27. *Tenochtitlán* (city)
28. *Tikal*
29. Draw a box around the approximate area of Mesoamerica.

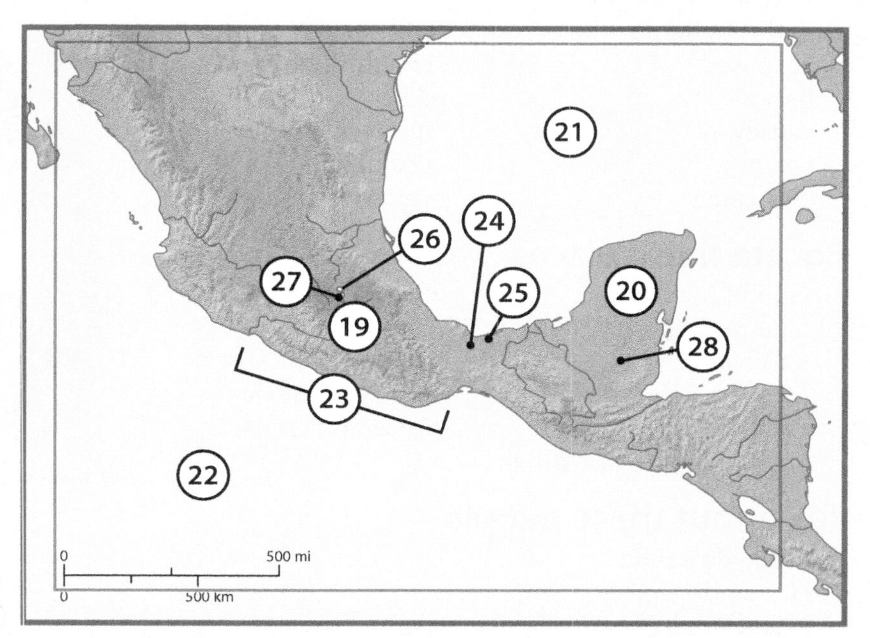

E. First, plan the essay on your own paper. Then, write your essay in the space below.

30. Compare and contrast the Aztecs with the Mayas. Include at least two differences and three similarities.

See the Venn diagram on page 170 for suggested differences and similarities that the student may include in his essay.

Chapter 11 Summary

Name ____________________

Define these terms

anthropologist
appease
basalt
causeway
cenote
chinampa
codex
conquistador
dike
maize
obsidian
stucco

I-shaped ball court of the Mayas

Locate these places

Gulf of Mexico
Lake Texcoco
La Venta
Mesoamerica
Pacific Ocean
San Lorenzo Tenochtitlán
Sierra Madre del Sur
Tenochtitlán
Tikal
Valley of Mexico
Yucatán Peninsula

Tell about these people

Diego de Landa
Hernando Cortés
Montezuma

Explain what happened

the building of Tenochtitlán (Mexico City)
the overthrow of the Aztec Empire

Be able to . . .

Write an essay describing the Mayan physical appearance and how it was achieved
Identify the two earliest civilizations in Mesoamerica
Identify the most famous archaeological find of the Olmecs
Identify the first people believed to have used rubber
Identify the geographic areas where the Mayas built their homes
Identify the Mayan achievements in arts, architecture, literature, math, and astronomy
Describe Mayan writing and the making of a codex
Identify the Mayan social classes
Describe the Mayan dress and architecture for the different social classes
Describe how Mayas farmed during the dry seasons
Identify the Mayan money
Describe how trade benefited the Mayan empire
Describe the Mayan ball game
Explain why the Mayas feared death
Identify the religious building in Tenochtitlán
Contrast the Mesoamerican beliefs with biblical truth
Describe why the Aztecs were feared
Compare and contrast the Aztecs with the Mayas

Chapter 12 Organizer

Name ______________________________

Use with Student Text pages 318–40.

Fill in the outline as you study the chapter.

I. Africa may be studied by its five regions.

A. Northern

B. Eastern

C. Western

D. Central

E. Southern

II. Africa may be studied by its topography.

A. A region with little rainfall and few plants— desert

1. In northern Africa— Sahara

2. In southern Africa—Namib and Kalahari

B. A region located on the Horn of Africa with little rain— rain shadow desert

C. A tropical area near the equator with huge trees and vines— rainforest

D. A grassland with few trees between the deserts— savanna

E. A raised area formed by volcanic activity— mountain ranges

III. Africa may be studied by various ways other than written records.

A. The study of the structure and changes of languages— linguistics

B. The study of plants and tracing the movement of people by their crops— botany

C. The study of ruins, burial sites, and artifacts from the past— archaeology

D. Stories passed from one generation to another by word of mouth— oral history

IV. Historians study Africa's early peoples by language.

A. The Berber language group—The greatest of these nomadic people were the Tuareg.

B. The Nilotic language group—The best known were the Maasai.

C. The Bantu language group

1. Bantu peoples

2. Some Pygmy tribes who lived in the Congo basin also spoke Bantu languages.

D. Click languages— Bushmen and Khoikhoi

V. Historians also study Africa's ancient peoples according to their empires or cities.

A. The empire of ___Aksum___—located in eastern Africa and ruled by King ___Ezana___ in the AD 300s

B. The empire of ___Ghana___—located along the ___Niger___ River; controlled the trade of ___salt___ and ___gold___

C. The empire of ___Mali___—conquered Ghana; ruled by ___Sundiata___

D. The empire of ___Songhai___—became independent of Mali

1. Ruler—___Sunni Ali___

2. Center of Islamic faith and learning—___Timbuktu___

E. The kingdom of ___Mwene Mutapa___—ancestors of a people that historians called the ___Shona___

1. Organized themselves into ___clans___

2. Built big stone houses called ___zimbabwes___

F. The eastern coastal cities built for trade—northernmost city of ___Mogadishu___ and southernmost city of ___Sofala___

1. The same religion—___Muslim___

2. The same language—___Swahili___

Africa's Regions

Name ______________________________

Use with Student Text pages 318–21.

A. Write a definition or description for each word. Use the glossary in the Student Text.

1. desert *a region with few plants that receives less than ten inches of rain a year*
2. equator *an imaginary line that divides the earth into northern and southern hemispheres*
3. Horn of Africa *a peninsula on the eastern coast of Africa*
4. oasis *a fertile area in the desert with water*
5. rain shadow desert *a lowland area that receives little rain because the wind blows water vapor high into nearby mountains*
6. rainforest *a tropical forest filled with huge trees and vines and a large variety of wildlife; receives annual rains of one hundred inches or more*
7. sand dune *a hill or ridge of wind-blown sand*
8. savanna *an area with tall grasses and few trees*

B. Write the five regions of Africa in the key. Color each region and the corresponding rectangle in the key.

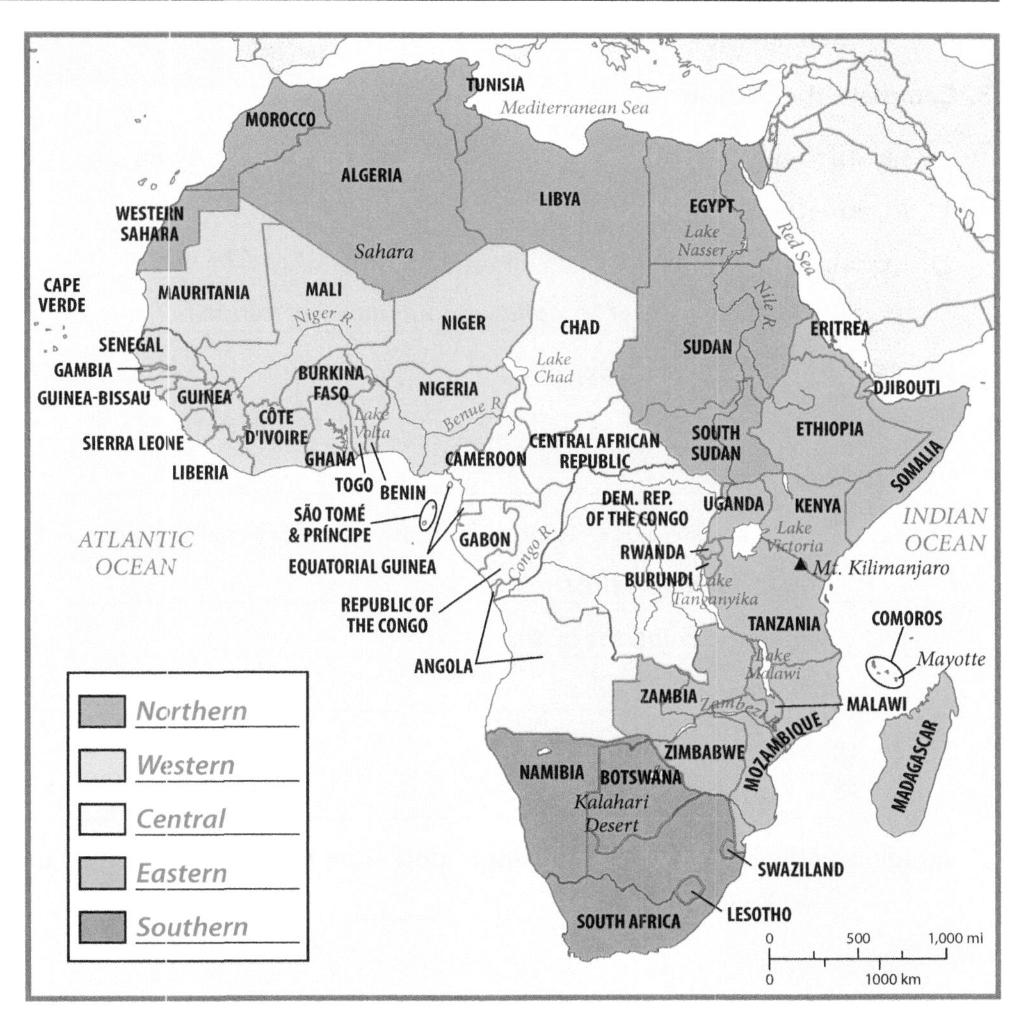

Study Guide

Name ______________________

Use with Student Text pages 318–23.

A. Match the description to the correct term.

C 1. an African oral storyteller

H 2. an area with tall grasses and few trees

A 3. a scientist who studies plants and traces the movements of people by their crops

F 4. stories about the past that are spoken instead of written down

E 5. a fertile area in the desert with water

G 6. a tropical forest filled with huge trees and vines and a large variety of wildlife; receives annual rains of one hundred inches or more

B 7. a region with few plants that receives less than ten inches of rain a year

D 8. the study of the structure and changes of languages

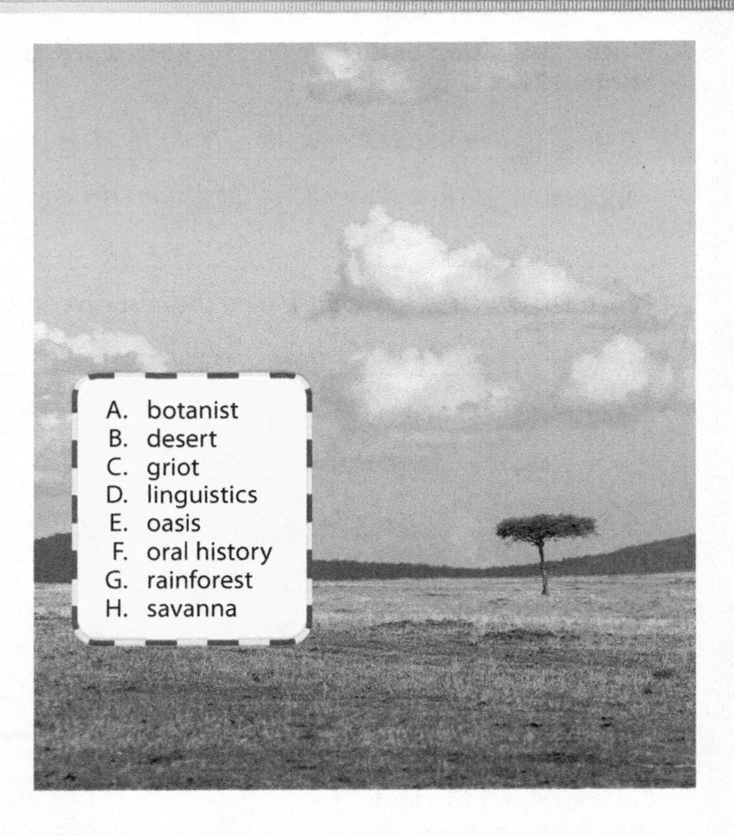

A. botanist
B. desert
C. griot
D. linguistics
E. oasis
F. oral history
G. rainforest
H. savanna

B. Complete the section.

9. Identify one way that geographers organize Africa for studying. *by regions (or by topography)*

10. Identify the peninsula on the eastern coast of Africa. *Horn of Africa*

11. Explain why Somalia is called a rain shadow desert. *The wind blows water vapor high into the mountains to the west of Somalia without allowing rain to fall on the lowlands.*

12. Name four ways of learning about people and their history other than written records.
    - *linguists*
    - *archaeology*
    - *botany*
    - *oral history*

13. Explain how a historian evaluates the truth of a story that has been passed down orally. *The historian compares the story with stories from different areas. If there are matching stories of the same past event, the historian can assume that the event really happened.*

14. Identify three land features of Africa. *possible answers: deserts, rain shadow desert, lakes and rivers, tropics or rainforests, mountain ranges*
    -
    -
    -

15. Identify the people whose migration route from the Benue River to southern Africa was traced by linguists. *Bantu*

Oral History

Name ______________________________

A. Answer the questions. *Wording may vary depending on the Bible version being used.*

1. What three things did God command be taught in Deuteronomy 6:1? *commandments, statues/ decrees, and judgments/laws/rules*
2. Why did God want these to be taught (Deut. 6:2)? *so people would fear the Lord God*
3. What phrase in this verse shows oral history being passed on? *"thou, and thy son, and thy son's son"*
4. What three benefits did God promise the Israelites in the Promised Land for keeping these commands (Deut. 6:2–3)?
   - *Their days would be prolonged/long.*
   - *It would be well with them.*
   - *They would increase mightily or multiply greatly.*
5. When were the Israelites to pass on the oral history (Deut. 6:7)? *When they sat in their houses, when they walked by the way, when they lay down, and when they rose up.*
6. What did Joshua ask each man to pick up as he crossed the Jordan River (Josh. 4:5)? *a stone*
7. What were these objects used for (Josh. 4:7)? *a memorial to the children of Israel forever*
8. What history did God want the Israelites to remember (Josh. 4:21–22)? *Israel crossed the Jordan on dry land.*

In Isaiah 43 God gives His people an oral history reminding them of His blessings.

9. What three civilizations are named in Isaiah 43:3? *Egypt, Kush/Cush/Ethiopia, and Seba*
10. What civilization is named in Isaiah 43:14? *Chaldean or Babylonian*
11. Why does God review the history of the Israelites (Isa. 43:11)? *He is reminding them that He is their Savior and their Lord.*

B. Write three sentences telling what God has done for you. This is part of your history to be passed on to your children and grandchildren.

12. ______________________________

13. ______________________________

14. ______________________________

Africa's People

Name ____________________

Use with Student Text pages 325–28.

A. Write the information under the correct heading.

Bantu peoples	measured wealth and social standing by the number of cattle they owned
Berber language group	Nilotic language group
blue turbans and loose garments	Pygmies
Bushmen	sounds made with the tongue, teeth, and lips
camels were most valuable possession	tall and slender
Khoikhoi	Tuareg
Maasai	

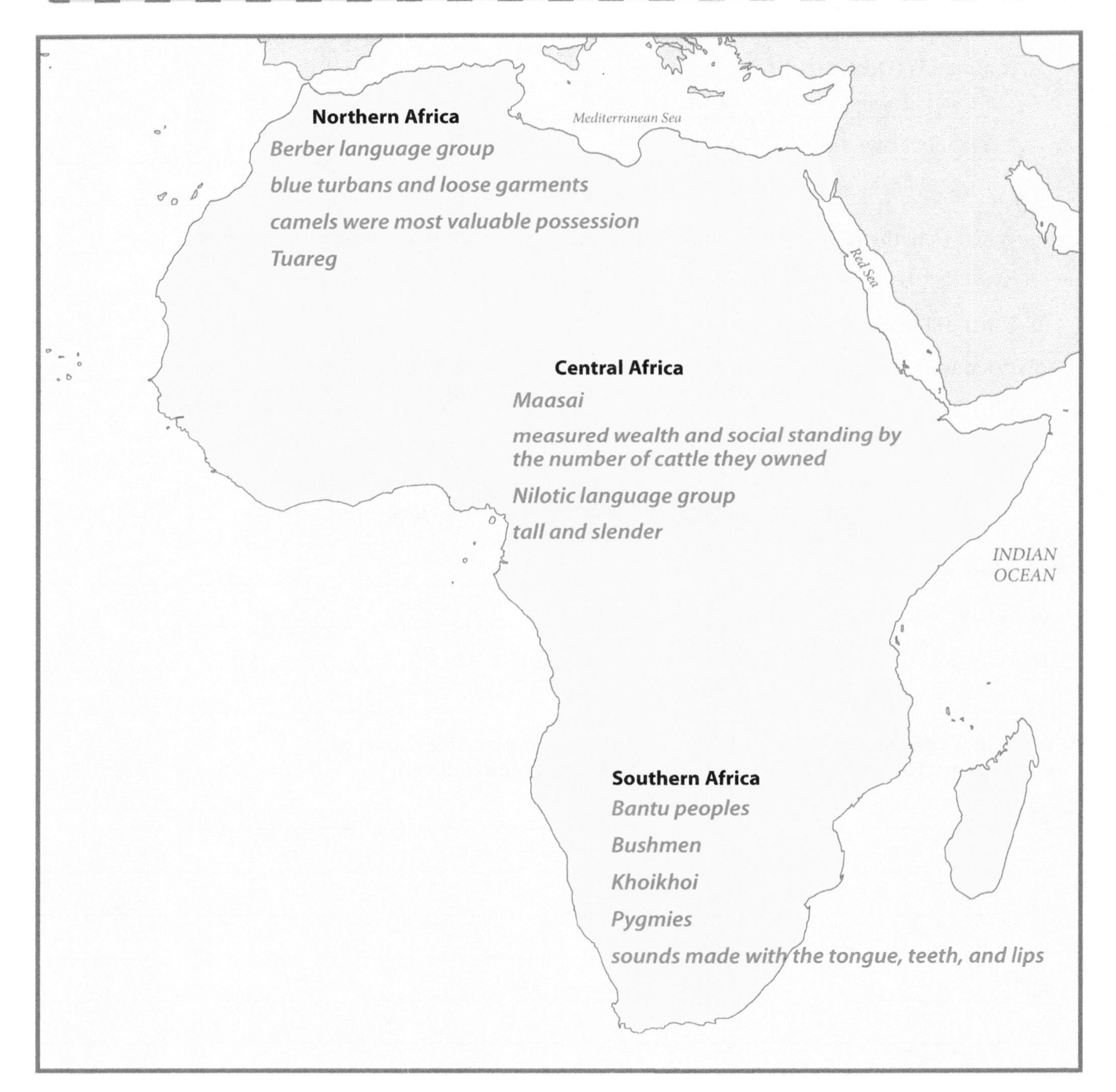

Africa's People

Name ______________________

Use with Student Text pages 325–28.

B. Contrast traditional African beliefs with biblical truth.

Traditional African beliefs	Biblical truth
Most Africans believed in a god who was a ___supreme being___ but relied on ___tradition___ to explain what this god was like.	The Bible teaches that God is ___Creator___ of the universe (Isa. 40:28). Christians rely on the ___Bible___ to explain what God is like (1 Thess. 2:13).
Most Africans believed that their god could be reached through ___sacrifices___ and offerings.	The Bible teaches that only Christ's sacrifice is sufficient to ___reconcile___ people to God (2 Cor. 5:19).
Most Africans believed that spirits controlled natural forces for ___good___ or for ___evil___. Many African religions taught ___animism___, which is the belief that spirits live in animals or things in nature such as trees and rivers.	The Bible teaches that there is only one God, Who ___created___ all things for His own glory, and He alone deserves to be worshiped (Rev. 4:11).
Most Africans relied on a man thought to have magical powers, such as a ___medicine man___ or a ___rainmaker___, to connect them with the supernatural world.	The Bible teaches that God may be approached only through ___Christ Jesus___ (1 Tim. 2:5).
Africans believed that the spirits of their departed relatives ___visited___ them and ___influenced___ their lives.	The Bible warns people not to try to ___contact___ the dead (Deut. 18:10–11; a necromancer is a person who inquires of the dead).

Ancient African masks that were sometimes used in religious ceremonies

Study Guide

Name ______________________

Use with Student Text pages 325–32.

A. Write one or two sentences to answer each statement.

1. Identify how historians divide Africa's early peoples into groups. *Historians divide Africa's early peoples into groups by common language.*

2. Identify the people of small stature who lived in the rainforest of the Congo basin. *The Pygmies lived in the rainforest of the Congo basin.*

3. Explain how Christianity became Aksum's official religion. *The king, Ezana, became a Christian, likely through the influence of his servant Frumentius, and made Christianity the official religion of Aksum.*

4. Describe how Ghana acquired Islam but kept its traditional beliefs. *Many traders converted to Islam after Arabian merchants brought Islam to Ghana, but the king of Ghana continued to practice traditional beliefs. Eventually, a separate Islamic community was founded there.*

B. Complete the chart.

5–7. Describe the dress, the occupations, and the valuable possession of the Tuareg.

	Tuareg
Dress	*dressed in loose, flowing garments; wrapped their heads with a long piece of dark blue cotton that acted as both a turban and a veil*
Occupations	*farmers, herders, traders, guides, warriors*
Valuable possession	*camels*

C. Write a sentence that contrasts the given characteristic of the civilizations. *Possible answers are given.*

8. Aksum's spoken language ◆ Aksum's written language *Aksum's educated people spoke Greek, but they developed a written language called Ge'ez.*

9. Aksum's religion ◆ Ghana's religions *Aksum's official religion was Christianity, while Ghana's religions included Islam and traditional African beliefs.*

10. Aksum's location ◆ Ghana's location *Aksum was in the area that is modern Ethiopia, and Ghana was located in modern Mauritania. (Students may also mention that Aksum was on the eastern side of Africa, while Ghana was on the western side.)*

11. goods Aksum traded ◆ goods Ghana traded *Aksum traded precious stones, gold, elephants, ivory, ebony, incense, and myrrh, while Ghana controlled the trade of salt and gold.*

Name ______________________

D. Write a sentence explaining the reason each factor was significant in making Ghana a wealthy empire.

12. Factor: Ghana's location was ideal.

    Reason: *It was on the edge of the Sahara and was near the only source of water for miles around.*

13. Factor: The gold mines were to the south of Ghana.

    Reason: *Ghana could control all the trade of salt and gold.*

14. Factor: The merchants of Ghana traded with European merchants.

    Reason: *They were able to trade gold for necessities as well as luxuries.*

E. Write *T* if the statement is true. If the statement is false, draw a line through the incorrect part and write the correction in the blank.

T 15. Maasai measured their wealth and social standing by the number of cattle they owned.

T 16. Young Maasai warriors had to go through certain ceremonies to prove their manhood.

cattle 17. Maasai men could buy a bride in exchange for ~~camels.~~

T 18. The Bushmen spoke an unusual click language.

southern 19. Both the Dutch and the English came to the ~~northern~~ tip of Africa.

T 20. The king of Ghana charged taxes on all trade with his kingdom, making himself wealthy.

Ezana 21. The empire of Aksum was ruled by King ~~Frumentius.~~

Ethiopia 22. Many scholars believe that the kingdom of Sheba was located in what is now ~~Egypt.~~

T 23. Jesus used the queen of Sheba as an example of the eager faith with which the Jews should have welcomed Him.

F. First, plan the essay on your own paper. Then, write it below.

24. Contrast traditional African beliefs with biblical truth.

The student's essay should include three of the following contrasts: Most Africans believed their god could be reached through sacrifices and offerings. The Bible teaches that only Christ's sacrifice is sufficient to reconcile people to God. Africans worshiped spirits who control natural forces for good or for evil. Many African religions taught that spirits lived in animals or things in nature such as trees and rivers. The Bible teaches that there is only one God, Who controls all the forces of nature for His own glory. He is the only One Who deserves to be worshiped. Africans often relied on a person thought to have magical powers to connect them with the supernatural world. The Bible teaches that God may be approached only through Jesus Christ. Africans believed that the spirits of their departed relatives visited them and influenced their lives. The Bible warns people not to try to contact the dead.

Africa's Time Zones

Name ______________________

Finding the time in areas other than your own involves addition or subtraction based on the directions of east and west. For every zone you travel to the *east*, you must *add one hour* to the time in your own time zone. For every zone you travel to the *west*, you must *subtract one hour* to the time in your own time zone.

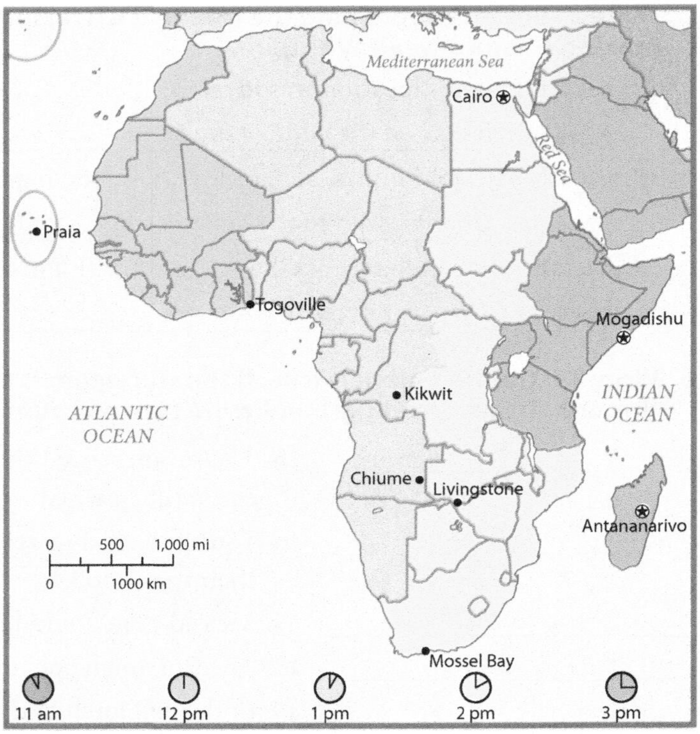

A. Answer the questions. Use the map on Student Text page 321.

1. A plane left Cairo, Egypt, at 1:00 PM and traveled to Praia, Cape Verde. The trip took 7 hours and 30 minutes. What time is 7 hours and 30 minutes later than 1:00 PM? *8:30 PM* Which direction did the plane travel? *west* Do you subtract or add? *subtract* How many times zones did the plane travel over? *3* What time did the plane reach Cape Verde? *5:30 PM*

2. Malkia met Rozi at a summer camp. Malkia lives in Kikwit in the Democratic Republic of the Congo. Rozi lives in Antananarivo, Madagascar. Malkia called Rozi at 10:00 AM. What direction did the phone call travel? *east* Do you subtract or add? *add* How many time zones did the phone call travel through? *2* What time did Rozi receive the phone call? *12:00 PM*

3. Mr. and Mrs. Jonas celebrated their anniversary at Victoria Falls. They left Chiume, Angola, at 8:00 AM. The trip took 6 hours, and they stopped for 1 hour to enjoy some local cuisine. What time did they arrive at their bed and breakfast in Livingstone, Zambia? *4:00 PM*

4. Miss Colas's last stop on the Horn of Africa was Mogadishu. Then she flew to Cairo, Egypt, for a Nile River boat ride. Her flight out of Mogadishu was at the early hour of 5:00 AM. She was able to get more sleep on the 3-hour flight. What time did Miss Colas land in Cairo, Egypt? *7:00 AM*

B. Complete the chart. Use the map on Student Text page 321.

From	To	Set your watch (back, forward)	Number of hours
Western Sahara	Algeria	*forward*	*1*
Uganda	Cameroon	*back*	*2*
Mossel Bay, South Africa	Togoville, Togo	*back*	*1*

Mali and Songhai

Name ______________________

Use with Student Text pages 334–36.

A. Match the description with the correct term.

12' ghana
21' Ibn Battuta
3° mansa
4' Mansa Musa
33" Sundiata
12" Sunni Ali
37° Timbuktu

__3°__ 1. the word for ruler in the Malian language

__4'__ 2. the ruler of Mali who was famous for his immense wealth and his devotion to Islam

__33"__ 3. the ruler of Mali known as the Lion King

__37°__ 4. Songhai's center of Islamic faith and learning

__21'__ 5. the traveler who described the people of Mali as loving justice and honesty

__12"__ 6. the ruler who establish the empire of Songhai

B. Write your answers from Section A in order on the blanks.

7. The latitude and longitude of Mount Kilimanjaro is __3°__ __4'__ __33"__ S, __37°__ __21'__ __12"__ E.

To show greater precision, degrees of longitude and latitude are divided into minutes (') and seconds ("). There are 60 minutes in each degree. Each minute is divided into 60 seconds.

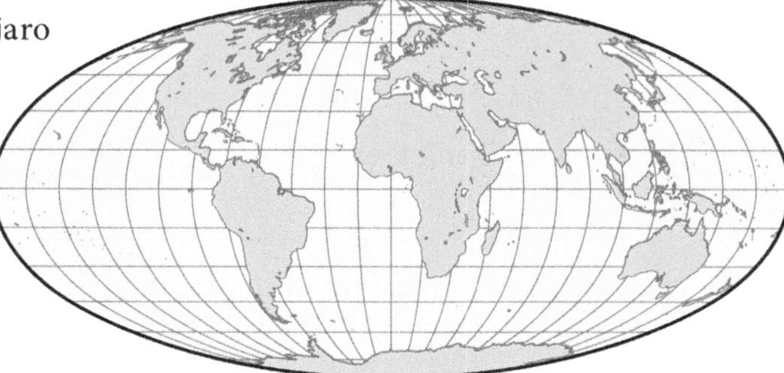

C. Draw a circle around the part of the sentence that states the cause. Underline the part of the sentence that states the effect.

8. Sundiata built his capital on the main trade route across the Sahara because he had gained control of the gold and salt trade.

9. Sundiata became known as the Lion King after he overcame a disability and miraculously began to walk after seven years of paralysis.

10. Mansa Musa was a devout Muslim, so he made a pilgrimage to Mecca.

11. Because there were no more strong kings after Mansa Musa's death, the Malian empire slowly weakened and broke apart.

12. The Moroccan army was better trained and had muskets; therefore, they defeated the empire of Songhai.

13. Most of the empires in ancient Africa rose to power because of wealth they gained through trade.

14. When people received free gold from Mansa Musa, the price of gold dropped.

Study Guide

Name ______________________

Use with Student Text pages 334–42.

A. Match the description to the correct term.

F 1. the ancestors of the Shona

C 2. a city of stone-slab buildings and the Great Enclosure

J 3. a big stone house

A 4. a group of families descended from a common ancestor

G 5. the strong ruler of Mali known as the Lion King

E 6. a Malian king famous for his immense wealth and his devotion to Islam

H 7. the ruler who established the empire of Songhai

I 8. Songhai's center of Islamic faith and learning

A. clan
B. Ezana
C. Great Zimbabwe
D. Madagascar
E. Mansa Musa
F. Mwene Mutapa
G. Sundiata
H. Sunni Ali
I. Timbuktu
J. zimbabwe

B. Complete the section.

9. Explain how Mali became an empire. *Sundiata and his army conquered Ghana, gained control of the gold and salt trade, and built a capital on the main trade route across the Sahara.*

10. Why did Mansa Musa travel to Mecca? *He was a faithful Muslim, and Muslims are required to make a pilgrimage to Mecca.*

11. Why did the price of gold go down in the region where Mansa Musa traveled? *He gave away so much gold that gold was no longer worth as much.*

12. Explain how the city of Songhai became an empire. *Sunni Ali led Songhai to win its independence from Mali and conquered the cities around Songhai to establish an empire.*

13. Describe the architecture of the Shona. *All the buildings had stone slabs tightly stacked on top of one another without any mortar. The walls were more than fifteen feet wide and up to thirty-two feet tall.*

C. Complete the chart.

14–17. List the similarities of the independent cities of eastern Africa's coast.

Religion	*Islam*
Goods for trade	*gold, ivory, rhinoceros horns, tortoise shells, and animal skins*
Language	*Swahili*
Occupations	*trading, fishing, farming, masonry, and shipbuilding*

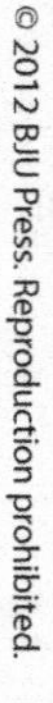

Study Guide

Use with Student Text pages 334–42.

Name ____________________

D. Write the number of each place on the map.

18. Atlantic Ocean
19. Horn of Africa
20. Indian Ocean
21. Kalahari Desert
22. Madagascar
23. Nile River
24. Sahara
25. Timbuktu

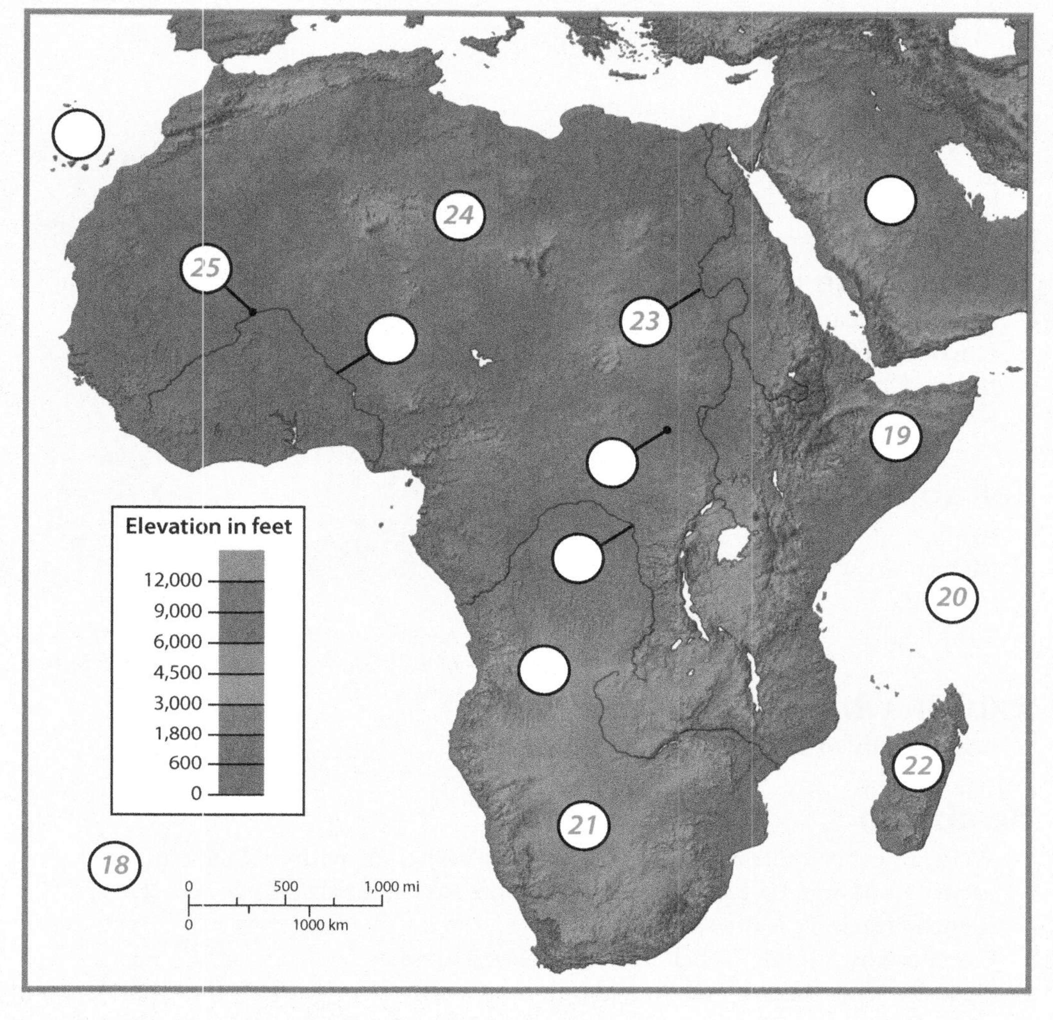

E. First, plan the essay on your own paper. Use the table on the previous page to help you. Then, write your essay below.

26. Describe the similarities of the independent cities of eastern Africa's coast.

The student's essay should include the following points: The cities shared the same religion of Islam. They shared the same language of Swahili. They produced many of the same goods for trade, such as gold, ivory, rhinoceros horns, tortoise shells, and animal skins. The people there had many of the same occupations, such as trading, fishing, farming, and building.

Chapter 12 Summary

Name ______________________

Define these terms

botanist
clan
desert
griot
linguistics
oasis
oral history
rainforest
savanna
zimbabwe

Aerial view of Victoria Falls. Compare the size of Victoria Falls with the size of the bridge on the right side of the picture.

Locate these places

Atlantic Ocean
Horn of Africa
Indian Ocean
Kalahari Desert
Madagascar
Nile River
Sahara
Timbuktu

Tell about these people

Ezana
Mansa Musa
Sundiata
Sunni Ali

Explain what happened

how the city of Songhai became an empire

Be able to . . .

Write an essay contrasting traditional African beliefs with biblical truth
Identify one way that geographers organize Africa for studying
Identify the land features of Africa
Explain why Somalia is called a rain shadow desert
Describe four ways of learning about people and their history other than written records
Identify the people whose migration route was traced by linguists
Explain how historians evaluate the truth of a story that has been passed down orally
Identify how historians divide Africa's early peoples into groups
Describe the dress, the occupations, and the valuable possession of the Tuareg
Describe the traditions of the Maasai
Identify the peoples who lived in the rainforest of the Congo basin
Identify the peoples who spoke unusual click languages
Identify the two groups of Europeans who came to the southern tip of Africa
Identify the modern country scholars believe the queen of Sheba was from
Explain how Jesus used the queen of Sheba as an example in the New Testament
Describe the ancient empire of Askum
Explain how Christianity became Aksum's official religion
Describe how Ghana acquired its great wealth and the religion of Islam while keeping traditional beliefs
Describe the empire of Mali
Identify the Mwene Mutapa as the ancestors of the Shona
Describe Great Zimbabwe
Describe the architecture of the Shona
Describe the similarities of the independent cities of eastern Africa's coast

Chapter 13 Organizer

Name ______________________

Use with Student Text pages 344–60.

Complete the lantern organizer as you read the chapter.

Geography

1. The name Japan comes from the Chinese phrase ___jih pen___, meaning "___origin of the sun___."

2. Japan is surrounded by the East China Sea, the ___Sea of Japan___, and the ___(North) Pacific Ocean___.

3. A large group of scattered islands is called an ___archipelago___.

4. The four main islands of Japan are ___Hokkaido___, ___Honshu___, ___Shikoku___, and ___Kyushu___.

Organization

5. An organized civilization was developed by the ___Yamato___ clan.

6. Wealth and power were symbolized by giant tomb mounds called ___kofuns___.

7. The Yamato claimed their emperors were descended from a mythical ancestor named ___Jimmu Tenno___.

8. The Japanese wanted a strong system of ___government___.

9. A constitution was developed by ___Prince Shotoku___.

10. Japanese culture, religion, and government were greatly influenced by the ___Chinese___.

Cut out the lantern pieces.

Fold in half lengthwise. Cut along solid lines. Do not cut to edge.

Attach short edges of paper.

Attach handle.

Chapter 13 Organizer

Name ______________________

Use with Student Text pages 344–60.

Complete the lantern organizer as you read the chapter.

Religion

11. The main religion of Japan was *Shintoism*.

12. Shintoists worship the spirits of animals, natural objects, and ideas like growth; these spirits are called *kami*.

13. God's Word warns people against worshiping *His creation* instead of Him.

14. According to Shintoism the purpose of existence is to lead a *moral* life, but the Bible teaches that a Christian should live a moral life to bring *glory* to God.

15. Prince Shotoku introduced a second religion to Japan, *Buddhism*.

Government

16. Political and economic changes came to Japan about *645*.

17. The "Great Change," or *Taika Reform*, weakened the influence of the *chieftains*.

18. The Taika Reform established a civil *service examination* like one the Chinese had.

Writing

19. The fine art of handwriting is known as *calligraphy*.

20. The man known as the father of this art form is *Wang Xizhi*.

Cut out the lantern pieces.

Fold in half lengthwise. Cut along solid lines. Do not cut to edge.

Attach short edges of paper.

Attach handle.

Chapter 13 Organizer

Name ____________________

Use with Student Text pages 344–60.

Complete the lantern organizer as you read the chapter.

Life at the Court During the Heian Period

21. The first permanent capital of Japan was ___Nara___. Later the capital moved to ___Heian-kyo___.

22. The nobles that live near, serve, and advise the emperor make up the ___imperial court___.

23. Strict rules of behavior at the imperial court stressed the importance of manners, or ___etiquette___.

24. The Heian period was known as the ___golden age___ of Japan.

Language and Literature

25. The official language of the men at the imperial court was ___Chinese___.

26. Women wrote in the common ___Japanese___ language.

27. One of the greatest writers of early Japan was ___Lady Murasaki Shikibu___, who is credited with writing the first ___novel___.

28. A Japanese poetry form that is popular today is the ___haiku___, a poem with ___seventeen___ syllables and an aspect of nature or the seasons.

Arts

29. One characteristic of Japanese art was its use of brilliant ___colors___.

30. A second characteristic of Japanese art was its use of everyday ___objects___.

Cut out the lantern pieces.

Fold in half lengthwise. Cut along solid lines. Do not cut to edge.

Attach short edges of paper.

Attach handle.

Chapter 13 Organizer

Name ______________________

Use with Student Text pages 344–60.

Complete the lantern organizer as you read the chapter.

Religion (Heian Period)

31. The Japanese would worship at the Shinto shrines to obtain help for their ___daily lives___.

32. The Japanese would worship at the Buddhist shrines to prepare for the ___life to come___.

Government (Heian Period)

33. A person who rules in place of a rightful ruler who is unable to fulfill his duties is a ___regent___.

34. During most of the Heian period, the Fujiwara family ___controlled___ the government but also brought ___corruption___ to it.

Feudal Japan

35. At the top of the Japanese feudal system were the emperor, his ___family___, and the ___military leader___.

36. The military leader who was chosen by the emperor and given supreme power over the government was the ___shogun___.

37. Below the emperor and the shogun in the feudal system were the ___daimyo___, who were the chief nobles and the powerful ___warlords___.

38. The next feudal class was the ___samurai___, warriors with the skills of horsemanship, fencing, ___archery___, and ___jujitsu___.

39. The last class of the feudal society was the ___peasants___, who were ranked in order from highest to lowest—farmers, ___artisans___, and then ___merchants___.

The Mongols

40. Both Mongol attacks against Japan ___failed___, the second because of a strong storm called a ___kamikaze___.

Cut out the lantern pieces.

Fold in half lengthwise. Cut along solid lines. Do not cut to edge.

Attach short edges of paper.

Attach handle.

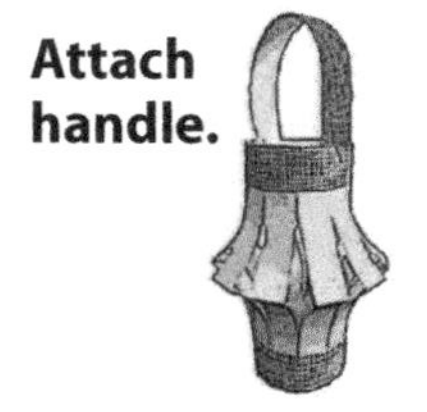

Origin of the Sun

Name ______________________________

Use with Student Text pages 344–47.

A. Define the terms.

1. archipelago ___a large group of scattered islands___
2. kofun ___a giant circular, square, or keyhole-shaped burial mound___

B. Complete the section.

3. The four main islands of Japan are ___Hokkaido___, ___Honshu___, ___Shikoku___, and ___Kyushu___.
4. The name Japan comes from *jih pen*, meaning "___origin of the sun___."
5. What names have archaeologists given the two earliest peoples of Japan?
   - ___Jomon___
   - ___Yayoi___
6. Describe the Japanese clans. ___Each clan had its own chieftain who protected his people from other clans. The people would then give part of their rice harvest to the chieftain. Each clan also had its own land and god.___
7. Name the clan that rose to power over all other clans. ___Yamato___
8. Name three areas that were influenced by the Chinese. *possible answers: the name of the country, government, concepts, religion, way of life*
   - ______________
   - ______________
   - ______________

C. Match the description with the correct term.

A. Jimmu Tenno
B. Prince Shotoku
C. Yamato clan

___B___ 9. developed a constitution
___A___ 10. mythical ancestor of Japanese emperors
___C___ 11. imperial or ruling family
___C___ 12. developed organized cities, a government, social classes, and a written language
___A___ 13. descendant of the sun goddess, Amaterasu
___B___ 14. encouraged the Chinese religion
___B___ 15. schooled in Buddhism and Confucianism
___A___ 16. was to be worshiped
___B___ 17. patterned the government after the Chinese

What shape is the kofun? *keyhole shaped*

Study Guide

Name ______________________

Use with Student Text pages 344–50.

A. Write *T* if the statement is true. If the statement is false, draw a line through the incorrect part and write the correction in the blank.

T 1. A large group of scattered islands is an archipelago.

Yamato 2. The imperial family of Japan was the ~~Yayoi~~ clan.

645 3. The Taika Reform took place around ~~794~~.

T 4. Wang Xizhi is credited with being the Father of Calligraphy.

Prince Shotoku 5. ~~Jimmu Tenno~~ developed a constitution to establish a strong system of government like China's.

kami 6. The gods or nature spirits of Shintoism are called ~~torii~~.

T 7. A kofun is a giant circular, square, or keyhole-shaped burial mound built by the Japanese aristocracy.

B. Complete the chart.

8–11. Contrast the Shinto beliefs with biblical truth.

Shinto beliefs	Biblical truth
Shintoists worship kami, which are the spirits of *animals*, *natural objects* like mountains or streams, and *ideas* like growth.	The Bible teaches that there is only *one God* to be *worshiped* and warns people against worshiping *His creation* (Rom. 1:18–25).
Shintoism teaches that the main purpose of existence is to *lead a moral life*.	The Bible teaches that a person should live a moral life by the power of the *Holy Spirit* (Rom. 8:1–17) to *bring glory* to God and to *serve* Him (1 Cor. 6:20).

C. First, plan the essay on your own paper. Then, write your essay in the space below.

12. Describe the changes that the Taika Reform brought to Japan.

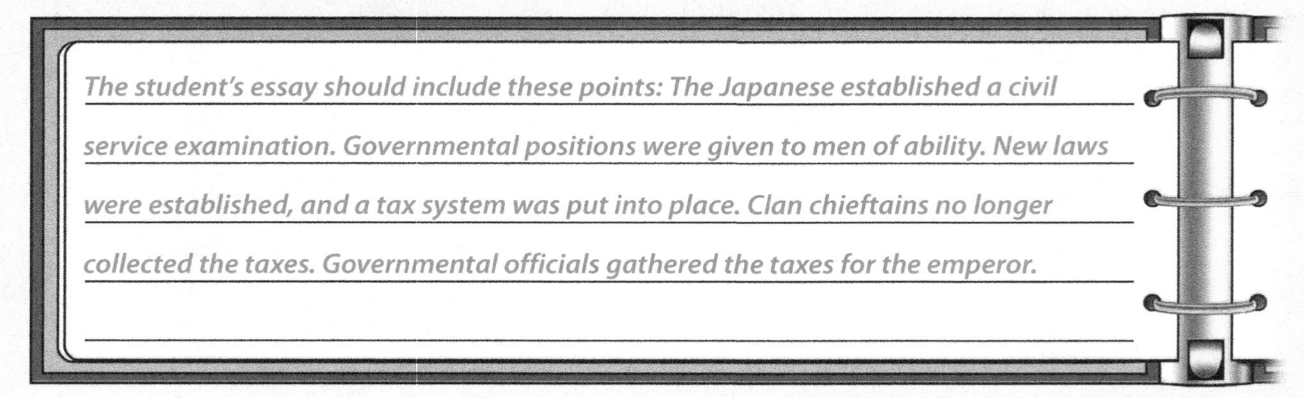

The student's essay should include these points: The Japanese established a civil service examination. Governmental positions were given to men of ability. New laws were established, and a tax system was put into place. Clan chieftains no longer collected the taxes. Governmental officials gathered the taxes for the emperor.

Study Guide

Use with Student Text pages 344–50.

Name ______________________

D. Complete the section.

13. Identify how the Japanese people were organized. ___*in clans*___
14. Identify the main religion of Japan. ___*Shintoism*___
15. Identify the religion Prince Shotoku introduced. ___*Buddhism*___ Where did it come from? ___*China*___
16. Identify the art of fine handwriting. ___*calligraphy*___
17. Who did the Japanese believe their emperor was a descendant of? ___*Jimmu Tenno*___, who was a descendant of ___*the sun goddess (Amaterasu)*___
18. Identify four areas of Chinese influence on Japan. *possible answers: the name of Japan, the system of government, the second religion of Buddhism, reading and writing Chinese, and literature and art in the Chinese style*
   - ______________________
   - ______________________
   - ______________________
   - ______________________

E. Complete the key and color the map according to your key. *Colors used for the key will vary.*

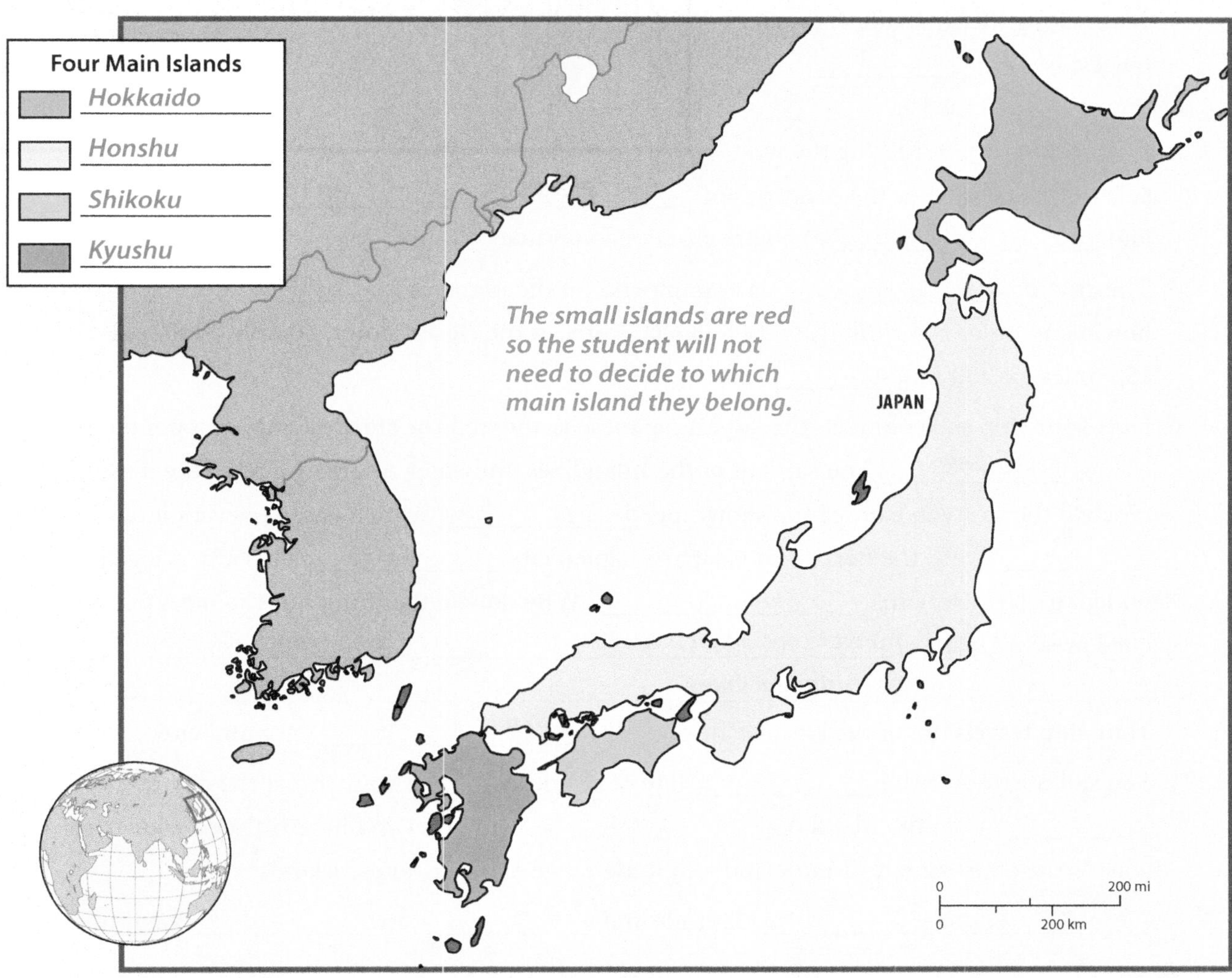

Trip Around the Archipelago

Name ____________________

Complete the section. Use this map and the one on Student Text page 347.

1. Begin at number 1. What is the latitude and longitude? ___45___ ° N, ___140___ ° E
2. At number 2 you are sailing around the northernmost of the four major islands of Japan. What is the name of this island? ___Hokkaido___
3. As you sail on, reaching number 3, what city do you see to the northwest? ___Sapporo___
4. At number 4 you are now sailing south along the west side of Japan's biggest island, ___Honshu___. Your ship is in the Sea ___of___ ___Japan___. Bordering the west side of the sea you see the countries of ___Russia___, ___North Korea___, and ___South Korea___. You are crossing longitude ___135° E___.
5. The city of ___Nagasaki___ is at number 5 on the island of ___Kyushu___. Roughly how many miles is it from this city to South Korea at the closest point: 50 miles, 100 miles, 150 miles, or 200 miles? ___150___ miles
6. Now your ship sails between the largest Japanese island and the smallest and least populous island, ___Shikoku___. You sail out of the Inland Sea and enter a narrow bay. In the distance to the east you can see the snowcapped ___Mt. Fuji___, which has an elevation of ___12,388 ft___. To the northwest is Japan's capital city, ___Tokyo___. This city is located on Japan's largest plain, ___Kanto Plain___. Why do you the think it is the most populated area in Japan? ___possible answer: It is the largest flat area to build homes, apartment complexes, and manufacturing facilities.___

   Your ship travels out of the bay and through the ___Pacific Ocean___ at number 6.
7. You sail north over the ___40° N___ line of latitude. You end your trip at the city of ___Kushiro___ on the island of ___Hokkaido___. Now that you have finished your trip, what is the approximate latitude and longitude range of the Japanese islands?

   ___30° N___ to ___45° N___ latitude and ___130° E___ to ___145° E___ longitude

Japanese Culture

Use with Student Text pages 352–55.

Name ____________________________

Complete the crossword puzzle.

			1 S								2 S		
	3 B		H		4 J		5 N				H		6 R
7 F	U	J	I	W	A	R	A		8 H	A	I	K	U
	D		N		P		R		E		K		L
	D		T		A		A		I		I		E
	H		O		N				A		B		S
	I		I		E				N		U		
	S		S		S					9 R			
	M		M		10 E	T	I	Q	U	E	T	T	E
										G			
						11 C	H	I	N	E	S	E	
										N			
										T			

The puzzle is on the Japanese character for *butterfly*.

Across

7. controlling family during much of the Heian period
8. Japanese poem about nature
10. manners
11. official language of the imperial court

Down

1. the religion to obtain help for daily life
2. the first name of the world's first novelist (In Japan a person's family name comes first, and the "first" name comes last.)
3. the religion to prepare for the life to come
4. the language women wrote in
5. the first permanent capital of Japan
6. strict ____ of behavior for imperial court
8. the period known as the golden age of Japan
9. a person who rules in place of the rightful ruler

Compare and Contrast Warriors

Name ____________________

The Samurai

In ancient Japan a samurai was a highly trained warrior. He mastered many skills such as horsemanship, fencing, archery, and jujitsu. Not only was a samurai skilled in fighting, but he was also a well-rounded individual. He wrote poetry and was familiar with fine arts and philosophy.

A samurai's obligation was to the warlord or chief noble. He lived by a strict code of conduct known as "the way of the warrior." This code demanded loyalty, honor, duty, justice, courage, sincerity, and courtesy. His duty was protecting the warlord at all costs, even unto death. Death with honor was chosen rather than surrender with defeat. A samurai had no fear of death and would take his own life rather than be captured or killed by the enemy.

Because of his loyalty and skills, a samurai was allowed to carry two swords, one long and one short. In later years his armor included a helmet to protect his head and neck, arm and shoulder protectors, a breastplate to protect the chest, a belly wrap, and protection for the legs.

The Christian Soldier

A person who has accepted Jesus Christ as Savior becomes a soldier of Christ. A Christian is in a spiritual army fighting a spiritual war. His responsibility is to fight against the spiritual enemy that is constantly warring against his Christian life. He is to read and study the Word of God to prepare him for everyday life (2 Tim. 2:15).

A Christian's obligation is to God. He should live according to the principles found in God's Holy Word. In a Christian's life the fruit of the Holy Spirit should be seen—love, joy, peace, patience, kindness, goodness, faithfulness, gentleness, and self-control (Gal. 5:22–23). As Christ ascended into heaven, He told Christians that their duty is to be His witness to the entire world (Acts 1:8). The Bible tells of Christians, such as Stephen, who met their deaths because they lived as Christians should. The chapter on ancient Rome in the Student Text tells about Christians who were burned, crucified, or sent to their deaths in the Roman arenas. Christians should have no fear of death but look forward to eternal life with their Savior in heaven.

Similar to the samurai,w a Christian soldier has armor that God has given him to wear (Eph. 6:13–17). He is to put on the belt of truth and the breastplate of righteousness. "For [God] hath made [Christ] to be sin for us, who knew no sin; that we might be made the righteousness of God in him" (2 Cor. 5:21). A Christian soldier wears shoes of the gospel of peace and carries a shield of faith. This shield protects his heart from the darts thrown by those against Christ. On his head the Christian wears the helmet of salvation. It protects his mind against the enemy's attacking his thoughts. Lastly, the Christian is given the sword of the Spirit. "For the word of God is quick, and powerful, and sharper than any twoedged sword, piercing even to the dividing asunder of soul and spirit, and of the joints and marrow, and is a discerner of the thoughts and intents of the heart" (Heb. 4:12).

The Warrior's End

Sadly, the samurai spent their lives serving a man who did not worship the true God. These same samurai died for their pagan beliefs and will spend eternity apart from God. Christians should live their whole lives showing Christ to others in everything they do. They will spend eternity with God.

Compare and Contrast Warriors

Name ____________________________

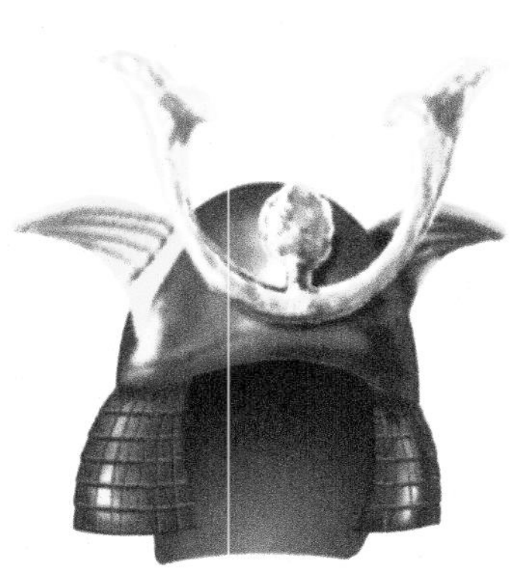

A. Complete the chart.

Answers may vary depending on the Bible translation used.

	Samurai	Christian soldier
Who	a highly trained *warrior* from *Japan*	a person who accepts *Jesus Christ* as *Savior*
Serves	*a warlord or chief noble*	*Jesus Christ*
Duty	to protect the *warlord* at all costs even unto death	to be Christ's *witness* to the entire world
Armor	a *belly wrap* to protect the torso	a belt of *truth*
	a *breastplate* to protect the chest	the *breastplate* of righteousness
	a *helmet* to protect the head and neck	the *helmet* of salvation
	a long and a short *sword*	the *sword* of the Spirit
	arm and shoulder *protectors* and protection for the *legs*	shoes of the *gospel of peace* and the shield of *faith*
Life's mission	the emphasis on serving a man who *did not worship the true God*	lives his whole life *showing others Christ in everything he does*

B. Answer the questions.

1. The Christian soldier's weapons are not carnal, or of the flesh. Describe the power of the weapons (2 Cor. 10:4). *They are "mighty through God to the pulling down of strongholds."*
2. What battle is the Christian soldier to fight (1 Tim. 6:12)? *"the good fight of faith"*
3. How is the Christian soldier to suffer (2 Tim. 2:3)? *"as a good soldier of Jesus Christ"*

Study Guide

Name ________________________________

Use with Student Text pages 352–60.

A. Match the description with the correct term. Some answers will not be used.

A.	Buddhism
B.	Chinese
C.	daimyo
D.	epic
E.	feudalism
F.	haiku
G.	Heian period
H.	Japanese
I.	Murasaki Shikibu
J.	regent
K.	samurai
L.	Shintoism
M.	shogun
N.	Wang Xizhi

__E__ 1. a system of organizing and governing society based on land and service

__G__ 2. the golden age of Japan

__L__ 3. the religion to obtain help for daily life

__A__ 4. the religion to prepare for the life to come

__B__ 5. the official language of the imperial court

__J__ 6. a person who rules in place of a rightful ruler who is unable to fulfill his duties

__F__ 7. a poem about nature with seventeen syllables

__M__ 8. a military leader who had the most political power and was chosen by the emperor

__C__ 9. a chief noble or powerful warlord who had military and economic power to rule over his land

__K__ 10. a warrior whose duty was to protect the chief noble or warlord

__I__ 11. the first true novelist

B. Complete the section.

12. Who was the family who rose to power during the Heian period? *Fujiwara*

13. Who wrote most of the literature that survived the Heian period? *women*

14. Name two characteristics of Japanese art. *the use of brilliant colors and the use of everyday objects*

15. Identify who was in control of the government before and after the civil war in the 1100s.
The imperial family was in control of the government before the civil war. After the civil war the emperor was the religious leader, but the shogun had the political power.

16. Why was Yoritomo appointed the first shogun? *for winning the war among the clans*

17. How did the first and second Mongol attacks end? *The shoguns turned back the Mongols in both attacks. In the second defeat the shogun had the help of a typhoon.*

18. What is the difference between the ancient meaning of *kamikaze* and its meaning during World War II? *A kamikaze in ancient times was a typhoon; during World War II it was a Japanese suicide pilot.*

Name ______________________

C. Complete the feudalism social pyramid. Write the names of the subclasses in the last social class level.

19. *emperor and shogun*
20. *daimyo*
21. *samurai*
22. *peasants*

a. *farmers* b. *artisans* c. *merchants*

D. Write the names of the numbered places.

23. *Nara*
24. *Heian-kyo*
25. *Pacific Ocean*
26. *Hokkaido*
27. *Honshu*
28. *Shikoku*
29. *Kyushu*

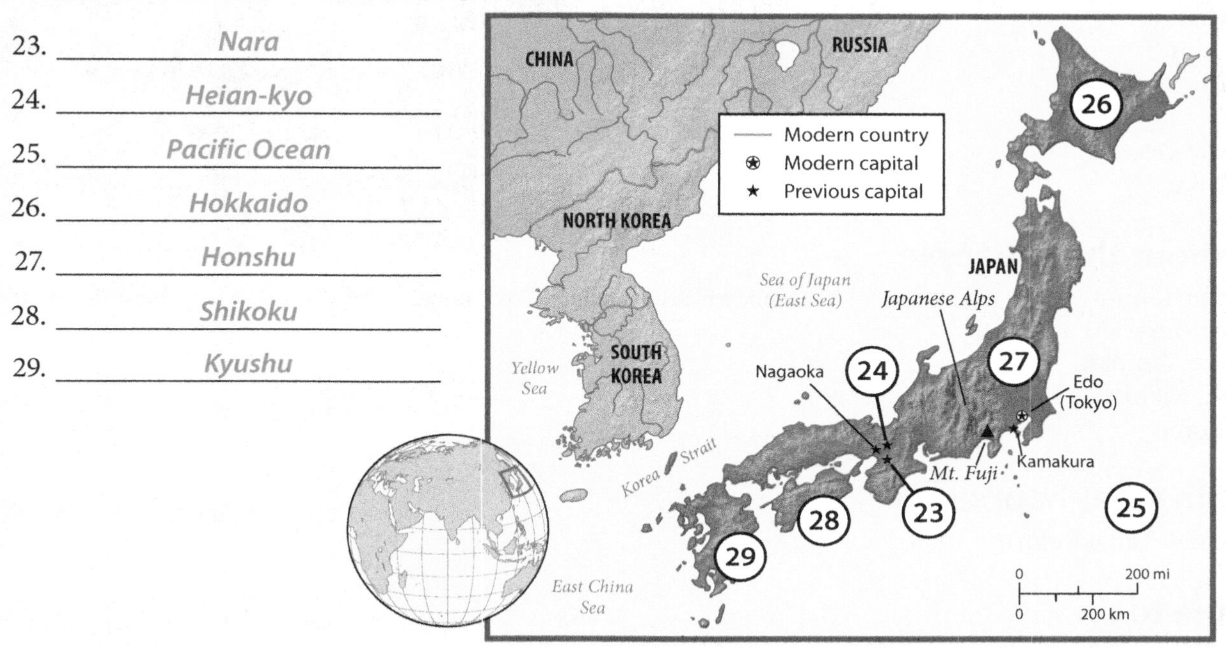

E. First, plan the essay on your own paper. Then, write your essay in the space below.

30. Describe the life of a samurai.

The student's essay should include the following points: The samurai warrior mastered the skills of horsemanship, fencing, archery, and jujitsu. The samurai worked under the daimyo. It was a samurai's duty to protect the daimyo. A samurai had additional privileges that included being able to have a surname, a family crest, and the right to carry two swords. The samurai lived by a strict code of conduct called the "way of the warrior." This code demanded loyalty, honor, duty, justice, courage, sincerity, and politeness.

Chapter 13 Summary

Name ________________________________

Define these terms

archipelago
calligraphy
daimyo
etiquette
feudalism
haiku
imperial court
kami
kamikaze
kofun
regent
samurai
shogun

Locate these places

Heian-kyo
Hokkaido
Honshu
Kyushu
Nara
Pacific Ocean
Shikoku

A torii, which is a traditional gate found at the entrance of or within a Shinto shrine

Tell about these people

Jimmu Tenno
Lady Murasaki Shikibu
Prince Shotoku
Wang Xizhi
Yoritomo

Explain what happened

ca. 645—Taika Reform

Be able to . . .

Identify how the Japanese people were organized
Identify who the Japanese believed their emperor was a descendant of
Identify the clan that was the imperial family of Japan
Identify who developed the constitution and the country he patterned the government after
Contrast Shintoism with the biblical truth
Identify the religion that Prince Shotoku introduced to Japan and its origin
Identify who influenced the Japanese in the arts and written language
Identify the family that rose to power during the Heian period
Describe the rules of behavior for life at court
Identify the official language of the Japanese court
Identify the Heian period as the golden age of Japan
Describe Japanese literature during the golden age
Describe two characteristics of Japanese art
Explain how the Japanese blended two religions
Identify who controlled the government before and after the civil war
Describe the social classes under feudalism
Describe the life of a samurai
Identify the cause of the Mongol defeats
Explain the difference in meaning of *kamikaze* in ancient times and during World War II

Chapter 14 Organizer

Name ____________________

Use with Student Text pages 362–88.

Complete the two-column organizer as you study the chapter.

Beginning (pp. 362–63)	The medieval period began . . .	in the year 476 and ended in 1400.
	Because the medieval period came between the fall of Rome and the Renaissance, . . .	it is also known as the Middle Ages.
	Once the Germanic warriors had conquered Roman lands, their rulers adopted . . .	the beliefs of the Roman Church.
The Roman Church (pp. 363–67)	Without an emperor to guide the people of the former Roman Empire, many turned . . .	to local leaders and the church.
	The patriarch of the church of Rome was . . .	called the pope.
	The religious leaders were called . . .	the clergy.
	Over time the priests began to teach that people could not receive God's grace . . .	without the help of a priest.
	Priests also taught that to be saved, a person had to participate in religious ceremonies . . .	called sacraments.
	Monks lived together in large secluded . . .	buildings called monasteries.
	Monks spent hours copying the Scriptures and . . .	the writings of early churchmen.
	Friars were traveling preachers who lived among the people and . . .	often begged for food.
	Women who took religious vows were . . .	called nuns.
	Benedict founded . . .	the Monte Cassino monastery.
	The Benedictine Rule encouraged monks to vary their daily routine between . . .	prayer, manual labor, and study of the Scriptures and other writings.
The Franks (pp. 369–72)	Of all the Germanic tribes, the Franks . . .	became the most powerful.
	The first Frankish king was . . .	Clovis.
	The conquests of Clovis would eventually . . .	become modern-day France.
	The Merovingian kings, Clovis's sons and descendants, plotted . . .	against one another.
	Charles Martel became famous for . . .	defeating Muslim invaders.
	Charles Martel and his descendants ruled . . .	the Carolingian Empire.
	Pepin the Short is best known for making . . .	an alliance with the Roman Church.
	Pepin defeated the . . .	Lombards.
	The conquered lands Pepin gave the church . . .	became known as the Papal States.
	Charlemagne was the greatest . . .	of the Carolingian kings.
	Charlemagne was crowned emperor of the Western Roman Empire by . . .	the pope in the year 800.
	Charlemagne divided his empire into small districts, and each district had several . . .	large farming communities called manors.
	Alcuin's writing style used both . . .	small and capital letters.
	After Charlemagne's death the empire went . . .	to his son and then to Louis's three sons.

Complete the two-column organizer as you study the chapter.

The Franks	Conflicts led to the empire's being divided . . .	into ___three___ parts.
	The weakened remains of Charlemagne's empire were invaded by . . .	the Norsemen, Northmen, or ___Vikings___.
Vikings (pp. 373–74)	The Viking attacks were always . . .	sudden and merciless, and they were ___feared___ by all.
	The Vikings' boats and expert sailing skills allowed . . .	them to sail up inland rivers and attack small, defenseless ___towns___.
	The Vikings were the first to discover . . .	___Iceland___, ___Greenland___, and the North American ___Atlantic coast___.
	Several days of the week echo the names of . . .	___Norse___ gods.
Feudalism (pp. 374–77)	Under the system of feudalism, wealthy landowners promised . . .	___protection___ to others in exchange for their ___services___.
	The king granted estates called . . .	___fiefs___ to nobles for their service.
	The nobles who were given an estate . . .	were called ___lords___.
	A lord would choose nobles who did not own land, called . . .	___vassals___, to manage portions of his fief.
	In exchange for the vassal's service, the lord . . .	gave him a ___piece of land___.
	A mounted soldier who defended the manor for the lord was . . .	called a ___knight___.
	A young boy who wanted to become a knight could take the first step . . .	at age ___seven___ and become a ___page___.
	The second step to become a knight was . . .	becoming a ___squire___ at age ___fourteen___.
	When there were no battles, the knights might plan . . .	mock battles called ___tournaments___.
	The emblem painted on a knight's shield was . . .	a ___coat of arms___, which helped identify him.
	A knight's code of behavior, called chivalry, taught a knight to be . . .	generous, loyal to his lord, skillful and brave in battle, faithful to the ___Roman Church___, and protective of ___women___.
	The manor was the center of . . .	___daily life___ during the Middle Ages.
	The peasants who paid rent to the lord and worked part-time for him were . . .	called ___serfs___.
	Serfs were bound to the same land all their lives unless . . .	they paid the ___lord___.
	More privileged peasants, or freemen, could move . . .	from ___manor___ to ___manor___ and paid less rent.

Chapter 14 Organizer

Name ______________________

Use with Student Text pages 362–88.

Complete the two-column organizer as you study the chapter.

Castle (pp. 384–85)	Castles were both . . .	a home and a *military fortress*.
	Some castles had a strong central tower called the . . .	*keep*, where the lord's family lived.
	To keep attackers from reaching the castle easily, builders . . .	dug a wide trench filled with water called a *moat*.
	A drawbridge crossed the moat . . .	to the *castle gate* and covered the gate during an attack.
	A large stronghold in the castle wall was . . .	called the *gatehouse*.
	Two weapons used to attack a castle were . . .	the battering *ram* and the *siege tower*.
Decline of feudalism (p. 387)	The Crusades helped to weaken . . .	the system of *feudalism*.
	By the 1500s European central governments were run . . .	by *kings*.
	Scholars and thinkers started to question . . .	the teachings of the *Roman Catholic Church*.
	Scholars no longer were just in monasteries and church-sponsored schools but could also be . . .	found in *universities* that were formed in the cities.
	A revival of learning resulted in . . .	new *discoveries* and *accomplishments*.

A castle in Poland

Europe

Name ______________________

Complete the section.

1. Name the European countries bordering the Baltic Sea. *Sweden, Finland, Estonia, Latvia, Lithuania, Poland, Denmark, Germany, and Russia*
2. Name the countries that border Greece on the north. *Albania, Macedonia, and Bulgaria*
3. Name the two countries Moldova is located between. *Ukraine and Romania*
4. Name the body of water to the west of France. *Bay of Biscay*
5. Name the body of water that is south of Ukraine and north of Turkey. *Black Sea*
6. Name the country that is bordered by France, Germany, Austria, and Italy. *Switzerland*
7. Name the direction you would travel to get from Greece to Estonia. *north*
8. Name the island country that is far northwest of the rest of Europe. *Iceland*
9. Name the two countries on the Iberian Peninsula. *Spain and Portugal*
10. Name the body of water that separates the United Kingdom from the mainland. *English Channel*

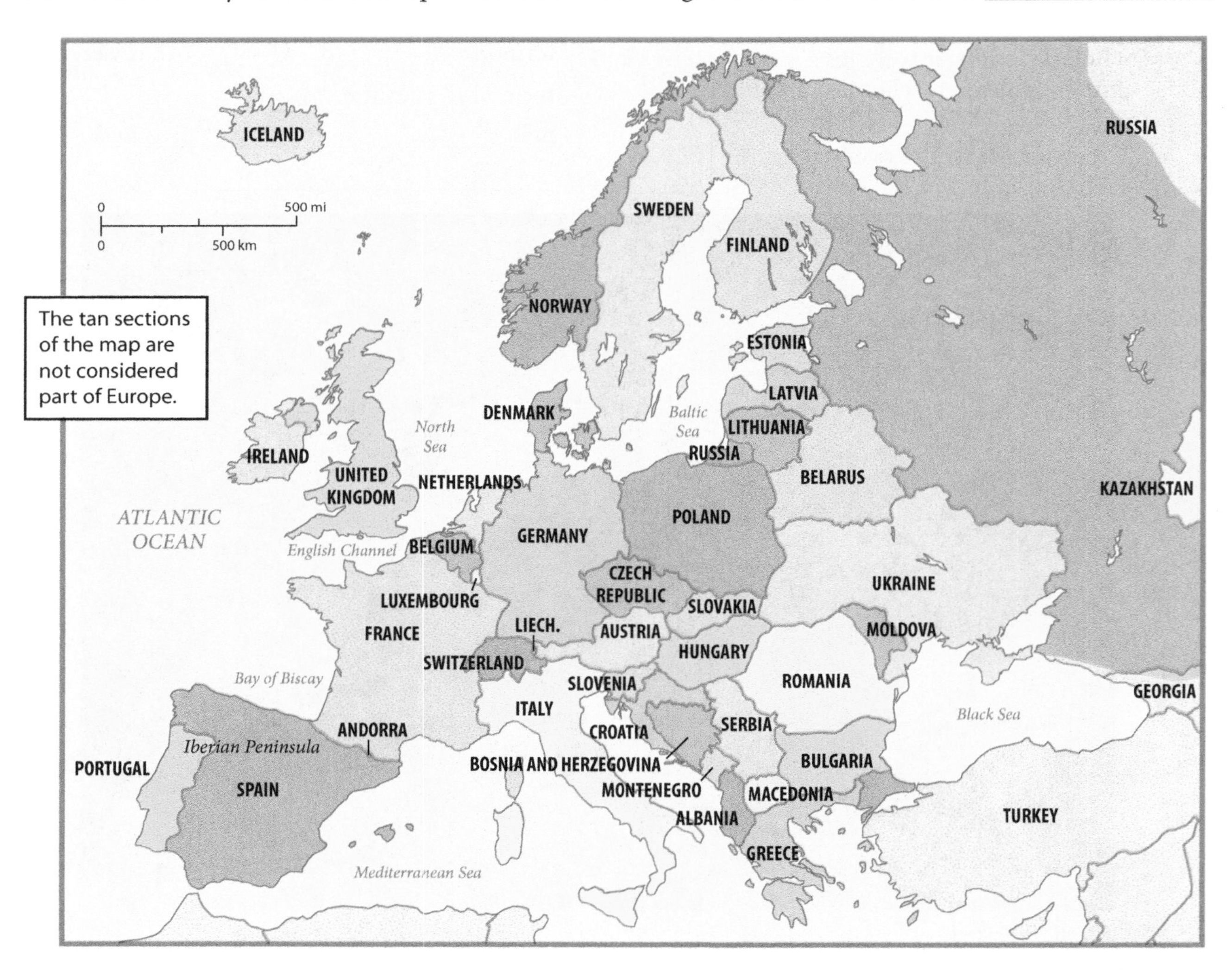

Study Guide

Use with Student Text pages 362–68.

Name ____________________

A. Define the terms. You may use the glossary in your Student Text.

1. clergy _religious leaders during the Middle Ages_
2. medieval _middle age; of or relating to the Middle Ages_
3. monastery _a large secluded dwelling where monks live and work_
4. sacrament _a religious ceremony developed by the Roman Catholic Church and believed to provide grace for salvation_

B. Match the description to the correct church leader.

A. friar
B. monk
C. nun
D. pope
E. priest

_B_ 5. rarely had contact with the outside world
_A_ 6. had a title meaning "brother"
_E_ 7. led services and instructed the people
_B_ 8. lived in a monastery
_E_ 9. preserved and developed many of the doctrines of the church
_A_ 10. lived among the people and was a traveling preacher
_D_ 11. served as patriarch of the church
_E_ 12. taught that people could not receive God's grace without his help
_B_ 13. spent hours copying the Scriptures and the writings of the early churchmen
_C_ 14. a woman who took religious vows
_D_ 15. directed the activities of the clergy

C. Complete the section.

16. The Middle Ages began with the fall of Rome in _476_ and ended with the beginning of the Renaissance in _1400_.
17. Explain why the citizens of the former Roman Empire turned to the church for leadership. _They had no emperor and needed a leader to guide them._
18. Benedict founded the Monte Cassino _monastery_ and produced a set of instructions for living as a monk that came to be known as the _Benedictine Rule_.

D. Complete the chart.

19–30. Contrast Roman Catholic beliefs with biblical truth.

Roman Catholic beliefs	Biblical truth
The Roman Catholic Church teaches that salvation comes at ___baptism___.	The Bible teaches that salvation is a gift of ___God___ (Rom. 6:23).
The Roman Catholic Church teaches that salvation is maintained through ___good works___ and ___penance___.	The Bible teaches that God's grace and salvation are received through ___faith___ alone and can never be earned (Eph. 2:8–9).
The Roman Catholic Church teaches that people cannot pray directly to God for forgiveness, but they must go to a ___priest___, whom they believe is a mediator between God and man.	The Bible teaches that Christ is the ___Mediator___ between God and man (1 Tim. 2:5). Because of Christ's death for sin and His resurrection, Christians can go directly to God to ask for ___forgiveness___ (1 John 1:9).
The Roman Catholic Church teaches that Communion (the Eucharist) must be taken to maintain ___salvation___.	The Bible teaches that observing Communion (the Lord's Supper) is a way for believers to ___remember___ Christ's sacrifice that made atonement for their sin (1 Cor. 11:23–26).
The Roman Catholic Church teaches that the bread and the wine are changed into Jesus' ___body___ and ___blood___.	The Bible teaches that the bread and the wine (or grape juice) are symbols of Jesus' ___body___ and ___blood___ to remind Christians of the cost of His sacrifice. They should ___examine___ their hearts for any sin that needs to be confessed to Him (1 Cor. 11:28).
The Roman Catholic Church teaches that a person needs to perform special rituals and prayers to prepare for ___death___.	The Bible teaches that anyone who has received salvation is already prepared for death because of Christ's ___resurrection___ from the dead (1 Cor. 15:53–57).

The Kings

Name ______________________

Use with Student Text pages 369–72.

A. Answer the questions.

1. Who were the three most important Frankish kings before Charlemagne? *Clovis, Charles Martel, and Pepin the Short*
2. Who conquered the last of the Romans? *Clovis*
3. Who made an alliance with the church of Rome? *Pepin the Short*
4. Who led an army that would keep the rest of Europe from Muslim rule? *Charles Martel*
5. Whom did the pope approve to take the Frankish crown from the Merovingians? *Pepin the Short*
6. Who was the first king of the Franks? *Clovis*
7. Who was known as the Hammer? *Charles Martel*
8. Who had a great interest in learning and encouraged scholarly pursuits? *Charlemagne*

B. Write *T* if the statement is true. If the statement is false, draw a line through the incorrect part and write the correction in the blank.

Great 9. Charlemagne's name means "Charles the ~~Hammer.~~"

T 10. The pope proclaimed Charlemagne emperor in 800 on Christmas Day.

community 11. A manor was a large ~~house~~ where farming took place.

Scandinavia 12. Vikings were raiders of Europe from ~~France.~~

T 13. France and Germany were two countries that were formed from the division of the Carolingian Empire.

C. Fill in the blanks.

14. Pepin the Short defended Rome against invaders called the *Lombards*.
15. The land that Pepin the Short gave to the Roman Church was called the *Papal States*.
16. During Charlemagne's reign, *learning* expanded and schools began for boys.
17. Viking invaders from Scandinavia were also called Northmen or *Norsemen*.
18. Charles Martel and his descendants ruled the *Carolingian Empire*.
19. Alcuin developed a style of handwriting that used both *small* and *capital* letters.
20. After Louis the Pious died, the Carolingian Empire divided into *three* parts.

Surnames

Name ______________________________

Have you ever wondered about where your last name came from? Not just what country but how your name even came to be? Learning about the original meaning and spellings of names is called *onomastics*. Last names, or surnames, were first used in China before Christ was born. The trend lasted for a time, but soon most people were using just one name again.

During the Middle Ages in Europe, a surname was not only popular but necessary. As the world became more crowded and people traveled more, it became important to be able to distinguish people with the same first name from one another. Surnames were a reflection of the lives of men. There were four main categories that surnames came from: familial, occupations, places, and nicknames.

Familial

The word *son* tagged on to the end of a name indicated that a person was the "son of" someone. A surname of Williamson would then say that a person was the son of William, and Robertson would be the son of Robert. Some other personal surnames are Johnson, Jackson, and Stevenson. Adding an *s* to the end of a name also meant "son of." Thus, Andrews would be a son of Andrew.

Occupations

Many surnames came from the jobs that men worked. For example, if a man named James was a baker, he might be called James Baker. Sons usually worked with their fathers, so then they would have the surname Baker as well. If James worked as a cook, he might be called James Cook. Some other occupational surnames include Smith, Potter, Cooper, Mason, Tailor, or Weaver.

Places

Sometimes a person was named based on where he lived. If someone lived near a wooded area, he might have the surname Woods. The name Green could be used for someone who lived by the village green. Someone with the last name of Stone probably lived near a large stone.

Nicknames

Sometimes a person was named because of the way he looked. Surnames such as Little and Small would describe someone who was short in stature. A person who had dark hair may have the surname of Black or Brown. Someone who had fair skin or hair might be called White. If a person had a handicap or a problem with a body part, he may be called by that part, such as Hand, Foot, or Head.

Your Name

Surnames were personal. They identified to everyone who the person was or where he may have come from. However, later on, it became a common practice that surnames were taken from the father. This practice helped eliminate a lot of confusion and helped to identify families better. This is the typical practice today, and it is probably how you got your last name. If you do not know the origin of your name, you may research it to find out more about where your ancestors came from, what they may have done for a living, or even if they had a peculiar physical quality.

Match the description with the best last-name choice.

F 1. son of Thomas
A 2. someone who has a beard
C 3. someone with gray hair
E 4. someone with really white hair
B 5. someone living near a road or a gate
D 6. a fast runner

A. Beard
B. Gates
C. Gray
D. Hare
E. Snow
F. Thompson

7. Do you know the origin of your last name? If so, explain it.

Answers will vary.

Study Guide

Use with Student Text pages 369–77.

Name ____________________

A. Match the description to the correct term. One term in A–J will be used twice, and terms K–N will be used more than once.

A.	chivalry
B.	coat of arms
C.	fief
D.	freeman
E.	knight
F.	lord
G.	manor
H.	serf
I.	tournament
J.	vassal

__E__ 1. a mounted soldier

__G__ 2. a large farming community

__D__ 3. a peasant who was a skilled craftsman

__H__ 4. a peasant who lived on the lord's land

__F__ 5. a noble who had been granted a fief

__J__ 6. a noble who did not own land but managed a portion of a fief

__G__ 7. the center of daily life in the Middle Ages

__I__ 8. a mock battle

__C__ 9. an estate given by a king to a lord

__B__ 10. an emblem that identified a knight in battle

__A__ 11. a code of behavior

K.	Clovis
L.	Charlemagne
M.	Charles Martel
N.	Pepin the Short

__M__ 12. defeated the Muslim invaders at Tours

__L__ 13. crowned by the pope on Christmas Day

__M__ 14. formed the Carolingian Empire with his descendants

__K__ 15. first king of the Franks

__N__ 16. made an alliance with the Roman Church

__K__ 17. conquered the last of the Romans in Gaul

__N__ 18. gave part of his conquered lands to the pope, who called them the Papal States

__L__ 19. expanded learning and extended the Frankish empire

B. Complete the section.

20. Identify three important Frankish kings before Charlemagne. *Clovis, Charles Martel, and Pepin the Short*

21. Describe the agreement Pepin the Short made to become king. *The pope approved of Pepin's taking the Frankish crown from the Merovingians in exchange for helping defend Rome against the Lombards.*

22. Explain why the Vikings were feared by European villagers. *Their attacks were sudden and fearless. During their attacks they stole things, killed people, and destroyed buildings.*

23. Describe the relationship between a lord and a vassal. *The lord chose the vassal to manage the fief; the vassal took an oath of faithfulness and service.*

24. Describe the knight's code of chivalry. *The code of chivalry taught a knight to be generous, loyal to his lord, skillful and brave in battle, faithful to the Roman Church, and protective of women.*

C. First, plan the essays on your own paper. Then, write them in the space provided.

25. Describe the steps in becoming a knight. Include the terms *page* and *squire*.

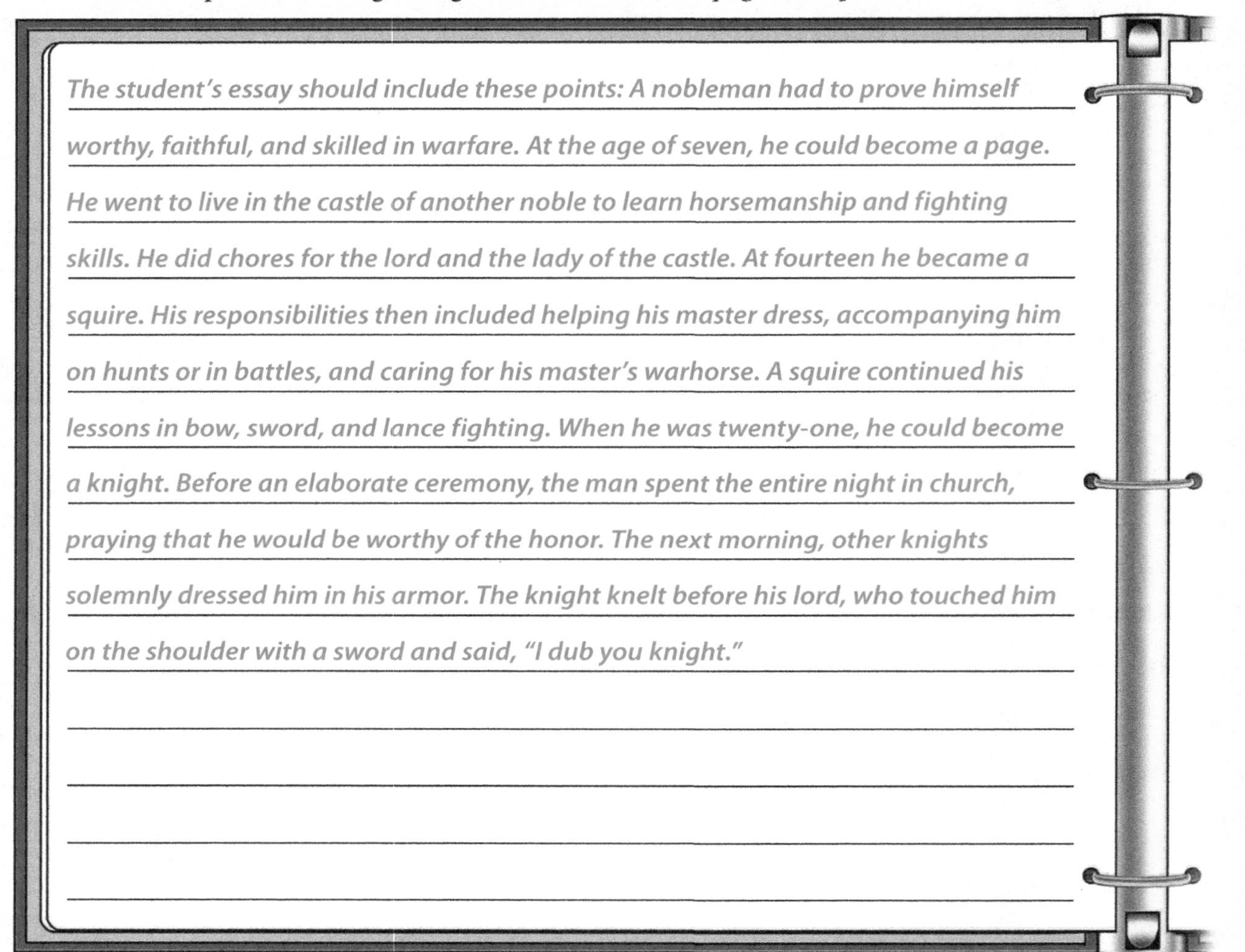

The student's essay should include these points: A nobleman had to prove himself worthy, faithful, and skilled in warfare. At the age of seven, he could become a page. He went to live in the castle of another noble to learn horsemanship and fighting skills. He did chores for the lord and the lady of the castle. At fourteen he became a squire. His responsibilities then included helping his master dress, accompanying him on hunts or in battles, and caring for his master's warhorse. A squire continued his lessons in bow, sword, and lance fighting. When he was twenty-one, he could become a knight. Before an elaborate ceremony, the man spent the entire night in church, praying that he would be worthy of the honor. The next morning, other knights solemnly dressed him in his armor. The knight knelt before his lord, who touched him on the shoulder with a sword and said, "I dub you knight."

Name ______________________________

26. Describe the work of the peasants on the manor.

The student's essay should include these points: The serfs paid rent to the lord and worked part-time for him. They farmed his land, cleared new lands, built and repaired buildings, dug ditches, and fixed roads. The serfs did not have many possessions of their own. They had to use the lord's mill to grind their grain into flour and had to bake their bread in the lord's oven. Often the lord made them pay to use these items. Serfs were bound to the same land all their lives. They could leave only if they paid the lord. The freemen, such as blacksmiths and carpenters, paid less rent and worked fewer hours for the lord. They were allowed to move from the manor if they wanted.

Name ____________________

Use with Student Text pages 379–82.

A. Define the terms. You may use your glossary.

1. shield wall _a wall formed when soldiers stood close together and held their shields tightly together_
2. trial by jury _a practice in which a group of local people help decide the outcome of a trial_
3. trial by ordeal _a practice in which a person had to undergo difficult physical circumstances to determine his guilt or innocence_
4. writ _a royal order_

B. Complete the section.

5. Explain the conflict known as the Battle of Hastings.
Harold Godwinson and Duke William of Normandy both claimed the throne of England and went to battle. Godwinson was killed in battle, and William became king of England.
6. Henry II's family was the _Plantagenets_.
7. Why was King John not popular with the people?
He imposed heavy taxes on the people and used his power to gain money and land for himself.
8. The Magna Carta was signed in _1215_ by _King John_.
9. The English people viewed the Magna Carta as a statement of _rights_ for all _citizens_.
10. American colonists used the rights granted in the Magna Carta as the basis for their _resisting unfair taxation by the king of England_.
11. The Magna Carta's legacy can be seen in the United States _Constitution_ and the _Bill of Rights_.
12. The legendary character of Robin Hood was regarded in England as a national hero because _he stood up for the rights of the poor during a time of tyranny_.

John Wycliffe

Name ____________________

Medieval Oxford, a city in England, had close ties to the king and to the political pulse of the whole country. Oxford's university was the center of intellectual activity and influenced the thinking of men across England. It was to Oxford's university that John Wycliffe went—a youth from Yorkshire in northern England—to be a student. After getting a bachelor's degree in theology, he became interested in biblical studies. Because of the interruptions of the Black Death, he was not able to earn his doctorate until 1372. By then he was already considered Oxford's leading philosopher and theologian. In 1374 Wycliffe became a rector, or member of the clergy over a church, in Lutterworth.

The pope demanded that the people of England pay Rome financial support. England was struggling to raise money to resist a possible French attack. Wycliffe advised his local lord to tell Parliament not to send any money. He argued that the church was already too wealthy. Wycliffe said that Christ had called His disciples to poverty and not wealth. He felt that the local authorities should keep the taxes. These opinions got Wycliffe into trouble with the church. The pope issued five bulls, or church edicts, against him. The church in England brought him to trial three times, and two more popes summoned him to Rome. Wycliffe was never put in prison, nor did he ever go to Rome.

Wycliffe wrote about the conflicts with the church. He believed the pope and the church were second in authority to the Word of God. He disagreed with the Roman Church that the bread and the wine taken at Communion were changed into the body and blood of Christ. Wycliffe believed that "The bread while becoming by virtue of Christ's words the body of Christ does not cease to be bread." From his studying, he disagreed with the church about confessions. "Private confession and the whole system of medieval confession was not ordered by Christ and was not used by the Apostles, for of the three thousand who were turned to Christ's Law on the Day of Pentecost, not one of them was confessed to a priest. . . . It is God who is the forgiver."

Wycliffe felt the common person should read about God's faith in his own language. He said that "Christ and His Apostles taught the people in the language best known to them. It is certain that the truth of the Christian faith becomes more evident the more faith itself is known. Therefore, the doctrine should not only be in Latin but in the vulgar tongue." So Wycliffe and some of his fellow scholars translated the Bible from the Latin Vulgate into English without the church's approval. Although Wycliffe was not alive when the translation was completed, he is credited with the first English translation of the Bible.

Wycliffe died in 1384 after his second stroke. In 1415 the Council of Constance condemned Wycliffe on 260 different counts and ordered that his writings be burned. His bones were to be dug up and cast out of consecrated ground. In 1428 the pope commanded that his remains be dug up again, burned, and scattered into the River Swift. Wycliffe is considered by many to be the forerunner of the Protestant Reformation, so he is sometimes referred to as the Morning Star of the Reformation.

Answer the questions.

1. What kept John Wycliffe from earning his doctorate until 1372? *the Black Death*
2. Why did Wycliffe first get into trouble with the Roman Catholic Church? *He thought that the church had enough money and did not need any more from the people.*
3. What are two beliefs that Wycliffe disagreed with the church on? *He disagreed with the church's thoughts on Communion and private confession to a priest.*
4. What is Wycliffe credited with writing? *the first English translation of the Bible*
5. What is Wycliffe sometimes called? *the Morning Star of the Reformation*

Study Guide

Name ______________________

Use with Student Text pages 379–87.

A. Match the description to the correct term or person.

A.	drawbridge
B.	gatehouse
C.	Henry II
D.	John
E.	keep
F.	moat
G.	shield wall
H.	trial by jury
I.	trial by ordeal
J.	writ

__B__ 1. a large stronghold in the castle wall

__H__ 2. a practice in which a group of local people help decide the outcome of a trial

__J__ 3. a royal order

__G__ 4. a barrier formed when soldiers stood close and held their shields tightly together

__C__ 5. king who developed England's legal system

__A__ 6. a feature of a castle that can be raised or lowered to prevent or allow passage

__I__ 7. a practice in which a person had to go through difficult physical circumstances to prove his guilt or innocence

__D__ 8. king who imposed heavy taxes to cover his military losses and used his power to gain money and land

__E__ 9. a castle tower where the lord and his family lived

__F__ 10. a wide water-filled trench surrounding the castle

B. Write *T* if the statement is true. If the statement is false, draw a line through the incorrect part and write the correction in the blank.

__1215__ 11. King John signed the Magna Carta in ~~1400~~.

__king's__ 12. The Magna Carta limited the ~~nobles'~~ powers and guaranteed certain rights to the people.

__T__ 13. Harold Godwinson and Duke William of Normandy were both nobles who claimed the throne of England.

__T__ 14. Henry II extended the English king's powers into new areas.

__Bill of Rights__ 15. The Magna Carta echoes in the United States Constitution and the ~~Declaration of Independence~~.

__T__ 16. At the Battle of Hastings, Harold Godwinson was killed and Duke William became the king of England.

__T__ 17. At a medieval banquet the lord and his guests were entertained by the court jesters who provided music, juggling, and acrobatics.

__his fingers__ 18. A guest at a medieval banquet ate with ~~a wooden fork~~ off a large, flat piece of bread.

__Plantagenet__ 19. In the late Middle Ages the ~~Norman~~ kings ruled England, while the Capets ruled France.

Name ______________________

C. Complete the section.

20. Explain why Robin Hood was considered a national hero in England. *The English people viewed him as a champion who stood up for the rights of the poor during a time of tyranny.*

21. What does the Bible teach about Robin Hood's methods? *The Bible teaches that stealing is wrong.*

22. Explain why the Crusades weakened feudalism and helped bring about its decline. *Fighting the Crusades was expensive, and most of the money was provided by the lords. Some lords had to sell or mortgage their properties to pay for Crusade expenses. Many serfs left their manors to fight. Since they enjoyed their freedom, they never returned to the manor.*

D. Identify the places numbered on the map.

23. *Atlantic Ocean*
24. *England*
25. *North Sea*
26. *Scandinavia*
27. *Mediterranean Sea*

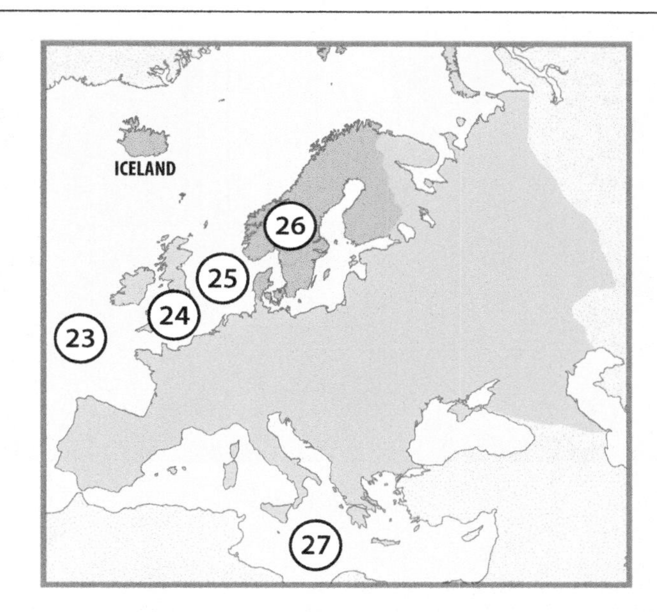

E. First, plan the essay on your own paper. Then, write your essay in the space below.

28. Explain the defense system of a medieval castle. Include the terms *moat*, *drawbridge*, and *gatehouse*.

The student's essay should include these points: The castle was surrounded by strong, thick stone walls. A moat surrounded the castle to keep attackers from reaching it easily. During an attack, the guards raised the drawbridge to cover the gate, cutting off the entrance to the castle. If attackers got safely across the moat, they had to face the gatehouse. If the attackers entered the gatehouse, castle defenders could lower a large screen to trap them inside.

Identify Simple Machines

Name ____________________

Use with Student Text page 388.

A. Identify the simple machines in each military defense.

Simple Machines
inclined plane
lever
pulley
screw
wedge
wheel and axle

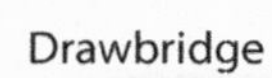
Drawbridge

1. *inclined plane*
lever
wheel and axle
____

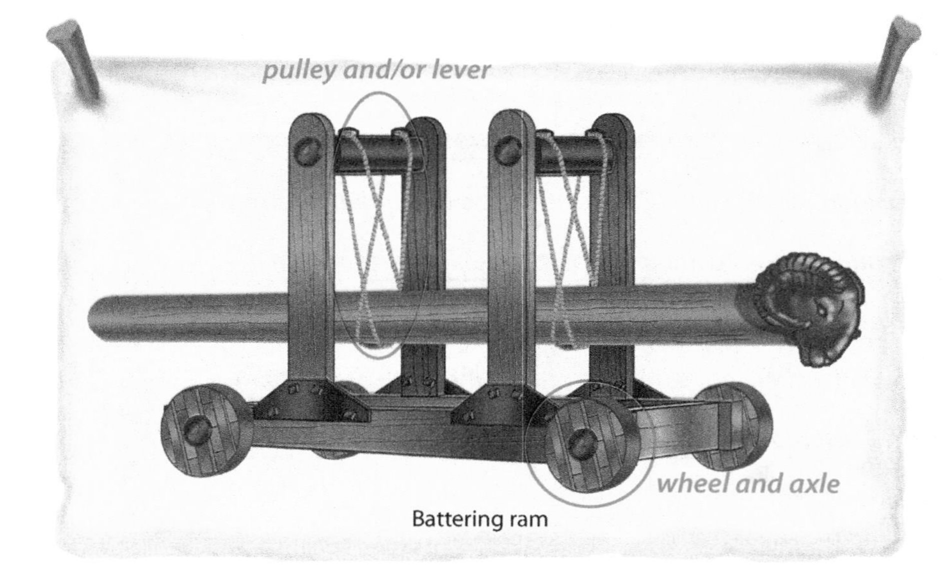

Battering ram

2. *lever*
pulley
wheel and axle
____

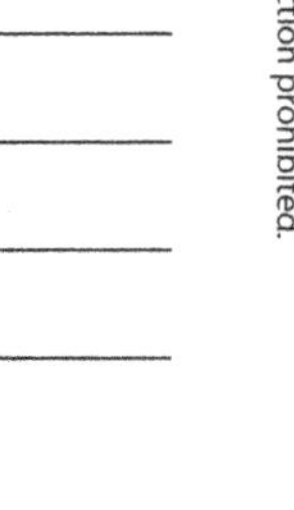

Identify Simple Machines

Name ______________________________

Use with Student Text page 388.

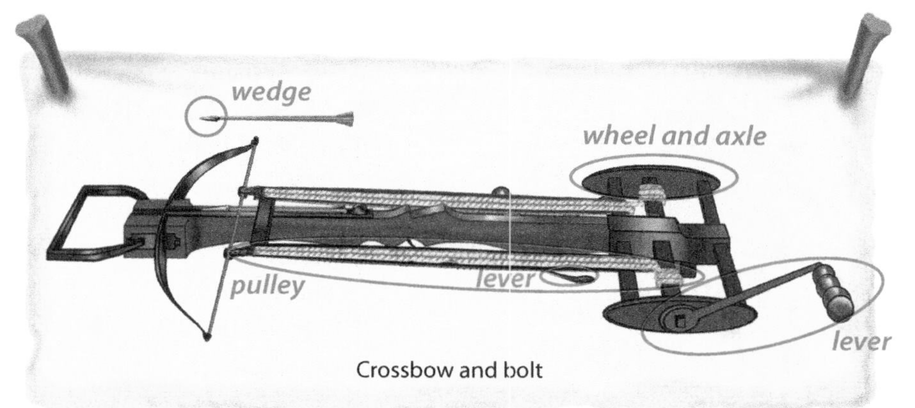

Crossbow and bolt

3. lever
   pulley
   wedge
   wheel and axle

Simple Machines
- inclined plane
- lever
- pulley
- screw
- wedge
- wheel and axle

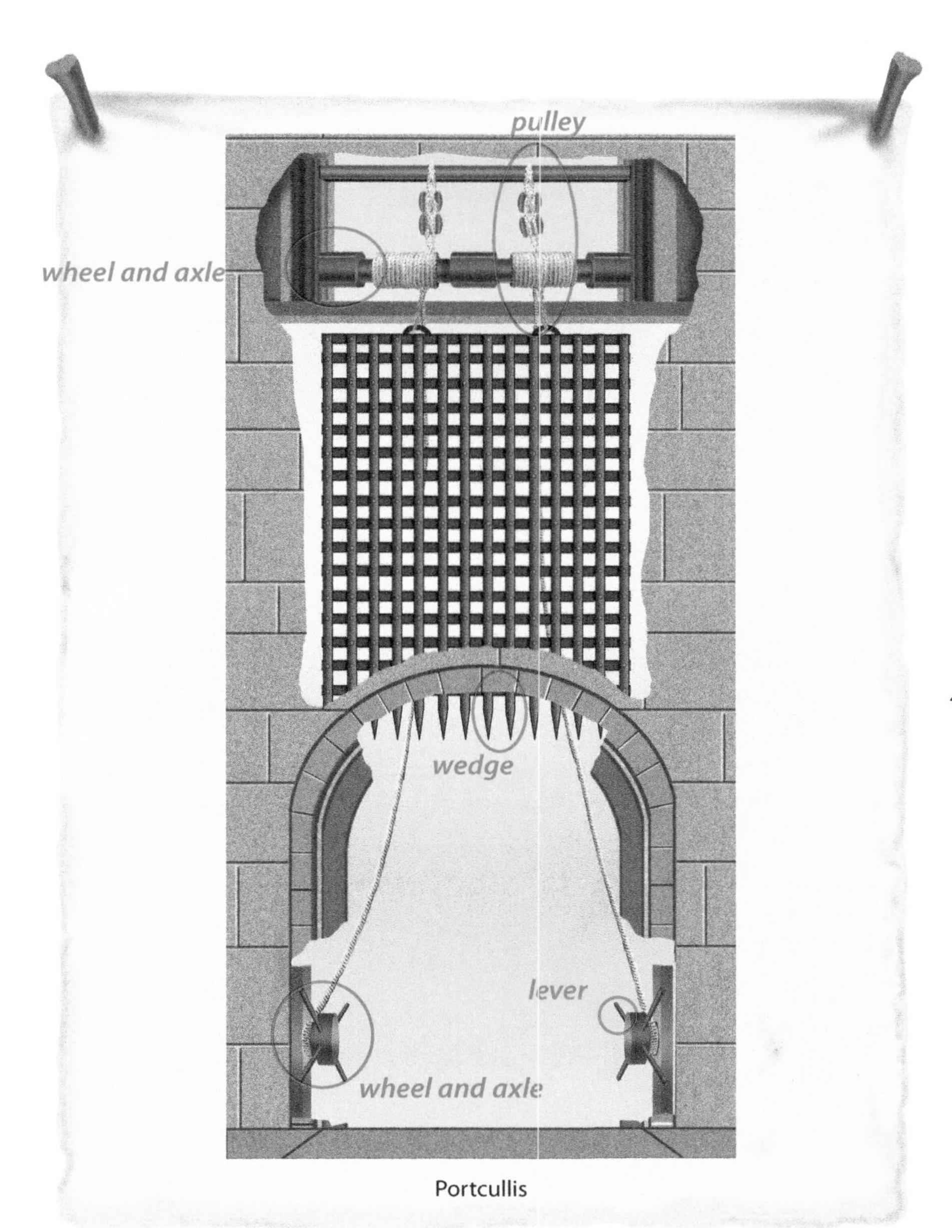

Portcullis

4. lever
   pulley
   wedge
   wheel and axle

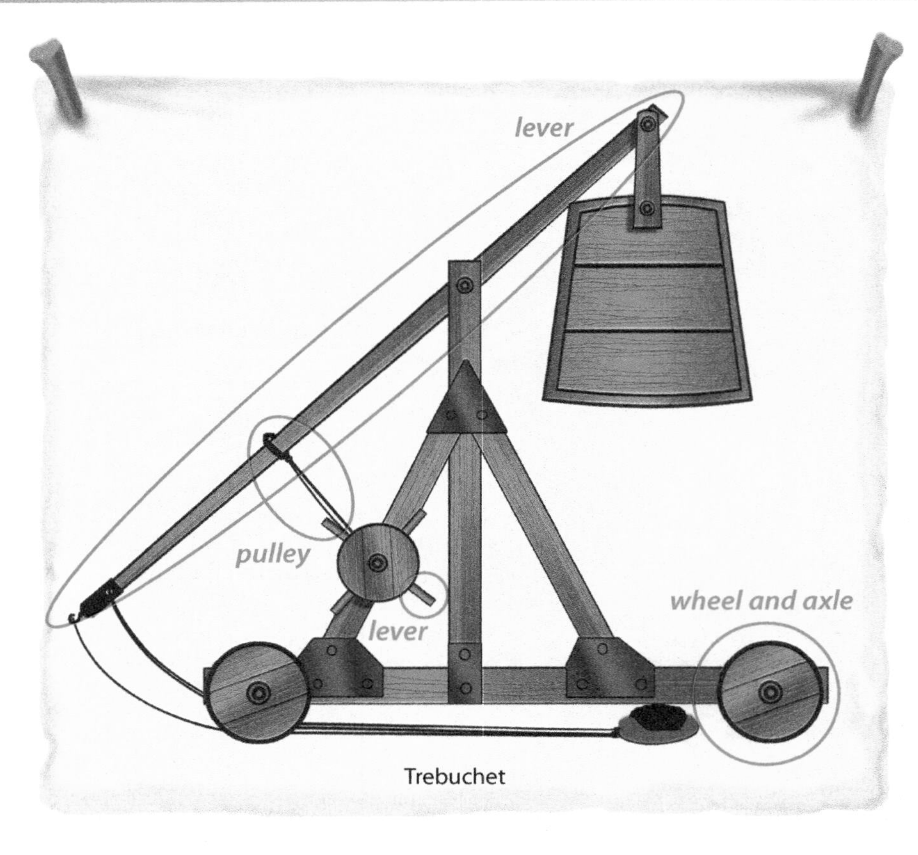

Trebuchet

Simple Machines
inclined plane
lever
pulley
screw
wedge
wheel and axle

5. lever
pulley
wheel and axle
____

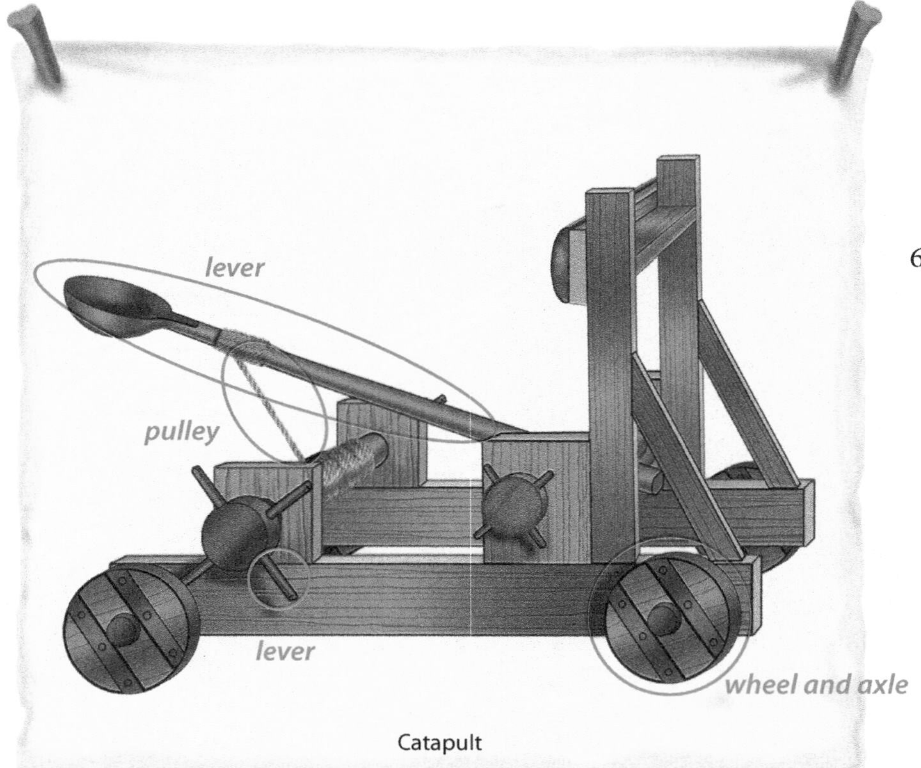

Catapult

6. lever
pulley
wheel and axle
____

Identify Simple Machines

Name ______________________________

Use with Student Text page 388.

B. Choose a castle defense or weapon to write about. Plan your essay on the lines below. Then write your essay in the space provided.

7. Describe how the simple machines give the castle defense or weapon a military advantage.

Castle defense or weapon: *Answers will vary*

Simple machines: ______________________________

Military advantages: ______________________________

____

____

Answers will vary.

Chapter 14 Summary

Name ________________________________

Define these terms

chivalry
clergy
coat of arms
drawbridge
fief
freeman
friar
gatehouse
keep
knight
lord
manor
medieval
moat
monastery
monk
nun
page
sacrament
serf
shield wall
squire
tournament
trial by jury
trial by ordeal
vassal
writ

Locate these places

Atlantic Ocean
England
Mediterranean Sea
North Sea
Scandinavia

Tell about these people

Benedict
Charlemagne
Charles Martel
Clovis
Henry II
King John
Pepin the Short

Explain what happened

476–1400—Middle Ages
800—crowning of Charlemagne by the pope
the Battle of Hastings
1215—signing of the Magna Carta

Be able to . . .

Identify the events that mark the beginning and end of the Middle Ages
Explain why the citizens of the former Roman Empire turned to the church for leadership
Identify the three types of clergymen in the Roman Church and their roles
Compare Roman Catholic beliefs with biblical truth
Identify the empire that Charles Martel and his descendants ruled
Identify the three important Frankish kings before Charlemagne and their accomplishments
Describe the agreement Pepin the Short made to become king
Identify the accomplishments that made Charlemagne the most memorable Frankish king
Explain why European villagers feared the Vikings
Describe the relationship between a lord and a vassal
Identify the steps to become a knight
Describe the knight's code of chivalry
Describe the work of the peasants on the manor
Describe the important development Henry II made in England's legal system
Explain why the legendary character of Robin Hood was regarded in England as a national hero
Explain the defense system of a medieval castle
Name some things that took place at medieval banquets
Name the family who ruled France during the later Middle Ages
Explain why the Crusades weakened feudalism and helped bring about its decline

Chapter 15 Organizer

Name ______________________

Use with Student Text pages 390–410.

Complete the outline as you study the chapter.

I. A Christian Worldview—how a Christian views and interprets history *(pp. 390–94)*

A. Creation

1. "Be fruitful, and multiply, and replenish the earth, and ___*subdue*___ it: and have ___*dominion*___ over . . . the earth" (Gen. 1:28).

   a. Egyptians harnessed the ___*Nile*___ and built the ___*pyramids*___.

   b. The Romans built ___*roads*___, new ___*cities*___, and systems of ___*government*___ that still exist.

   c. The Greeks and Persians developed ___*philosophies*___ that lived on.

2. The greatness of each civilization had a single source—the ___*image of God*___ in man.

   a. People can do creative, intelligent things because an ___*intelligent God*___ created them to be like Him.

   b. God deserves praise and glory for the greatness and contributions of ___*civilizations*___.

B. The Fall

1. People used the abilities that God gave them to ___*rebel*___ against Him.

2. False religions and philosophies formed because people ___*rejected*___ God's truth.

C. Redemption

1. Jesus came as both a man and a king to ___*redeem*___ the world.

2. When Jesus died, He paid the ___*penalty*___ for sinful people in all times and in all places.

3. Those who turn from their sin to Christ for salvation receive His ___*righteousness*___.

4. Jesus' kingdom spreads as more and more people enter it by placing their ___*faith*___ in Him.

II. The Spread of Christ's Kingdom

A. Egypt *(pp. 396–98)*

1. Isaiah prophesied that Egyptians would be considered God's ___*people*___.
2. One of the most important places for early Christianity was the Egyptian city ___*Alexandria*___.
3. Muslims conquered Egypt and threatened death to Christians who did not convert to ___*Islam*___.

B. Mesopotamia and Persia *(pp. 398–99)*

1. God used several Persian kings to ___*protect*___ and ___*provide*___ for His people.
2. After the Roman emperor Constantine converted to Christianity, the Persians feared the ___*Christians*___ would side with Rome and fight against them.
3. Since Constantine's time, Persian Christians have suffered ___*persecution*___ during various periods of history.

C. Greece, Rome, and Europe *(pp. 400–401)*

1. Both Greek and Roman cultures worshiped many different ___*gods*___.
2. Many errors in doctrine and practice had crept into the ___*church*___ by the Middle Ages.
3. Martin Luther realized that a person is justified simply by putting his ___*faith*___ in Jesus' life and His death on the cross.
4. Luther and many others began a movement known as the Protestant Reformation, in which they wanted the Roman Catholic Church to ___*reform*___ its teachings.
5. The Reformation is considered one of the most important events in history for ___*spreading*___ Christ's kingdom.

Mosaic of the Roman emperor Constantine

Chapter 15 Organizer

Name ______________________

Use with Student Text pages 390–410.

Complete the outline as you study the chapter.

D. India *(pp. 401–3)*

1. Hinduism held people captive in its ___*caste system*___.
2. Buddhism gave people the false hope that they could end their suffering by following a path of ___*good works*___ to a state called nirvana.
3. Trading companies were more concerned with making ___*money*___ than they were with the eternal future of the Indians.
4. William Carey was a Baptist missionary from ___*England*___.
5. England passed a law that required the British East India Company to permit ___*missionary work*___ in the areas the company controlled.

E. Africa *(pp. 403–4)*

1. After Christ's time on earth, the gospel spread from Israel to Egypt and other parts of ___*northern*___ Africa.
2. Portuguese explorers attempted missionary work among the people of Africa's ___*interior*___.
3. Robert Moffat set up a mission ___*station*___, translated the Bible into the local ___*language*___, and began a ___*church*___ in southern Africa.

F. Latin America *(pp. 406–7)*

1. As the Reformation took place in Europe, Hernando Cortés was introducing Roman Catholicism to ___*Mesoamerica*___.
2. Missionary efforts in Latin America were greatly aided by ___*immigrants*___.
3. The immigrants were better able to minister to the Latin American people after learning to speak ___*Spanish*___ and ___*Portuguese*___.

Cortés meeting Montezuma II

G. China (pp. 407–9)

1. Christianity seemed to be kept out of China by the country's ___isolation___.
2. Robert Morrison was an English missionary who dressed like the Chinese to avoid ___attention___.
3. Morrison translated the entire Bible into Chinese, making a tremendous impact on the ___evangelization___ of China.
4. Another English missionary, Hudson Taylor, insisted his workers ___support___ themselves rather than be paid with foreign funds.
5. After World War II, ___Communists___ took over China.
6. The Chinese church was able to stand on its own when missionaries were forced to leave because it had long been ___self-supporting___.

H. Japan (pp. 409–10)

1. Japan's two main religions were ___Shintoism___ and ___Buddhism___.
2. An American diplomat negotiated a ___trade agreement___ with Japan, which helped open it to missionary work.

III. Christ's Kingdom and You (p. 410)

A. The kingdom of Christ will one day include people from every ___tribe___ and ___nation___ who will sing His praises before His throne.

B. Part of God's plan for Christians is to carry the message of ___salvation___ to all the world.

Kamikaze pilots believed the highest gift one could give the emperor was one's life.

God's Plan

Name ____________________

Use with Student Text pages 390–94.

A. Complete the section.

1. Explain the difference between the non-Christian worldview of history and the Christian worldview. *The non-Christian rejects the account of history in the Bible. The Christian sees how God's plan has unfolded in the past.*
2. What were God's first words to mankind? *"Be fruitful, and multiply, and replenish the earth, and subdue it: and have dominion over the fish of the sea, and over the fowl of the air, and over every living thing that moveth upon the earth" (Gen. 1:28).*
3. Give two examples of how man has had dominion over the earth. *possible answers:*
   - *The Egyptians harnessed the Nile. The Egyptians built pyramids. The Romans built an empire. The*
   - *Romans built roads, new cities, and systems of government. The Greeks and Persians developed philosophies that lived on. The student may also list other examples from past chapters.*
4. What is the one source for the greatness in each civilization? *the image of God in man*
5. What feature of every civilization causes historians to marvel? *intelligence*
6. Why did all the world's religions and philosophies form? *People rejected God's truth.*
7. What does "they are brought out of the kingdom of darkness and placed into the kingdom of His light" mean? *People who turn from their sin to trust Christ for salvation receive His righteousness.*

B. First, plan the essay on your own paper. Then, write your essay in the space below.

8. Explain God's plan of redemption.

The student's essay should include a reasonable amount of the following information: God's plan has always been to redeem mankind from sin and its effects in the world. History is very important to God's plan of redemption. God gave the Israelites His law and promises of a Savior and King. This King would rule and save Israel as well as people from every nation of the world. Jesus came to earth as both a man and a king to redeem the world. He lived a perfect life. He died and paid the penalty for sinful people in all times and in all places. Those who turn from their sin to trust Him for salvation receive His righteousness.

Making Inferences

Name ____________________

Use with Student Text page 395.

Make inferences about each paragraph.

> **MAKING INFERENCES**
>
> 1. What topic is the writer describing?
> 2. What facts are given?
> 3. What can you infer from the information?
> 4. What conclusions can you draw?

The Hanging Gardens of Babylon were one of the wonders of the ancient world. The gardens were probably built by Nebuchadnezzar for his wife, who was from another country. The terraced gardens contained tropical palms, trees, and flowers. From the ground the gardens seemed to hang in the air. The Euphrates River ran under the wall and through the middle of the city. It watered the gardens and provided a water supply for the city.

1. What topic is the writer describing? *Hanging Gardens of Babylon*
2. What facts are given? *Possible answers are given.*
   - *The gardens were probably built by Nebuchadnezzar for his wife.*
   - *The terraced gardens had tropical palms, trees, and flowers.*
   - *The Euphrates River ran under the wall and through the city.*
   - *The river watered the gardens.*
   - ____________________
3. What can you infer about Nebuchadnezzar's wife from the information? *possible answers: The plants that Nebuchadnezzar planted were to remind his wife of her homeland. The plants that Nebuchadnezzar planted were from his wife's homeland. Nebuchadnezzar's wife enjoyed gardening or nature.*
4. What conclusions can you draw? *possible answer: Nebuchadnezzar's wife liked plants and missed those of her homeland.*

Many Chinese believers worked with Hudson Taylor's China Inland Mission. He insisted, however, that the workers support themselves rather than be paid with foreign funds. In 1899, as a result of the Boxer Rebellion, many foreigners were driven from the Chinese empire. Some missionaries as well as Chinese Christians were attacked and even killed. When the Communists took over China after World War II, all the missionaries were forced to leave. Believers continued worshiping Christ and spreading the gospel.

5. What topic is the writer describing? *missionaries and believers in China*

6. What facts are given? *Possible answers are given.*
   - *Missionary workers supported themselves.*
   - *Foreigners were driven out during the Boxer Rebellion.*
   - *Missionaries and Chinese Christians were killed.*
   - *All missionaries were forced to leave after World War II.*
   - *Believers continued worshiping and spreading the gospel.*
7. What can you infer about the believers from the information? *possible answer: The believers supported themselves and did not use foreign funds.*
8. What conclusions can you draw about the believers? *possible answer: The believers were able to stand on their own when the foreign missionaries were forced out.*

Robert Moffat and Mary Smith were married in Cape Town. They set up mission stations, first in the village of Lattakoo and later in the town of Kuruman. Progress in both stations was slow. Mary became very sick and nearly died before the birth of their first child. A time of drought came, and the water supply ran low. In addition the mission station they lived at was threatened by tribal warfare.

A friend in England wrote to Mary and asked her if there was anything she needed. "Please send us a communion set," Mary wrote back, knowing that goods shipped from England could take months to arrive. "Some day we will need it."

9. What topic is the writer describing? *the missionaries Robert and Mary Moffat*
10. What facts are given? *Possible answers are given.*
    - *Robert and Mary Moffat set up mission stations.*
    - *Progress with the Africans was slow.*
    - *They endured hardships—sickness, drought, and tribal warfare.*
    - *Mary asked for a communion set.*
    - ______________________
11. What can you infer about the Africans or Mary Moffat from the information? *possible answers: The Africans did not show any interest in the gospel at first. Mary believed that Africans would eventually be saved.*
12. What conclusions can you draw about the Africans or Mary Moffat? *possible answers: Since progress was slow, there were few Africans who showed interest in the gospel. Mary Moffat had faith that one day an African would trust the Lord, and they would need a communion set.*

Study Guide

Use with Student Text pages 390–99.

Name ____________________

A. Define the terms. Use the glossary in the Student Text.

1. dominion *the authority to rule*
2. gospel *the message of God's redemption of man through Jesus Christ*
3. worldview *how a person sees and interprets the universe and everything in it*

B. Mark the correct answer.

4. How did persecution help the spread of Christianity?
   - ● Believers carried the gospel with them as they fled to other parts of the world.
   - ○ Believers went into hiding and formed underground churches.
   - ○ The spread of Christ's kingdom is not consistent in all places and at all times.
5. Which is the worldview held by most non-Christians?
   - ○ They look at the Israelites to see how God's plan has unfolded in the Bible.
   - ● They look at the Israelite civilization and reject its history as recorded in the Bible.
   - ○ They read the Bible to see what happened to Israel and how to think about what has happened.
6. Which is an illustration of how man has had dominion over the earth?
   - ○ Both the Bushmen and the Khoikhoi spoke unusual click languages.
   - ○ Roman general Hannibal is one of the greatest generals in ancient history.
   - ● The Egyptians and the Mesopotamians used irrigation to water their crops.
7. What promise did Jesus give about His kingdom?
   - ○ If believers were not faithful, their churches would be removed.
   - ● Jesus promised His kingdom would continue to grow gradually.
   - ○ Egyptians would be considered God's people, just as Israel was.
8. What is the source of the intelligence that made each civilization great?
   - ● the image of God in man
   - ○ the mercy of God in man
   - ○ the grace of God in man
9. Where are God's first words to mankind recorded?
   - ○ Genesis 1:3
   - ● Genesis 1:28
   - ○ Genesis 2:16–17
10. Why did all the world's false religions and philosophies form?
    - ○ People wanted to use the abilities God gave them as bearers of His image.
    - ○ People built structures such as cathedrals and pyramids.
    - ● People rejected God's truth.
11. What happened to Christianity in Egypt so that it is no longer strong?
    - ○ The Egyptian city of Alexandria grew to be one of the most important places for early Christianity.
    - ● Muslims threatened death, placed restrictions on Christians, and seized church property.
    - ○ Christians embraced the teaching that Athanasius had spent his life defending.
12. How was Constantine instrumental in preserving Christianity?
    - ● After his conversion, he declared that Christianity would be tolerated.
    - ○ He allowed the temple to be rebuilt.
    - ○ He wrote sermons and a hymnal.

Compare-Contrast Essay

Name ______________________________

Use with Student Text page 405.

A. Choose a topic from two civilizations to compare and contrast. Use the T-chart to help you take notes on your topic.

Topic: ______________________________

Civilization:	**Civilization:**

B. Use the Venn diagram to help you organize the information you have collected.

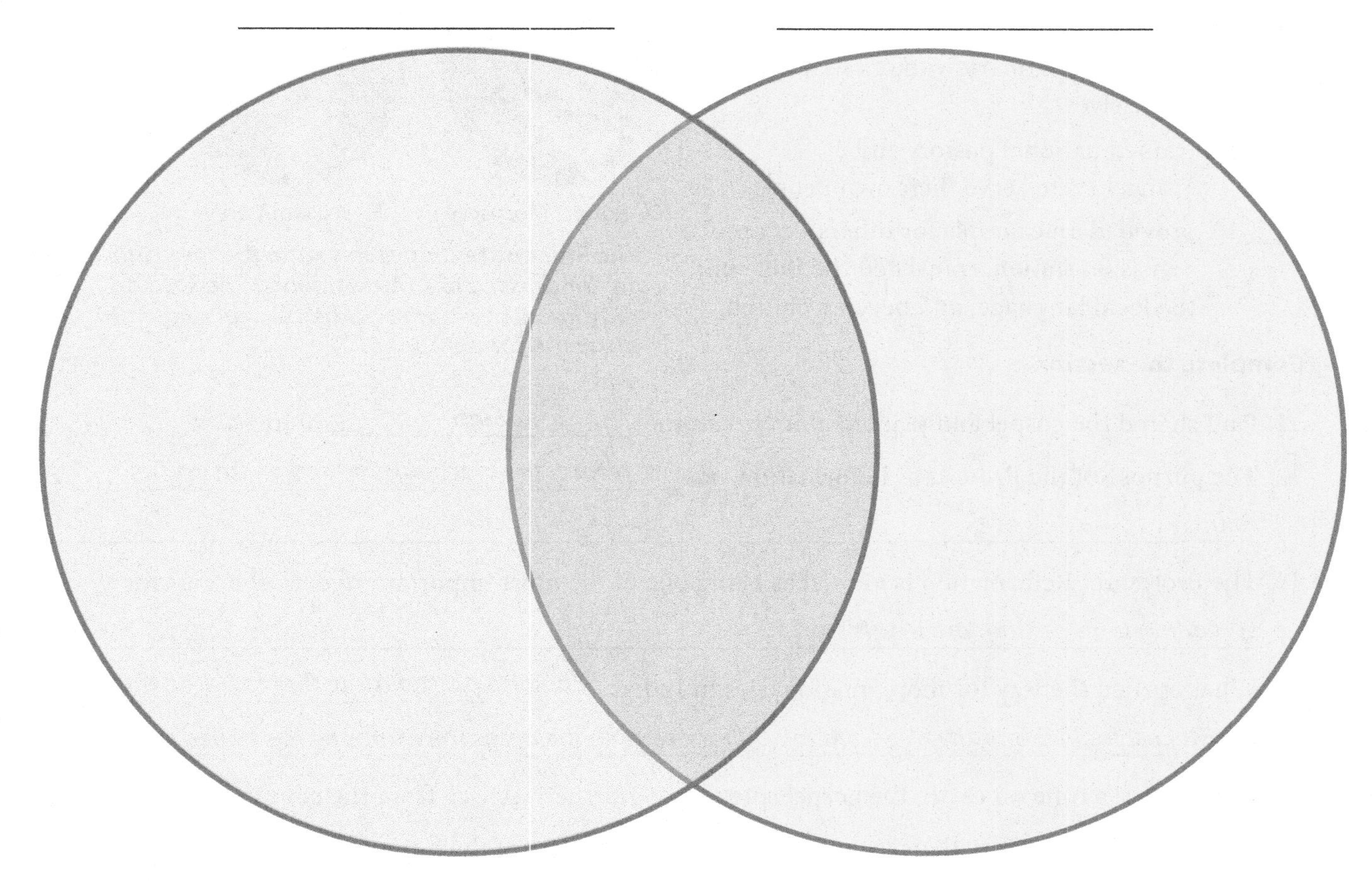

C. Circle how you will organize your essay.

by similarities and differences

by subject

D. Complete your essay using the steps on Student Text page 405.

Study Guide

Name ______________________

Use with Student Text pages 400–410.

A. Match the description to the correct person.

C 1. a missionary to southern Africa

D 2. did not openly evangelize; learned the language

B 3. started the Protestant Reformation

A 4. started the China Inland Mission

B 5. taught that justification was by faith alone

D 6. a missionary to China who dressed like the residents

E 7. a missionary to India

A 8. insisted missionary workers support themselves

E 9. trained national pastors and evangelists to serve their own people

C 10. provided an example for others—set up a mission station, translated the Bible into the local language, and began a church

A. Hudson Taylor

B. Martin Luther

C. Robert Moffat

D. Robert Morrison

E. William Carey

The Student Text does not state that Hudson Taylor dressed like the residents. The student may know this from another source and answer A for number 6.

B. Complete the section.

11. Paul shared the gospel and planted churches in the *Roman* Empire.

12. The purpose of the Protestant Reformation was *to reform the teachings of the Roman Catholic Church*.

13. The Protestant Reformation is viewed as being one of the most important historical events for *spreading Christ's kingdom in this world*.

14. What opened the way for more missionaries in India? *England passed a law that required the British East India Company to permit missionary work in the areas the company controlled.*

15. After Christ's time on earth, the gospel spread into northern Africa from the country of *Israel*.

16. Whom do African Christians want to provide the leadership of their churches today? *They want to provide their own leadership rather than have foreign missionaries lead them.*

17. What was happening to the Aztecs as the Protestant Reformation was taking place in Europe? *Hernando Cortés and the Spaniards were conquering the Aztecs.*

18. What religion did the Spaniards bring to Latin America? *Roman Catholicism*

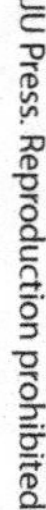

19. What kept Christianity out of China for so long?
    China's isolation

20. Why did Hudson Taylor feel that the mission workers needed to support themselves?
    The Chinese church would be able to stand on its own even if the foreigners were driven out.

The Fall of the Pekin Castle depicts a battle during the Boxer Rebellion.

21. What was the result of the Boxer Rebellion?
    Many foreigners were driven from China. Some missionaries and Chinese Christians were attacked and killed.

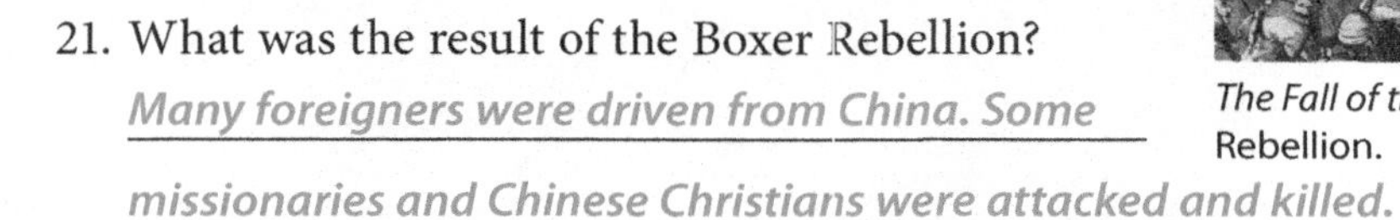

22. Who took over China after World War II and forced the missionaries to leave? *the Communists*

23. Many Christians in China have had to endure *persecution* and meet in *secret*.

24. The book of Revelation says that the kingdom of Christ will one day include people from every *tribe* and *nation* who will sing His praises before His *throne*.

C. First, plan the essay on your own paper. Then, write your essay in the space below.

25. Describe how missionaries and immigrants helped spread the gospel in Latin America.

The student's essay should include a reasonable amount of the following information: The Spaniards and Hernando Cortés brought Roman Catholicism to the area. Some of the first Protestant missionaries to come to Brazil were from Switzerland, but the French colonists drove them away. After three hundred years Protestant missionaries were invited to come. African Americans from the United States moved to Haiti and the Dominican Republic to spread the gospel there. Immigrants from Europe and the United States started churches in Latin America. After living in the culture, the immigrants learned to speak Spanish and Portuguese and were better able to minister. The British Bible Society and the American Bible Society also sent missionaries to Latin America. Bibles in Portuguese, Spanish, and other languages helped to spread the gospel.

Chapter 15 Summary

Name ______________________________

Define these terms

dominion
gospel
worldview

Locate these places

None

Tell about these people

Hudson Taylor
Martin Luther
Robert Moffat
Robert Morrison
William Carey

Explain what happened

Protestant Reformation

Be able to . . .

Compare the worldviews of a non-Christian and a Christian
Identify the Bible verse that records God's first words to mankind
Illustrate how man has had dominion over the earth
Identify the source of man's intelligence and why he is able to do intelligent things
Explain why the world's false religions and philosophies formed
Explain God's plan of redemption
Explain how persecution helped the spread of Christianity
Explain the promise Jesus gave about His kingdom
Identify what happened to Christianity in Egypt
Describe Constantine's role in preserving Christianity
Identify the empire that Paul shared the gospel and planted churches in
Describe what opened the way for more missionaries in India
Identify how Christianity entered northern Africa
Explain who African Christians want for church leadership
Describe what was happening in Latin America at the time of the Protestant Reformation
Explain how missionaries and immigrants helped spread the gospel in Latin America
Describe what kept Christianity out of China for so long
Explain what happened in China as a result of the Boxer Rebellion
Describe Christianity in China today
Explain who the book of Revelation says will be included in the kingdom of Christ

Essay Writing Steps & Vocabulary

Name ____________________

STUDY SKILL

Essay Writing Steps

1. Read the question.
2. Underline key words.
3. Plan the response.
4. Order the main points.
5. Write an opening statement.
6. Write the main points with supporting facts and details.
7. Write a closing statement.
8. Evaluate the essay.

Essay Vocabulary

analyze—examine critically to identify causes, key factors, possible results, and relationships

classify—sort into groups based on shared characteristics

compare—show how things are similar or alike

contrast—show how things are different

demonstrate—show clearly by using examples

describe—tell about

evaluate—judge something's significance or importance using evidence to support

explain—make clear or give reasons for

identify—name or recognize

illustrate—explain by using examples, pictures, or comparisons

interpret—give the meaning or importance of

justify—support a position with specific facts and reasons

list—provide a series of details or steps

predict—tell what will happen in the future based on an understanding of the past

state—give information clearly in words

summarize—write a short account of the main points

trace—follow the development or steps of something in chronological order

Essay Rubric			
	0	1	2
Content	includes none of the required facts, reasons, or comparisons	includes part of the required facts, reasons, or comparisons	includes all the required facts, reasons, or comparisons
Construction	no topic sentence or paragraph form	partial paragraph form—missing either a topic sentence or well-written supporting sentences	correct paragraph form—includes a topic sentence and well-written supporting sentences

History TimeLine

Africa

3000 BC	2800 BC	2600 BC	2400 BC

ca. 3000 BC
Upper and Lower Egypt united under Menes

ca. 2700–2200 BC
Old Kingdom in Egypt

Americas

3000 BC	2800 BC	2600 BC	2400 BC

Asia

3000 BC	2800 BC	2600 BC	2400 BC

ca. 3000 BC
Sumer civilization

ca. 2350 BC
Akkadian Empire

Europe

3000 BC	2800 BC	2600 BC	2400 BC

Africa

2200 BC | 2000 BC | 1800 BC | 1700 BC | 1600 BC

ca. 2250 BC
Kushite capital at Kerma

ca. 2040–1783 BC
Middle Kingdom in Egypt

ca. 2270 BC
Sargon, ruler of Kish

ca. 1570–1075 BC
New Kingdom in Egypt

Old Kingdom in Egypt
(ca. 2700–2200 BC)

Americas

2200 BC | 2000 BC | 1800 BC | 1700 BC | 1600 BC

Asia

2200 BC | 2000 BC | 1800 BC | 1700 BC | 1600 BC

ca. 2300 BC
Harappan
civilization

ca. 2000 BC
Hittite settlement
in Asia Minor

1700–1500 BC
Disappearance of Harappan civilization

ca. 2050 BC
Beginning of Ur-Nammu's
reign in Sumer

Harappan artifact

ca. 2091 BC
God's revelation
to Abraham

ca. 2100 BC
God's calling of Abraham
out of Ur in Mesopotamia

Ruins of the temple complex in Ur

Europe

2200 BC | 2000 BC | 1800 BC | 1700 BC | 1600 BC

ca. 2000–1400 BC
Minoan civilization in Greece

Africa

1500 BC | 1400 BC | 1300 BC | 1200 BC

1500 BC
Kush conquered by Egypt

1446 BC
Exodus from Egypt

ca. 1400 BC
Songhai's independence from Mali

ca. 1358 BC
Beginning of King Tut's reign in Egypt

King Tut

1200 BC
Beginning of Sundiata's reign in Mali

Americas

1500 BC | 1400 BC | 1300 BC | 1200 BC

ca. 1200–400 BC
Olmec civilization

Asia

1500 BC | 1400 BC | 1300 BC | 1200 BC

ca. 1500 BC
Aryan civilization in India

Rig-Veda (India)

ca. 1500–1000 BC
Shang dynasty in China

ca. 1406 BC
First book of the Pentateuch written by Moses

Shang dynasty ting

Moses given the Law by God

Europe

1500 BC | 1400 BC | 1300 BC | 1200 BC

ca. 1400–1200 BC
Mycenaean civilization in Greece

ca. 1200s BC
Life of Homer, Greek poet and storyteller

Gold mask found at Mycenae

Homer

Africa

1100 BC | 1000 BC | 900 BC | 800 BC

New Kingdom in Egypt
(ca. 1570–1075 BC)

ca. 1000 BC
Egypt conquered by Kush

Kushite temples and artifacts were covered or moved when the Aswan High Dam was built.

Americas

1100 BC | 1000 BC | 900 BC | 800 BC

Olmec civilization (**ca. 1200–400 BC**)

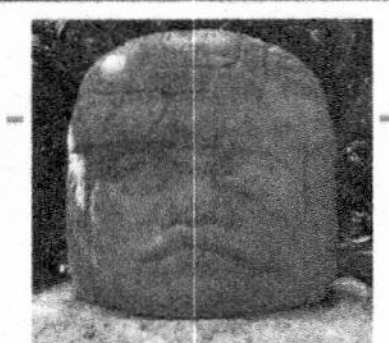

Asia

1100 BC | 1000 BC | 900 BC | 800 BC

1020 BC
Saul anointed as Israelite king

922 BC
Death of King Solomon; beginning of Rehoboam's reign; Israel divided in two

961 BC
Death of Israelite king David; beginning of Solomon's reign

Shang dynasty in China (**ca. 1500–1000 BC**)

ca. 1000–771 BC
Chou dynasty in China

ca. 1000 BC
Chaldean settlement around Babylon

King Wu of the Chou dynasty

Europe

1100 BC | 1000 BC | 900 BC | 800 BC

753 BC
Legendary founding of Rome by Romulus and Remus

1150–750
Grecian dark age

A Spartan warrior

Africa

700 BC | 600 BC | 500 BC | 400 BC

ca. 650 BC
Assyrian invasion of Egypt under Kushite rule

500 BC
Kushite capital, Meroë

Kushite pyramids

Americas

700 BC | 600 BC | 500 BC | 400 BC

Olmec ceramic fish container

Asia

700 BC | 600 BC | 500 BC | 400 BC

ca. 750 BC
Assyrian Empire built

722 BC
Assyrian captivity of Israel

612 BC
Destruction of Nineveh by Chaldeans/Medes

586 BC
Babylonian destruction of Jerusalem

571 BC
Nebuchadnezzar's destruction of mainland Tyre

ca. 559–530 BC
Reign of Cyrus II (the Great) in Persia

551–479 BC
Life of Confucius

539 BC
Cyrus the Great's conquest of Babylon; Israelites freed

ca. 522–486 BC
Reign of Darius I (the Great) in Persia

ca. 500s BC
Life of Zoroaster, founder of Zoroastrianism

ca. 500 BC
Buddhism founded by Siddhartha Gautama

The Babylonian Chronicles

Darius I

Europe

700 BC | 600 BC | 500 BC | 400 BC

509–31 BC
Roman Republic

ca. 500 BC
Athenian democracy

ca. 500–323 BC
Grecian classical age

499 BC
Greek city-states' rebellion against Persia

490–479 BC
Persian wars with Greece

480 BC
Battle of Salamis between Persians and Greeks

ca. 470–399 BC
Life of Socrates, Greek philosopher and teacher

431–404 BC
Peloponnesian War between Athens and Sparta

ca. 400s BC
Life of Greek scholar Herodotus

Life of Greek historian Thucydides

Greek war ship

300 BC 200 BC 100 BC 0

Africa

ca. 248–183 BC
Life of Hannibal

ca. AD 10–600
Aksum Empire

300 BC 200 BC 100 BC 0

Americas

300 BC 200 BC 100 BC 0

Asia

273–233 BC
Beginning of Asoka's reign of Mauryan Empire

ca. 140–87 BC
Reign of Wu Ti, emperor of Han dynasty in China

4 BC
Birth of Christ

171 BC
Control of Parthians extended

63 BC
Herod made king of Judea by Caesar

ca. 320–184 BC
Mauryan Empire in India

176 BC
Beginning of Antiochus IV's reign in Judea

184 BC
Mauryan Empire conquered by invaders

326 BC
Alexander the Great's conquest of northwestern India

ca. 250 BC–AD 224
Parthian period in Persia

ca. 200 BC
Formation of Japanese clans

Birth of Christ

334 BC
Fall of Persia to Alexander the Great

202 BC–AD 220
Han dynasty in China

221–210 BC
Reign of Qin Shih Huang Ti

221–202 BC
Qin dynasty in China

300 BC 200 BC 100 BC 0

Europe

312 BC
Beginning of construction on the Roman Appian Way

264–241 BC
First Punic War between Rome and Carthage

218–201 BC
Second Punic War between Rome and Carthage

149–146 BC
Third Punic War between Rome and Carthage

106–43 BC
Life of Cicero

31 BC
Battle of Actium between Octavian and Anthony; beginning of Octavian's reign of Roman Empire

338 BC
Greece under Macedonian king Philip II's control

ca. 200 BC
Roman Republic's domination of Italian Peninsula and western Mediterranean region

44 BC (Ides of March)
Caesar assassinated

60 BC
Triumvirate formed in Rome

Second Punic War

Grecian classical age (ca. 500–323 BC)

31 BC–AD 476
Roman Empire

Roman Republic (509–31 BC)

Africa

AD 100 AD 200 AD 300 AD 400

AD 330
Kush conquered by Aksum

ca. AD 300
Beginning of King Ezana's reign in Aksum

King Ezana

Americas

AD 100 AD 200 AD 300 AD 400

ca. AD 250–900
Mayan civilization

Asia

AD 100 AD 200 AD 300 AD 400

AD 72
Fall of two Jewish strongholds to Romans

AD 70
Roman destruction of Jerusalem and temple; end of Israelite nation

AD 400
Beginning of Indian golden age

ca. AD 250–700
Yamato clan in Japan

ca. AD 224–642
Sassanid period in Persia

Europe

AD 100 AD 200 AD 300 AD 400

AD 68
Civil war in Roman Empire

AD 180
End of Pax Romana

ca. AD 284–305
Diocletian's reign of Roman Empire

AD 306–337
Reign of Roman emperor Constantine

AD 312
End of Roman persecution of Christians

AD 313
Edict of Milan (Rome)

AD 330
Roman capital moved to Constantinople

AD 325
Council of Nicea (Rome)

AD 395
Roman Empire divided by Theodosius I

AD 378
Battle of Adrianople between Romans and Visigoths

Roman Colosseum

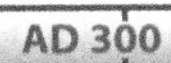

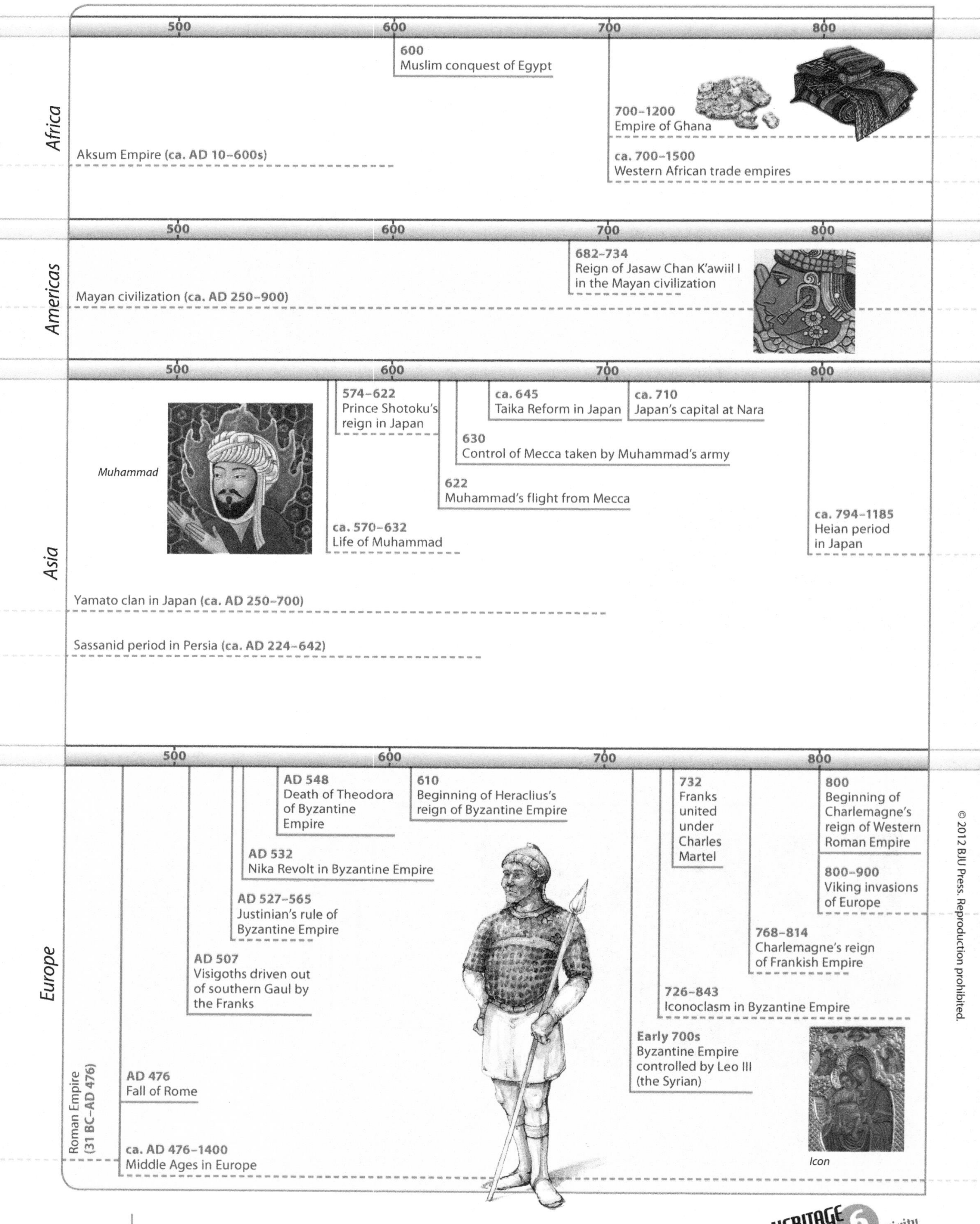
500
600
700
800
Africa
600
Muslim conquest of Egypt
700–1200
Empire of Ghana
Aksum Empire (ca. AD 10–600s)
ca. 700–1500
Western African trade empires
Americas
682–734
Reign of Jasaw Chan K'awiil I in the Mayan civilization
Mayan civilization (ca. AD 250–900)
Asia
574–622
Prince Shotoku's reign in Japan
ca. 645
Taika Reform in Japan
ca. 710
Japan's capital at Nara
630
Control of Mecca taken by Muhammad's army
Muhammad
622
Muhammad's flight from Mecca
ca. 794–1185
Heian period in Japan
ca. 570–632
Life of Muhammad
Yamato clan in Japan (ca. AD 250–700)
Sassanid period in Persia (ca. AD 224–642)
Europe
AD 548
Death of Theodora of Byzantine Empire
610
Beginning of Heraclius's reign of Byzantine Empire
732
Franks united under Charles Martel
800
Beginning of Charlemagne's reign of Western Roman Empire
AD 532
Nika Revolt in Byzantine Empire
800–900
Viking invasions of Europe
AD 527–565
Justinian's rule of Byzantine Empire
768–814
Charlemagne's reign of Frankish Empire
AD 507
Visigoths driven out of southern Gaul by the Franks
726–843
Iconoclasm in Byzantine Empire
Early 700s
Byzantine Empire controlled by Leo III (the Syrian)
AD 476
Fall of Rome
Roman Empire (31 BC–AD 476)
ca. AD 476–1400
Middle Ages in Europe
Icon

900 1000 1100 1200

Africa

ca. 900
Coastal trade cities established in western Africa

ca. 900–1400
Mwene Mutapa kingdom

900 1000 1100 1200

Americas

ca. 869
Mayas' sudden exit from cities

900 1000 1100 1200

Asia

1099
European crusaders' capture of Jerusalem from Muslims

1096–1099
First Crusade

1200
Middle East under control of Muslim Turks

1192
Yoritomo appointed as the first shogun

1187
Jerusalem recaptured from Crusaders by Muslims

Heian Palace

900 1000 1100 1200

Europe

911
Treaty between Carolingian kings and Viking chieftain

ca. 900
Beginning of Viking line of kings

976–1025
Basil II's reign of Byzantine Empire

1066
Battle of Hastings

1054
Split between Roman Catholic Church and Eastern Orthodox Church

Henry II

1154–1189
Henry II's reign in England

1198
Innocent III made pope

1199
Beginning of King John's reign in England

ca. 1200
Seven sacraments instituted by Roman Catholic Church

1215
Signing of Magna Carta by King John

1204–1261
Constantinople ruled by Venetians and crusaders

1202–1204
Fourth Crusade

850–1050
Byzantine Empire's golden age

Magna Carta signed

Africa

1300 | 1400 | 1500 | 1600

1312–1337 Reign of Mansa Musa in Mali

ca. 1400–1808 Slave trade in the West

Mwene Mutapa kingdom (**ca. 900–1400**)

Western African trade empires (**ca. 700–1500**)

Americas

1300 | 1400 | 1500 | 1600

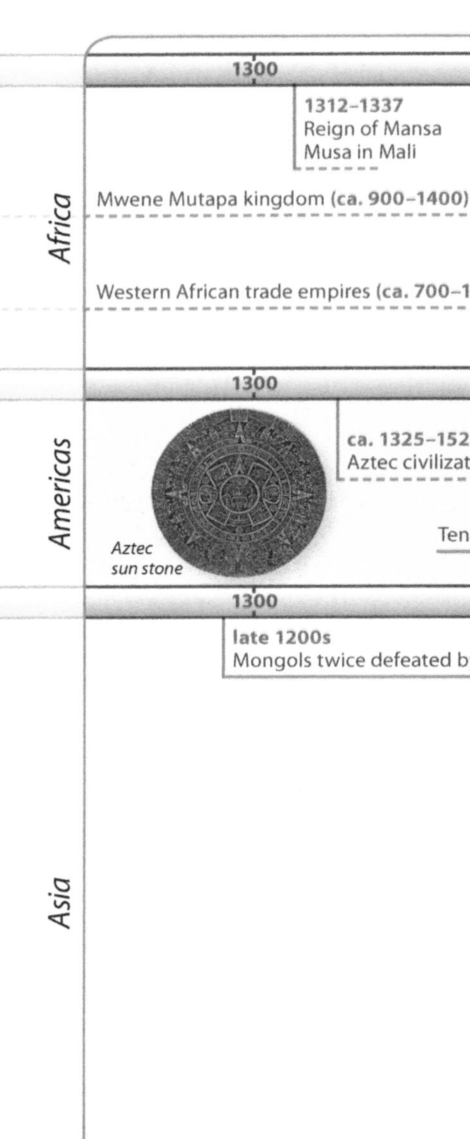

Aztec sun stone

ca. 1325–1521 Aztec civilization

ca. 1466–1520 Montezuma II

1562 Mayan books burned by De Landa

1500 Tenochtitlán's domination of all Mesoamerican cities

1519 Conquistadors' landing in Mesoamerica

Asia

1300 | 1400 | 1500 | 1600

late 1200s Mongols twice defeated by Japanese

1642 Dutch Reformed missionaries in Taiwan

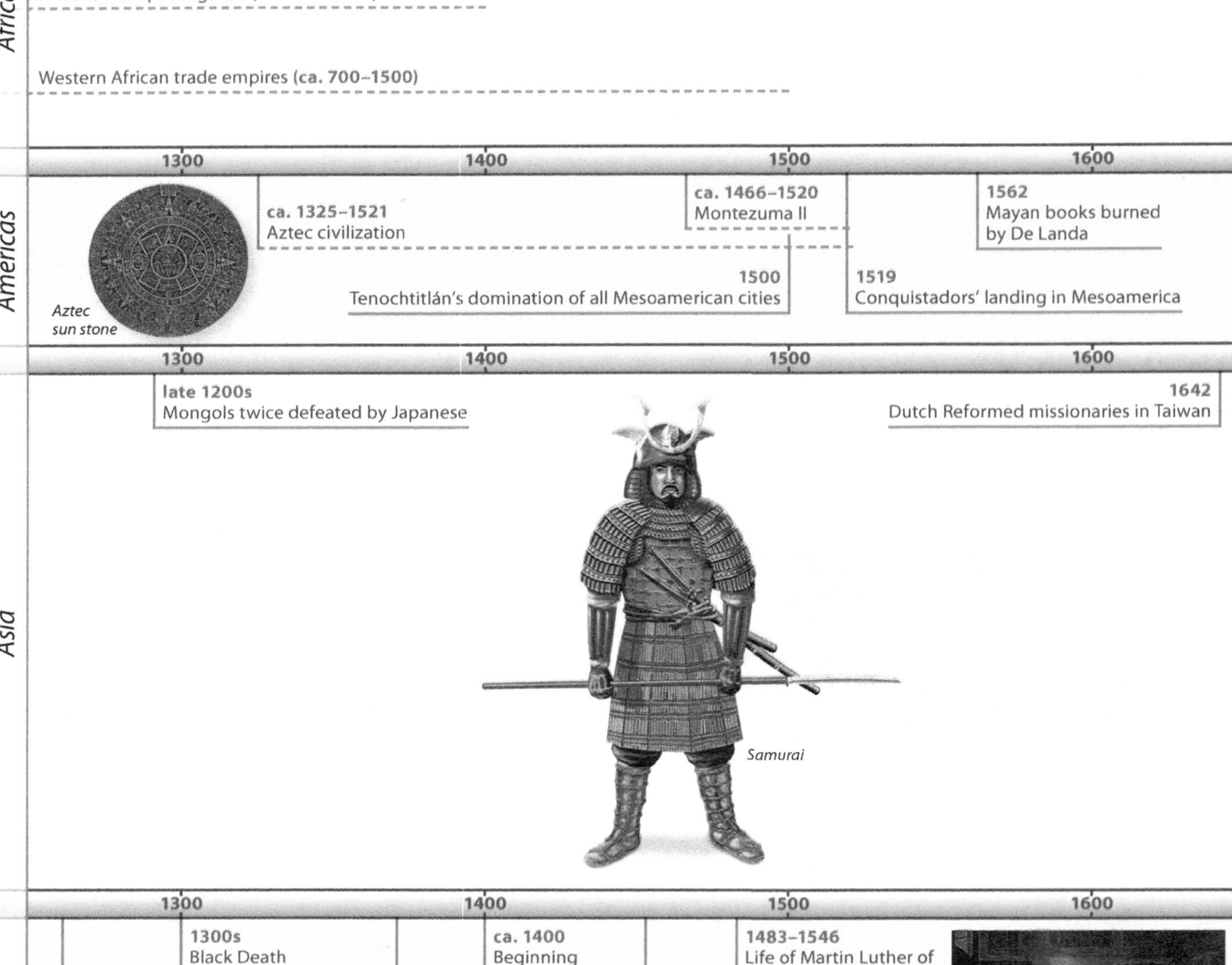

Samurai

Europe

1300 | 1400 | 1500 | 1600

1300s Black Death

1261 Constantinople recaptured by Michael VIII

ca. 1400 Beginning of the Italian Renaissance

1371 All Byzantine Empire except Constantinople conquered by Ottomans

1483–1546 Life of Martin Luther of Protestant Reformation

1453 Constantinople conquered by Ottoman Turks

Fall of Byzantine Empire

Martin Luther

Constantinople ruled by Venetians and Crusaders (**1204–1261**)

Ottoman attack

Middle Ages in Europe (**ca. AD 476–1400**)

Africa

1700 | 1800 | 1900 | 2000

1799
Rosetta stone discovered

1817
Scottish missionary Robert Moffat in southern Africa

Robert Moffat

1822
Jean-François Champollion's translation of Rosetta stone hieroglyphics in Egypt

ca. 1900
Modern state of Egypt formed

1922
Howard Carter's discovery of King Tut's tomb in Egypt

1970
Aswan High Dam completed

Americas

1700 | 1800 | 1900 | 2000

1970
Mayan hieroglyphics understood

Asia

1700 | 1800 | 1900 | 2000

William Carey

1792
English missionary William Carey in India

1807
English missionary Robert Morrison in China

1813
Missionaries allowed into all of India

1853
Beginning of trade between Japan and America

1864
J. E. Taylor's excavation of ziggurat at Ur, Iraq

1879
Cylinder seal at ancient Babylonian temple found by Hormuzd Rasam

1899–1900
Boxer Rebellion

1920
Discovery of Harappa and Mohenjo-Daro by Sir John Marshall

1922
Sir Leonard Wooley's excavation of Ur, Iraq

1947
Indian independence from England

1948
Nation of Israel reborn

1974
Terra-cotta army found in China

Europe

1700 | 1800 | 1900 | 2000

1782–1834
Life of English missionary Robert Morrison

Robert Morrison working on the Chinese Bible

Photograph Credits

The following agencies and individuals have furnished materials to meet the photographic needs of this textbook. We wish to express our gratitude to them for their important contribution.

BigStockPhoto.com
BJU Photo Services
Bob Jones University Museum & Gallery
Fotolia
Gospel Fellowship Association
Harry S Truman Library
Images of Asia
iStockphoto
Library of Congress
Map Resources
Craig Oesterling
Overseas Missionary Fellowship
Panoramio
Saudi Aramco World / SAWDIA
SuperStock
Thinkstock
Wikimedia Commons

Cover
Craig Oesterling

Chapter 1
Hemera/Thinkstock 1; © iStockphoto.com/Floriano Rescigno 3

Chapter 2
Michael Spencer / Saudi Aramco World / SAWDIA 17, 19; Getty Images/Hemera/Thinkstock 29

Chapter 3
© iStockphoto.com/bojan fatur 35; © I, Rémih / Wikimedia Commons / GNU 1.2 / CC 3.0 46; © iStockphoto.com/Sculpies 50

Chapter 4
© iStockphoto.com/Nancy Louie 57; © iStockphoto.com/brytta 58; Getty Images/iStockphoto/Thinkstock 65 (left); © iStockphoto.com/manwolste 65 (right); © iStockphoto.com/ra-photos 68

Chapter 5
Deeptrivia / Wikimedia Commons / GNU 1.2 / CC 3.0 69; BJU Photo Services 72; © iStockphoto.com/Ajay Bhaskar 73; Rene Drouyer/Hemera/Thinkstock 80; Dew/Wikimedia Commons 84

Chapter 6
© iStockphoto.com/Robert Churchill 86; © iStockphoto.com/Maria Toutoudaki 87; © iStockphoto.com/Daniel Padavona 94; © iStockphoto.com/graham kiotz 100

Chapter 7
Getty Images/Hemera/Thinkstock 103; Nicola e Pina/www.panoramio.com 106; Andrew Dunn / Wikimedia Commons / CC 2.0 111; Getty Images/iStockphoto/Thinkstock 112

Chapter 8
Getty Images/iStockphoto/Thinkstock 114, 128; BJU Photo Services 118; Getty Images/Photos.com/Thinkstock 119; Ablestock/Getty Images/Thinkstock 123

Chapter 9
Matt H. Wade /Wikimedia Commons / CC 3.0 132 (left); Getty Images/Comstock/Thinkstock 132 (right); Getty Images/iStockphoto/Thinkstock 136, 138; © Marie-Lan Nguyen / Wikimedia Commons / CC 2.5 140; © iStockphoto.com/Martin Lovatt 142

Chapter 10
Alex Popov / Getty Images /iStockphoto / Thinkstock 147; Getty Images/Photos.com/Thinkstock 153; Getty Images/iStockphoto/Thinkstock 158

Chapter 11
Glysiak / Wikimedia Commons / GNU 1.2 / CC 3.0 159; El Comandante / Wikimedia Commons / GNU 1.2 / CC 3.0 162; Volker Kreinacke / Getty Images / iStockphoto / Thinkstock 168 (top); Getty Images/iStockphoto/Thinkstock 168 (bottom); Adalberto Hernandez Vega / Wikimedia Commons / CC 2.0 174

Chapter 12
Konstantin Kalishko / Getty Images / Hemera / Thinkstock 178; Andrey Turchaninov / Getty Images /Hemera / Thinkstock 181; © iStockphoto.com/Jan Zoetekeouw 188

Chapter 13
National Land Image Information (Color Aerial Photographs), Ministry of Land, Infrastructure, Transport and Tourism / Wikimedia Commons 197; © iStock photo.com/chrisp0 206

Chapter 14
Getty Images/Hemera/Thinkstock 209; Getty Images / Digital Vision / Thinkstock 214; © iStockphoto.com/Andrew Dernie 226

Chapter 15
The York Project / Wikimedia Commons / Public Domain 228; Getty Images/Thinkstock 229; Harry S Truman Library 230; Overseas Missionary Fellowship 236 (top left); Wikimedia Commons / Public Domain 236 (top center); Wikimedia Commons / Public Domain 236 (center left); Wikimedia Commons / Public Domain 236 (center right); Library of Congress 237; Gospel Fellowship Association 238

History Timeline
Getty Images/Hemera/Thinkstock 241 (top); Bowen Collection of Antiquities, Bob Jones University Museum & Gallery 241 (bottom); Tor Eigeland / The Egyptian Antiquities Organization /Saudi Aramco World / SAWDIA 242 (top); Images of Asia 242 (center left); BJU Photo Services 242 (center right); Getty Images/iStockphoto/Thinkstock 242 (bottom); Bjørn Christian Tørrissen / Wikipedia / CC 3.0 243 (top); Moonb007/BigStockPhoto.com 243 (center right); Mountain / Wikimedia Commons / GNU 1.2 / CC 3.0 243 (center left); DieBuche / Wikimedia Commons / GNU 1.2 / CC 3.0 243 (bottom left); Przemyslaw "Blueshade" Idzkiewicz / Wikimedia Commons / CC 2.0 244 (top); Glysiak / Wikimedia Commons / GNU 1.2 / CC 3.0 244 (center); Madman / Wikimedia Commons / GNU 1.2 / CC 3.0 245 (center); © De Agostini/SuperStock 245 (top); © iStockphoto.com/Jeroen Peys 245 (bottom right); ChrisO / Wikimedia Commons / CC 3.0 / located at the British Museum 245 (bottom left); © iStockphoto.com/Grafissimo 246 (top); BJU Photo Services 246 (bottom right); Steerpike / Wikimedia Commons / CC 3.0 247 (center); iStockphoto/Thinkstock 247 (bottom); Getty Images/iStockphoto/Thinkstock 248 (bottom right); © iStockphoto.com/Razvan 249 (center); Getty Images/Photos.com/Thinkstock 250 (bottom left); *Martin Luther Discovering Justification by Faith,* Edward Matthew Ward, From the Bob Jones University Collection 250 (bottom right); © PB/Fotolia 250 (top left); Wikimedia Commons / Public Domain 251 (all)

All maps © 2011 Map Resources or BJU Press Art Department